J. O. Bird
B.Sc. (Hons), F.Coll.P., F.I.M.A
I.Eng. C.Math

A. J. C. May
B.A., C.Eng., M.I.Mech., E.F.I.T.E., A.M.B.I.M.

Algebra and Calculus for technicians

Level 3

Longman
Scientific &
Technical

Longman Scientific & Technical,
Longman Group UK Limited,
Longman House, Burnt Mill, Harlow,
Essex CM20 2JE, England
and Associated Companies throughout the world.

First published 1985
Fourth impression 1992

British Library Cataloguing in Publication Data

Bird, J. O.
   Algebra and calculus for technicians.
   Level 3.
   1. Algebra   2. Calculus
   I. Title   II. May, A. J. C.
 512′.15′0246   QA155

ISBN 0-582-41371-0

Produced by Longman Singapore Publishers (Pte) Ltd
Printed in Singapore.

Contents

Page 17
38
143
153.

Preface

This textbook provides coverage of the Business and Technician Education Council level 3 half units in Algebra and Calculus, the two half units forming the full unit of Mathematics 3.

However, it can be regarded as a basic textbook in Algebra and Calculus suitable for a much wider range of courses, such as for GCE A level Mathematics or for Australian TAFE courses.

Each topic considered in the text is presented in a way that assumes in the reader only the knowledge attained at BTEC level 2 Mathematics or its equivalent.

The aims of the book are to extend such previous knowledge which requires the development of algebraic and trigonometrical methods, to enable the student to differentiate and integrate simple functions, to solve certain first-order differential equations and to apply calculus to scientific and technological problems.

The book provides a natural follow-on to Technician Mathematics levels 1 and 2 written by the same authors.

This practical book contains some 120 illustrations, 220 detailed worked problems, followed by over 800 further problems with answers.

The authors would like to express their appreciation for the friendly co-operation and helpful advice given to them by the publishers and to thank Mrs. Elaine Woolley for the excellent typing of the manuscript.

Finally, the authors would like to add a word of thanks to their wives, Elizabeth and Juliet, for their patience, help and encouragement during the preparation of this book.

J. O. BIRD
A. J. C. MAY

Highbury College of Technology
Portsmouth

Section I

Algebra

Chapter 1

The binomial expansion

1 The expansion of $(a + b)^n$, where n is a small, positive integer, using Pascal's triangle

Table 1

Term	Expansion
$(a + b)^0 =$	1
$(a + b)^1 =$	$1a + 1b$
$(a + b)^2 =$	$1a^2 + 2ab + 1b^2$
$(a + b)^3 =$	$1a^3 + 3a^2b + 3ab^2 + 1b^3$
$(a + b)^4 =$	$1a^4 + 4a^3b + 6a^2b^2 + 4ab^3 + 1b^4$
$(a + b)^5 =$	$1a^5 + 5a^4b + 10a^3b^2 + 10a^2b^3 + 5ab^4 + 1b^5$
$(a + b)^6 =$	$1a^6 + 6a^5b + 15a^4b^2 + 20a^3b^3 + 15a^2b^4 + 6ab^5 + 1b^6$

The word binomial indicates a 'two-number' expression. When n is a small positive integer, up to, say, 10, the expansion of $(a + b)^n$ can be done by multiplying $(a + b)$ by itself n times. The result of doing this is shown in Table 1 for values of n from 0 to 6.

An examination of Table 1 shows that patterns are forming and the following observations can be made.

(i)   The power of a, when looking at each term in any of the expansions and moving from left to right, follows the pattern:

$n, n-1, n-2, \ldots, 2, 1, 0$ (since $a^0 = 1$).
Thus for $n = 5$, the 'a' part of each term is:

a^5, a^4, a^3, a^2, a and 1.

(ii) The power of b, when looking at each term in any of the expansions and moving from left to right, follows the pattern:

0, (since $b^0 = 1$), $1, 2, 3, \ldots, n-2, n-1, n$.
For $n = 5$, the 'b' part of each term is:

$1, b, b^2, b^3, b^4$ and b^5.

(iii) The values of the coefficients of each of the terms in any of the expansions are symmetrical about the middle coefficient when n is even and symmetrical about the middle two coefficients when n is odd. This can be seen in Table 1, where for n being an even number, say 4, the coefficients of $(a + b)^4$ are 1, 4, 6, 4, 1, i.e. symmetrical about 6, the middle coefficient. When n is odd, say 5, the coefficients of $(a + b)^5$ are 1, 5, 10, 10, 5, 1, i.e. symmetrical about the two 10's, the middle two coefficients.

Table 2 shows the coefficients of the expansions of $(a + b)^n$, where n is a positive integer and varies from 0 to 6.

Table 2

Term	Values of coefficients in the expansion
$(a + b)^0$	1
$(a + b)^1$	1 1
$(a + b)^2$	1 2 1
$(a + b)^3$	1 3 3 1
$(a + b)^4$	1 4 6 4 1
$(a + b)^5$	1 5 10 10 5 1
$(a + b)^6$	1 6 15 20 15 6 1

The coefficient of, say, the fourth term in the expansion of $(a + b)^6$ is obtained by adding together the 10 and 10 immediately above it, giving a result of 20, this being shown by the triangle in the table. An examination of Table 2 shows that the first and last coefficients of any expansion of the form $(a + b)^n$ are 1's. To obtain the coefficients of, say, $(a + b)^4$, the first and last coefficients are 1's. The second coefficient, 4, is obtained from adding the 1 and 3 from the line above it. Similarly the third coefficient, 6, is obtained by adding the 3 and 3 from the line above it, and so on. The configuration shown in Table 2 is called **Pascal's triangle**. It is used to determine the coefficients of the expansion $(a + b)^n$ when n is a relatively small positive integer.

Worked problems on the expansion of the type $(a + b)^n$, where n is a small positive integer, using Pascal's triangle.

Problem 1. Find the expansion of $(a + b)^7$.

The coefficients of the terms are determined by producing Pascal's triangle as far as the seventh power and selecting the last line.
From Table 2, the coefficients of $(a + b)^6$ are:
1, 6, 15, 20, 15, 6, 1

The coefficients of $(a + b)^7$ are therefore:

1, since the first and last coefficients are always 1's;
7, obtained by adding the first and second coefficients of $(a + b)^6$, i.e., $1 + 6$;
21, obtained by adding the second and third coefficients of $(a + b)^6$, i.e.,
$\quad 6 + 15$;
and so on, giving the coefficients of $(a + b)^7$ as:

1, 7, 21, 35, 35, 21, 7, 1

The 'a' terms are $a^7, a^6, a^5, \ldots, a, 1$
The 'b' terms are $1, b, b^2, \ldots, b^6, b^7$
Combining these results gives:

$$(a + b)^7 = a^7 + 7a^6b + 21a^5b^2 + 35a^4b^3 + 35a^3b^4 + 21a^2b^5 + 7ab^6| + b^7$$

A check for blunders can be made by adding the powers of a and b for each term. These should always be equal to n. In this problem, adding the powers of a and b together for each term gives:

$7+0 = 7, 6+1 = 7, 5+2 = 7, 4+3 = 7, 3+4 = 7, 2+5 = 7, 1+6 = 7,$ and $0+7 = 7$.

Thus no blunder has been made in determining the powers of a and b.

Problem 2. Find the expansion of $(1 - 3x)^{12}$ as far as the term in x^4.

Comparing $(1 - 3x)^{12}$ with $(a + b)^n$ shows that $a = 1, b = (-3x)$, (note the minus sign) and $n = 12$. Hence the 'a' terms are
$1^{12}, 1^{11}, 1^{10}, \ldots, 1^1, 1^0$
The 'b' terms are $(-3x)^0, (-3x)^1, (-3x)^2, (-3x)^3, (-3x)^4$, and only five

terms of the expansion are required since the expansion is as far as the term in x^4. Also, only the first five coefficients of each line of Pascal's triangle are necessary. Taking the first five coefficients of the seventh-power expansion from Problem 1 and calculating the first five coefficients as far as the twelfth power gives:

$$
\begin{array}{ccccccccc}
 & & & 1 & & 7 & & 21 & & 35 & & 35 \\
 & & 1 & & 8 & & 28 & & 56 & & 70 \\
 & 1 & & 9 & & 36 & & 84 & & 126 \\
 1 & & 10 & & 45 & & 120 & & 210 \\
1 & & 11 & & 55 & & 165 & & 330 \\
1 & 12 & & 66 & & 220 & & 495
\end{array}
$$

Thus $(1-3x)^{12} = 1(1)^{12} + 12(1)^{11}(-3x) + 66(1)^{10}(-3x)^2 + 220(1)^9(-3x)^3 +$
$+ 495(1)^8(-3x)^4$ as far as the term in x^4, i.e.

$$(1-3x)^{12} = 1 - 36x + 594x^2 - 5\,940x^3 + 40\,095\,x^4 \text{ as far as the term in } x^4.$$

Problem 3. Expand $\left(-1 - \dfrac{3}{y}\right)^7$ to five terms.

Comparing $\left(-1 - \dfrac{3}{y}\right)^7$ with $(a + b)^n$ shows that $a = (-1), b = \left(-\dfrac{3}{y}\right)$

and $n = 7$. Note that the minus signs must be included for both the 'a' and 'b' terms. The first five coefficients of the seventh power are obtained using Pascal's triangle as shown in Problem 1 and are:

$$
\begin{array}{ccccc}
 & 1, & 7, & 21, & 35 \text{ and } 35
\end{array}
$$

The 'a' terms are $\quad (-1)^7, \quad (-1)^6, \quad (-1)^5, \quad (-1)^4 \text{ and } (-1)^3$

The 'b' terms are $\left(\dfrac{-3}{y}\right)^0, \quad \left(\dfrac{-3}{y}\right)^1, \quad \left(\dfrac{-3}{y}\right)^2, \quad \left(\dfrac{-3}{y}\right)^3 \text{ and } \left(\dfrac{-3}{y}\right)^4$

Hence the first five terms of the expansion of $\left(-1 - \dfrac{3}{y}\right)^7$ are:

$$(1)(-1)^7 \left(\dfrac{-3}{y}\right)^0 + (7)(-1)^6 \left(\dfrac{-3}{y}\right)^1 + (21)(-1)^5 \left(\dfrac{-3}{y}\right)^2 + (35)(-1)^4\left(\dfrac{-3}{y}\right)^3$$

$$+ (35)(-1)^3 \left(\dfrac{-3}{y}\right)^4$$

that is, $(1)(-1)(1) + (7)(1) \left(\dfrac{-3}{y}\right) + (21)(-1) \left(\dfrac{9}{y^2}\right) + (35)(1)\left(\dfrac{-27}{y^3}\right)$

$$+ (35)(-1)\left(\dfrac{81}{y^4}\right)$$

i.e. $-1 - \dfrac{21}{y} - \dfrac{189}{y^2} - \dfrac{945}{y^3} - \dfrac{2\,835}{y^4}$

Problem 4. Determine the expansion of $\left(2x + \dfrac{y}{2}\right)^9$ as far as the term in y^5.

Taking the first six coefficients of the seventh-power expansion from Problem 1 and calculating the first six coefficients as far as the ninth power gives:

$$
\begin{array}{ccccccc}
& 1 & 7 & 21 & 35 & 35 & 21 \\
1 & 8 & 28 & 56 & 70 & 56 \\
1 & 9 & 36 & 84 & 126 & 126
\end{array}
$$

The 'a' terms in the $(a + b)^n$ expansion are replaced by $2x$ and are:

$(2x)^9, (2x)^8, (2x)^7, (2x)^6, (2x)^5, (2x)^4$

The 'b' terms in the $(a + b)^n$ expansion are replaced by $\dfrac{y}{2}$ and are:

$\left(\dfrac{y}{2}\right)^0, \left(\dfrac{y}{2}\right)^1, \left(\dfrac{y}{2}\right)^2, \left(\dfrac{y}{2}\right)^3, \left(\dfrac{y}{2}\right)^4$, and $\left(\dfrac{y}{2}\right)^5$

Combining these three results gives:

$$\left(2x + \frac{y}{2}\right)^9 = 1(2x)^9 \left(\frac{y}{2}\right)^0 + 9\,(2x)^8 \left(\frac{y}{2}\right)^1 + 36\,(2x)^7 \left(\frac{y}{2}\right)^2$$

$$+ 84\,(2x)^6 \left(\frac{y}{2}\right)^3 + 126\,(2x)^5 \left(\frac{y}{2}\right)^4 + 126\,(2x)^4 \left(\frac{y}{2}\right)^5$$

as far as the term in y^5.

Thus, $\left(2x + \dfrac{y}{2}\right)^9 = 2^9 x^9 + 9\,(2)^7 x^8 y + 36(2)^5 x^7 y^2 + 84(2)^3 x^6 y^3$

$$+ 126(2)x^5 y^4 + \frac{126}{2} x^4 y^5$$

as far as the term in y^5. That is,

$$\left(2x + \frac{y}{2}\right)^9 = 512 x^9 + 1\,152\,x^8 y + 1\,152\,x^7 y^2 + 672\,x^6 y^3 + 252\,x^5 y^4$$

$$+ 63\,x^4 y^5, \text{ as far as the term in } y^5.$$

Further problems on the expansion of the type $(a + b)^n$, *where n is a small positive integer, using Pascal's triangle, may be found in Section 4 (Problems 1–10), p. 14.*

2. The general expansion of $(a + b)^n$, where n is any positive integer

The value of the coefficients of the expansion of $(a + b)^n$ for integer values of n from 0 to 6 are shown in Table 2. This table shows that the coefficients for $(a + b)^6$ are:

1, 6, 15, 20, 15, 6 and 1

Instead of using Pascal's triangle to derive these coefficients, they could have been obtained using a factor method from the relationships:

$$1, \quad \frac{6}{1} = 6, \quad \frac{(6)(5)}{(1)(2)} = 15, \quad \frac{(6)(5)(4)}{(1)(2)(3)} = 20, \quad \frac{(6)(5)(4)(3)}{(1)(2)(3)(4)} = 15,$$

$$\frac{(6)(5)(4)(3)(2)}{(1)(2)(3)(4)(5)} = 6 \text{ and } \frac{(6)(5)(4)(3)(2)(1)}{(1)(2)(3)(4)(5)(6)} = 1$$

Replacing $(a + b)^6$ by $(a + b)^n$ and building up the coefficients by a factor method using those for $(a + b)^6$ as a pattern, gives:

$$1, n, \quad \frac{n(n-1)}{(1)(2)}, \quad \frac{n(n-1)(n-2)}{(1)(2)(3)}, \quad \frac{n(n-1)(n-2)(n-3)}{(1)(2)(3)(4)}, \text{ and so on.}$$

For example, the value of the third coefficient of $(a + b)^5$ is obtained from $\frac{n(n-1)}{(1)(2)}$ where n is 5, and is $\frac{(5)(4)}{(1)(2)}$, i.e. 10. Similarly, the value of the fourth coefficient of $(a + b)^4$ is determined using $\frac{n(n-1)(n-2)}{(1)(2)(3)}$ where n is equal to 4, and is $\frac{(4)(3)(2)}{(1)(2)(3)}$, i.e. 4.

Combining this factorial method of writing coefficients with the observations previously made for $(a + b)^n$ shows that the terms in 'a' are $a^n, a^{n-1}, a^{n-2}, \ldots,$ and the terms in 'b' are $b^0, b, b^2, b^3, \ldots$ Thus the general expansion of $(a + b)^n$ is:

$$(a+b)^n = a^n + n\,a^{n-1} b + \frac{n(n-1)}{(1)(2)}\, a^{n-2}\, b^2 + \frac{n(n-1)(n-2)}{(1)(2)(3)}\, a^{n-3}\, b^3 \text{ and so on.}$$

The product $(1)(2)(3)$ is usually denoted by 3!, called 'factorial 3'. In general, $(1)(2)(3)(4) \ldots (n)$ is denoted by $n!$, (factorial n). Hence,

$$(a + b)^n = a^n + n\,a^{n-1}\, b + \frac{n(n-1)}{2!}\, a^{n-2}\, b^2 + \frac{n(n-1)(n-2)}{3!}\, a^{n-3}\, b^3 + \ldots$$

This expansion is the **general binomial expansion** of $(a + b)^n$.

Practical problems can arise, for example, in the binomial distribution in statistics, where it is required to find the value of just one or two terms of a binomial expansion. The fifth term of the expansion of $(a + b)^n$ is

$$\frac{n(n-1)(n-2)(n-3)}{4!}\, a^{n-4}\, b^4$$

It can be seen that in the fifth term of any expansion the number 4 is very evident. There are four products of the type $n(n-1)(n-2)(n-3)$; 'a' is raised to the power $(n-4)$; 'b' is raised to the power of 4, and the denominator of the coefficient is 4!. For any term in a binomial expansion, say the rth term, $r-1$, is very evident. The value of the coefficient of the rth term is given by:

$$\frac{n(n-1)(n-2)}{(r-1)!} \ldots \text{to } (r-1) \text{ terms}$$

The power of 'a' for the rth term is $n-(r-1)$ and the power of 'b' is $(r-1)$. Thus the rth term of the expansion of $(a+b)^n$ is:

$$\frac{n(n-1)(n-2)\ldots\text{to } (r-1) \text{ terms}}{(r-1)!} \; a^{n-(r-1)} \; b^{(r-1)}$$

For example, to find the fifth term in the expansion of $(a+b)^{15}$, n is 15 and r is 5 and $(r-1)$ is 4. Hence the fifth term is

$$\frac{(15)(14)(13)(12)}{4!} \; a^{15-4}b^4, \text{ i.e. } 1\,365\,a^{11}\,b^4$$

Worked problems on the general expansion of $(a+b)^n$, where n is any positive integer

---

Problem 1. Expand $(x+y)^{20}$ as far as the fifth term.

The general binomial expansion for $(a+b)^n$ is

$$a^n + na^{n-1}\,b + \frac{n(n-1)}{2!}\,a^{n-2}\,b^2 + \frac{n(n-1)(n-2)}{3!}\,a^{n-3}\,b^3 + \ldots$$

Substituting in this general formula, $a = x$, $b = y$ and $n = 20$ gives:

$$(x+y)^{20} = x^{20} + 20x^{(20-1)}\,y + \frac{20(20-1)}{(2)(1)}\,x^{(20-2)}y^2$$

$$+\; \frac{20(20-1)(20-2)}{(3)(2)(1)}\,x^{(20-3)}\,y^3 + \frac{20(20-1)(20-2)(20-3)}{(4)(3)(2)(1)}\,x^{(20-4)}\,y^4 + \ldots$$

That is:

$$(x+y)^{20} = x^{20} + 20x^{19}\,y + \frac{20(19)}{2}\,x^{18}y^2 + \frac{20(19)(18)}{6}\,x^{17}y^3$$

$$+\; \frac{20(19)(18)(17)}{24}\,x^{16}y^4 + \ldots$$

i.e. $(x+y)^{20} = x^{20} + 20x^{19}y + 190x^{18}y^2 + 1\,140x^{17}y^3 + 4\,845x^{16}y^4$ when expanded as far as the fifth term.

Problem 2. Determine the expansion of $\left(p - \dfrac{4}{p^2}\right)^{15}$ as far as the term containing p^3.

Substituting $a = p$, $b = \left(\dfrac{-4}{p^2}\right)$ and $n = 15$ in the general expansion of $(a + b)^n$ gives:

$$\left(p - \frac{4}{p^2}\right)^{15} = (p)^{15} + 15(p)^{14}\left(\frac{-4}{p^2}\right) + \frac{15(14)}{(2)(1)}(p)^{13}\left(\frac{-4}{p^2}\right)^2$$

$$+ \frac{15(14)(13)}{(3)(2)(1)}(p)^{12}\left(\frac{-4}{p^2}\right)^3 + \frac{15(14)(13)(12)}{(4)(3)(2)(1)}(p)^{11}\left(\frac{-4}{p^2}\right)^4 + \dots$$

i.e., $\left(p - \dfrac{4}{p^2}\right)^{15} = p^{15} + 15p^{14}\left(\dfrac{-4}{p^2}\right) + 105p^{13}\left(\dfrac{16}{p^4}\right) + 455p^{12}\left(\dfrac{-64}{p^6}\right)$

$$+ 1\,365p^{11}\left(\frac{256}{p^8}\right) + \dots$$

i.e. $\left(p - \dfrac{4}{p^2}\right)^{15} = p^{15} - 60p^{12} + 1\,680p^9 - 29\,120p^6 + 349\,440p^3$ when

expanded as far as the term in p^3.

Problem 3. Determine the sixth term of the expansion of $\left(\dfrac{1}{m} + \dfrac{m^2}{2}\right)^{14}$

The rth term of the expansion of $(a + b)^n$ is given by

$$\frac{n(n-1)(n-2)\dots \text{ to } (r-1) \text{ terms}}{(r-1)!}\, a^{n-(r-1)}\, b^{(r-1)}$$

Substituting $a = \dfrac{1}{m}$, $b = \dfrac{m^2}{2}$, $n = 14$, and $(r-1) = 5$ (since $r = 6$), in this expression gives:

$$\frac{(14)(13)(12)(11)(10)}{(5)(4)(3)(2)(1)}\left(\frac{1}{m}\right)^{14-5}\left(\frac{m^2}{2}\right)^5$$

$$= 2\,002\left(\frac{1}{m}\right)^9\left(\frac{m^2}{2}\right)^5$$

$$= \frac{1\,001}{16}\,m$$

Thus the sixth term of the expansion of $\left(\dfrac{1}{m} + \dfrac{m^2}{2}\right)^{14}$ is $\dfrac{1\,001}{16}\,m$.

Problem 4. Find the middle term of the expansion of $\left(3u - \dfrac{1}{3v}\right)^{18}$.

In any expansion of the form $(a + b)^n$ there are $(n + 1)$ terms. Hence, in the expansion of $\left(3u - \dfrac{1}{3v}\right)^{18}$ there are 19 terms. Tne middle term is the 10th term. Using the general expression for the rth term, where $a = 3u$,

$b = \left(-\dfrac{1}{3v}\right)$, $n = 18$ and $(r-1) = 9$, gives:

$$\frac{18(17)(16)(15)(14)(13)(12)(11)(10)}{9\ (8)\ (7)\ (6)\ (5)\ (4)\ (3)\ (2)\ (1)}\ (3u)^9\ \left(-\dfrac{1}{3v}\right)^9$$

$$= 48\,620\ (3)^9\ (u^9)\ \frac{(-1)^9}{3^9 v^9} = -\,48\,620\ \left(\dfrac{u}{v}\right)^9$$

Thus the middle term of the expansion of $\left(3u - \dfrac{1}{3v}\right)^{18}$ is $-48\,620\ \left(\dfrac{u}{v}\right)^9$.

Problem 5. Derive the term containing y^{12} in the expansion of $\left(y^2 - \dfrac{x}{4}\right)^{10}$.

The y terms are $(y^2)^{10}, (y^2)^9, (y^2)^8, (y^2)^7, (y^2)^6$, and so on. Hence the term involving y^{12} is the fifth term. Using the expression for the rth term, where

$a = y^2, b = \left(-\dfrac{x}{4}\right)$, $n = 10$ and $(r-1) = 4$, gives

$$\frac{10(9)(8)(7)}{4(3)(2)(1)}\ (y^2)^{10-4}\ \left(-\dfrac{x}{4}\right)^4$$

i.e. $\dfrac{105}{128}\ y^{12}\ x^4$.

Thus the term containing y^{12} in the expansion of $\left(y^2 - \dfrac{x}{4}\right)^{10}$ is $\dfrac{105}{128}\ y^{12}\ x^4$.

Further problems on the expansion of $(a + b)^n$ *where n is any positive integer may be found in Section 4 (Problems 11–20), p. 15.*

3. The application of the binomial expansion to determining approximate values of expressions

The general binomial expansion of $(a + b)^n$ is:

$$(a + b)^n = a^n + n\,a^{n-1}b + \frac{n(n-1)}{2!}\,a^{n-2}\,b^2 + \frac{n(n-1)(n-2)}{3!}\,a^{n-3}\,b^3 + \dots$$

When $a = 1$ and $b = x$, then

$$(1+x)^n = (1)^n + n(1)^{n-1}x + \frac{n(n-1)}{2!}\,(1)^{n-2}x^2 + \frac{n(n-1)(n-2)}{3!}\,(1)^{n-3}x^3 + \dots$$

i.e. $(1 + x)^n = 1 + nx + \dfrac{n(n-1)}{2!}x^2 + \dfrac{n(n-1)(n-2)}{3!}x^3 + \dots$

If the first term of the expression on the right of this equation is u_1, the second term u_2, the third term u_3, the nth term u_n, and so on and if the sum S_N is given by $S_N = u_1 + u_2 + u_3 + \ldots u_n$, then provided that S_N approaches a definite finite value when N is large, the series is said to be **convergent**. An example of a convergent series is $1 + \dfrac{1}{1!} + \dfrac{1}{2!} + \dfrac{1}{3!} + \dfrac{1}{4!} + \ldots$ which approaches a value of $2.71828 \ldots$ when N is large.

The series for $(1 + x)^n$ given above is convergent provided x lies between -1 and 1. For example, if x is 0.6 and n is 0.5, $(1 + x)^n = 1.6^{0.5} = \sqrt{1.6} \approx 1.265$. The series for $(1 + x)^n$ is

$$1 + (0.5)(0.6) + \frac{(0.5)(-0.5)(0.6)^2}{2} + \frac{(0.5)(-0.5)(-1.5)(0.6)^3}{3 \times 2} + \ldots$$

that is, $1 + 0.3 - 0.045 + 0.0135 - \ldots \approx 1.269$. Thus, when N is only 4 terms, the series is already approaching its definite finite value of $\sqrt{1.6}$.

If an expression is written in the form $(1 + x)^n$ where x is small compared with 1, then terms such as $x^2, x^3, x^4, \ldots$ become very small and can be ignored if only an approximate result is required. Approximate values of expressions which could be written in this form used to be found in this way before electronic calculators came into widespread use. However solving problems of this sort using the binomial expansion, assists the understanding and provides practice in the expansion of two numbers into a series. A series of the form $1 + ax + bx^2 + cx^3 + \ldots$ where $a, b, c, \ldots$ are constants is called a **power series** since it is expressed in terms of powers of x. Thus the binomial expansion is used to produce a power series for a two-number expansion. Using this method to find the value of, say, $(1.002)^7$ correct to four decimal places, the expression is written as $(1 + 0.002)^7$ and since 0.002 is small compared with 1, only a few terms of the binominal expansion are required. Thus

$$(1 + 0.002)^7 \approx 1 + 7(0.002) + \frac{7(6)}{2}(0.002)^2 + \ldots$$

$$\approx 1 + 0.014 + 21(0.000\,004) + \ldots$$
$$\approx 1 + 0.014 + 0.000\,084 + \ldots$$
$$= 1.014\,1 \text{ correct to four decimal places}$$

The fourth term of the expansion is $\dfrac{(7)(6)(5)}{(1)(2)(3)}(0.002)^3$ and does not affect the result, to the accuracy required.

In experimental work, measurements are taken in the workshop or laboratory under the conditions prevailing at the time and corrections are subsequently made to enable results to be obtained more accurately. For example, the radius and height of a cylinder are measured and the volume is calculated. Later on, corrections are made due to temperature fluctuations or inherent inaccuracies within the measuring devices. The measured value of the radius has an error of 2½ per cent too large and the measured value of the height has an error of 1½ per cent too small. The binomial expansion can be used to find an approximate value of the error made in calculating the volume, when the other errors are known.

Let the correct values be volume V, radius r and height h. Then the correct value of volume is given by $V = \pi r^2 h$ for a cylinder. The uncorrected value of the radius is $\dfrac{102.5}{100}$ r or $(1 + 0.025)r$, since the radius is 2½ per cent too large. The uncorrected value of the height is $\dfrac{98.5}{100}$ h or $(1 - 0.015)h$ since the measured value of the height is 1½ per cent too small. Thus the uncorrected value of the volume, V_1, based on these measurements is given by:

$$V_1 = \pi \left[(1 + 0.025)r\right]^2 (1 - 0.015)h$$
$$= (1 + 0.025)^2 (1 - 0.015) \pi r^2 h$$

Using the binomial expansion to evaluate $(1 + 0.025)^2$ and ignoring the term containing $(0.025)^2$, since $(0.025)^2 = 0.000\,625$, which is small compared with 1, gives:

$$V_1 \simeq (1 + 2\,(0.025))\,(1 - 0.015)\,\pi r^2 h$$
$$\simeq (1 + 0.05)\,(1 - 0.015)\,\pi r^2 h$$
$$\simeq [1 + 0.05 - 0.015 + (0.05)(-0.015)]\,\pi r^2 h$$

When approximate values are required, it is also usual to ignore the products of small terms. In general, in any binomial expansion, both products of small terms and powers of small terms can be ignored. This is because numbers less than unity get progressively smaller both when multiplied together and when they are raised to larger powers.

Hence $V_1 \simeq (1 + 0.05 - 0.015)\,\pi r^2 h$

$$\simeq 1.035\,\pi r^2 h \text{ or } 1.035\,V \text{ or } \dfrac{103.5}{100}\,V$$

That is, the uncorrected value V_1 is approximately 3.5 per cent larger than the correct value.

Worked problems on determining approximate values using the binomial expansion

---

Problem 1. Find the value of $(1.003)^{10}$ correct to: (a) three decimal places: and (b) six decimal places, using the binomial expansion.

Writing $(1.003)^{10}$ as $(1 + 0.003)^{10}$ and substituting $x = 0.003$ and $n = 10$ in the general expansion of $(1 + x)^n$ gives:

$$1 + 10\,(0.003) + \dfrac{10(9)}{(2)(1)}\,(0.003)^2 + \dfrac{10(9)(8)}{(3)(2)(1)}\,(0.003)^3 + \dots$$

or $(1.003)^{10} = 1 + 0.03 + 0.000\,405 + 0.000\,003\,24 + \dots$
Hence $(1.003)^{10} = 1.030$ correct to three decimal places
and **1.030 408** correct to six decimal places.

Problem 2. Find the value of $(0.98)^7$ correct to five significant figures by using the binomial expansion.

$(0.98)^7$ is written as $(1 - 0.02)^7$. Using the $(1 + x)^n$-type expansion gives:

$$(1 - 0.02)^7 = 1 + 7(-0.02) + \frac{7(6)}{(2)(1)}(-0.02)^2 + \frac{(7)(6)(5)}{(3)(2)(1)}(-0.02)^3$$

$$+ \frac{(7)(6)(5)(4)}{(4)(3)(2)(1)}(-0.02)^4 + \ldots$$

$$= 1 + 7(-0.02) + 21(0.0004) + 35(-0.000008)$$
$$+ 35(0.00000016) + \ldots$$
$$= 1 - 0.14 + 0.0084 - 0.00028 + 0.0000056 - \ldots$$
$$= \mathbf{0.86813} \text{ correct to five significant figures.}$$

Problem 3. Find the value of $(8.016)^4$ correct to six significant figures using the binomial expansion.

$(8.016)^4$ is written in the $(1 + x)^n$ form as follows:

$$\begin{aligned}(8.016)^4 &= [8(1.002)]^4 \\ &= 8^4 (1.002)^4 \\ &= 8^4 (1 + 0.002)^4\end{aligned}$$

$$(1 + 0.002)^4 = 1 + 4(0.002) + \frac{4(3)}{2}(0.002)^2 + \ldots$$

$$= 1 + 0.008 + 0.000024 + \ldots$$
$$\simeq 1.008024$$

Hence $(8.016)^4$
$$\begin{aligned} &\simeq 8^4 (1.008024) \\ &\simeq 4096(1.008024) \\ &= \mathbf{4128.87} \text{ correct to six significant figures.}\end{aligned}$$

Problem 4. Pressure p and volume v are related by the expression
$$pv^3 = C, \text{ where } C \text{ is a constant.}$$

Find the approximate percentage change in C when p is increased by 2 per cent and v decreased by 0.8 per cent.

Let p and v be the original values of pressure and volume.

The new values are $\frac{102}{100}p$ or $(1 + 0.02)p$ and $\frac{99.2}{100}v$ or $(1 - 0.008)v$.

Let the new value of C be C_1, then

$$\begin{aligned} C_1 &= (1 + 0.02)p\,[(1 - 0.008)v]^3 \\ &= (1 + 0.02)(1 - 0.008)^3\, pv^3 \\ &\quad (1 - 0.008)^3 \simeq 1 - (3)(0.008) + \ldots \\ &\quad\quad\quad \simeq 1 - 0.024 \end{aligned}$$

Hence $C_1 \quad\quad \simeq (1 + 0.02)(1 - 0.024)\,C$

and neglecting the products of small terms, this becomes
$$C_1 \simeq (1 + 0.02 - 0.024)C$$
$$\simeq (1 - 0.004)C$$
Hence the value of C is reduced by approximately 0.4 per cent when p is increased by 2 per cent and v decreased by 0.8 per cent.

Problem 5. The resonant frequency of a vibrating shaft is given by $f = \dfrac{1}{2\pi}\sqrt{\left(\dfrac{k}{I}\right)}$,

where k is the stiffness and I is the inertia of the shaft. Determine the approximate percentage error in determining the frequency using the measured values of k and I, when the measured value of k is 3 per cent too large and the measured value of I is 1.5 per cent too small.

Let f, k and I be the true values of frequency, stiffness and inertia respectively. Since the measured value of stiffness, k_1 is 3 per cent too large,
$k_1 = \dfrac{103}{100}k = (1 + 0.03)k$. The measured value of inertia, I_1 is 1.5 per cent

too small, hence $I_1 = \dfrac{98.5}{100}I = (1 - 0.015)I$.

The measured value of frequency,

$$f_1 = \frac{1}{2\pi}\sqrt{\left(\frac{k_1}{I_1}\right)} = \frac{1}{2\pi}\frac{k_1^{\frac{1}{2}}}{I_1^{\frac{1}{2}}} = \frac{1}{2\pi}k_1^{\frac{1}{2}}I_1^{-\frac{1}{2}}$$

$$= \frac{1}{2\pi}\left[(1 + 0.03)k\right]^{\frac{1}{2}}\left[(1 - 0.015)I\right]^{-\frac{1}{2}}$$

$$= \frac{1}{2\pi}(1 + 0.03)^{\frac{1}{2}}k^{\frac{1}{2}}(1 - 0.015)^{-\frac{1}{2}}I^{-\frac{1}{2}}$$

$$= \frac{1}{2\pi}k^{\frac{1}{2}}I^{-\frac{1}{2}}(1 + 0.03)^{\frac{1}{2}}(1 - 0.015)^{-\frac{1}{2}}$$

i.e., $f_1 = (1 + 0.03)^{\frac{1}{2}}(1 - 0.015)^{-\frac{1}{2}}f$

$$\simeq \left(1 + \left(\frac{1}{2}\right)(0.03)\right)\left(1 - \left(-\frac{1}{2}\right)(0.015)\right)f$$

$$\simeq (1 + 0.015)(1 + 0.0075)f$$

Neglecting the products of small terms,

$$f_1 \simeq (1 + 0.015 + 0.0075)f \simeq 1.0225f$$

Thus, the percentage error based on the measured values of k and I is approximately $(1.0225)(100) - 100$, i.e., **2.3 per cent too large**.

Further problems on determining approximate values, using the binomial expansion, may be found in the following section (4) (Problems 21–32), p. 15.

4. Further problems

Expansions of the type $(a + b)^n$ where n is a small positive integer using Pascal's triangle

1. Determine the expansion of $(a + b)^8$.

   $[a^8 + 8a^7b + 28a^6b^2 + 56a^5b^3 + 70a^4b^4 + 56a^3b^5 + 28a^2b^6 + 8ab^7 + b^8]$

2. Find the expansion of $(x - y)^5$.

   $[x^5 - 5x^4y + 10x^3y^2 - 10x^2y^3 + 5xy^4 - y^5]$

3. Find the expansion of $(2p - 3q)^6$.

   $[64p^6 - 576p^5q + 2\,160p^4q^2 - 4\,320p^3q^3 + 4\,860p^2q^4 - 2\,916pq^5$
   $+ 729q^6]$

4. Expand $(p + 3q)^{11}$ as far as the term containing q^4.

   $[p^{11} + 33p^{10}q + 495p^9q^2 + 4\,455p^8q^3 + 26\,730p^7q^4]$

5. Find the expansion of $(x - 2y)^{10}$ as far as the term containing y^5.

   $[x^{10} - 20x^9y + 180x^8y^2 - 960x^7y^3 + 3\,360x^6y^4 - 8\,064x^5y^5]$

6. Determine the expansion of $\left(-m - \dfrac{n}{2}\right)^7$ as far as the term containing n^4.

   $\left[-m^7 - \dfrac{7}{2}m^6n - \dfrac{21}{4}m^5n^2 - \dfrac{35}{8}m^4n^3 - \dfrac{35}{16}m^3n^4\right]$

7. Determine the expansion of $\left(\dfrac{w}{2} - \dfrac{x}{3}\right)^4$.

   $\left[\dfrac{1}{16}w^4 - \dfrac{1}{6}w^3x + \dfrac{1}{6}w^2x^2 - \dfrac{2}{27}wx^3 + \dfrac{1}{81}x^4\right]$

8. Find the expansion of $(3 + 4y)^6$ and express the result in the form $a + by + cy^2 + \ldots$, where $a, b, c, \ldots$ are constants.

   $[729 + 5\,832y + 19\,440y^2 + 34\,560y^3 + 34\,560y^4 + 18\,432y^5 + 4\,096y^6]$

9. Determine the expansion of $\left(\dfrac{x}{4} - 7\right)^5$ and express the result in the form

   $ax^5 + bx^4 + cx^3 + \ldots$, where $a, b, c, \ldots$ are constants.

   $\left[\dfrac{x^5}{1\,024} - \dfrac{35}{256}x^4 + \dfrac{245}{32}x^3 - \dfrac{1\,715}{8}x^2 + \dfrac{12\,005}{4}x - 16\,807\right]$

10. Expand $\left(-5 - \dfrac{p}{3}\right)^8$ as far as the term containing p^4.

    $\left[390\,625 + \dfrac{625\,000}{3}p + \dfrac{437\,500}{9}p^2 + \dfrac{175\,000}{27}p^3 + \dfrac{43\,750}{81}p^4\right]$

Expansions of the type $(a + b)^n$ where n is any positive integer

11. Find the expansion of $(a + b)^{12}$ as far as the term containing b^5.

$[a^{12} + 12a^{11}b + 66a^{10}b^2 + 220a^9b^3 + 495a^8b^4 + 792a^7b^5]$

12. Determine the expansion of $\left(x - \dfrac{y}{2}\right)^{16}$ as far as the term containing y^4.

$\left[x^{16} - 8x^{15}y + 30x^{14}y^2 - 70x^{13}y^3 + \dfrac{455}{4}x^{12}y^4\right]$

In problems 13–15, find the first four terms of the expansions of the expressions given.

13. $\left(m - \dfrac{n^2}{2}\right)^{13}$ $\left[m^{13} - \dfrac{13}{2}m^{12}n^2 + \dfrac{39}{2}m^{11}n^4 - \dfrac{143}{4}m^{10}n^6\right]$

14. $(-p^2 - 2q)^{17}$ $[-p^{34} - 34p^{32}q - 544p^{30}q^2 - 5\,440p^{28}q^3]$

15. $\left(-\dfrac{1}{x} + \dfrac{3}{y}\right)^{19}$ $\left[-\dfrac{1}{x^{19}} + \dfrac{57}{x^{18}y} - \dfrac{1\,539}{x^{17}y^2} + \dfrac{26\,163}{x^{16}y^3}\right]$

16. Determine the middle term of the expansion of $(x^2 - y^2)^{14}$.

$[-3\,432\,x^{14}y^{14}]$

17. Find the eleventh term of the expansion of $\left(2p - \dfrac{q}{2}\right)^{21}$.

$[705\,432\,p^{11}q^{10}]$

18. Find the value of the middle term of the expansion of $\left(2c^2 - \dfrac{1}{2c^2}\right)^{12}$.

$[924]$

19. Determine the two middle terms of the expansion of $\left(2p - \dfrac{1}{3p}\right)^9$.

$\left[\dfrac{1\,344p}{27}, -\dfrac{224}{27p}\right]$

20. Find the term involving a^{12} in the expansion of $\left(a^3 - \dfrac{b}{2}\right)^{14}$.

$\left[\dfrac{1\,001}{1\,024}a^{12}b^{10}\right]$

Determining the approximate values of expressions

21. Use the binomial expansion to calculate the value of $(0.995)^{12}$ correct to (a) 4 decimal places; and (b) 6 decimal places. $[0.941\,6, 0.941\,623]$

22. Find the value of $(1.05)^3(0.98)^4$ correct to 5 significant figures by using binomial expansions. $[1.067\,8]$

23. Determine the value of $(3.036)^3$ correct to 3 decimal places by using the binomial expansion.   [27.984]

24. Use the binomial expansion to find the value of $(2.018)^5$ correct to 6 significant figures.   [33.466 2]

25. An error of 3.5 per cent too large was made when measuring the radius of a sphere. Ignoring the products of small quantities, determine the approximate error in calculating: (a) the volume; and (b) the surface area when they are calculated using the correct radius measurement.   [10.5 per cent too large, 7 per cent too large]

26. The area of a triangle is given by $A = \frac{1}{2}ab \sin C$, where C is the angle between the sides a and b of a triangle. Calculate the approximate change in area (ignoring the products of small quantities), when: (a) both a and b are increased by 2 per cent; and (b) when a is increased by 2 per cent and b is reduced by 2 per cent.   [4 per cent increase, no change]

27. The moment of inertia of a body about an axis is given by $I = kbd^3$ where k is a constant and b and d are the dimensions of the body. Determine the approximate percentage change in the value of I when b is increased by 5 per cent and d reduced by 1 per cent, if products of small quantities are ignored.   [2 per cent increase]

28. The radius of a cone is reduced by 4.5 per cent and its height increased by 1.5 per cent. Determine the approximate percentage change: (a) in its volume, neglecting the products of small quantities.
     [7.5 per cent reduction]

29. The power developed by an engine is given by $I = kPLAN$ where k is a constant. Find the approximate percentage increase in power when P, L, A and N are each increased by 3.5 per cent.   [14 per cent]

30. The modulus of rigidity G is given by

$$G = \frac{R^4 \theta}{L}$$

where R is the radius, θ the angle of twist, and L the length. Find the approximate percentage error in G where R is measured 1.5 per cent too large and θ is measured 5 per cent too small.   [1 per cent too large]

31. The degree of hydrolysis of methyl ethanoate is given by the equation $\alpha = \sqrt{[K_w/(K_a C)]}$, where K_w is a constant. If there is an error of $+1.2$ per cent in K_a and -2.5 per cent in C, determine the resultant error in α.   [0.65 per cent]

32. The viscosity (η) of a liquid is given by:

$$\eta = \frac{a\, r^4}{vl}, \text{ where } a \text{ is a constant.}$$

If there is an error in r of $+3$ per cent, in v of $+4$ per cent and l of -2 per cent, what is the resultant error in η?   [10 per cent]

Chapter 2

Exponential functions and Naperian logarithms

1 The exponential function

In calculus and more advanced mathematics, a mathematical constant e is frequently used. This constant is called the exponent and has a value of approximately 2.7183. A function containing e^x is called an **exponential function** and can also be written as exp x. e^x is a function which increases at a rate proportional to its own magnitude (see Chapter 3).

All the natural laws of growth and decay are of the form $y = ae^{kx}$ (see Chapter 3) and therefore the exponent is of considerable importance in Science and Engineering.

In the same way that logarithms to the base 10 were introduced to facilitate calculations based on powers of 10, logarithms to the base e were developed by Napier to simplify calculations involving the exponential function (see Section 3).

2 Evaluating exponential functions

The value of e^x may be determined by using:

(a) the power series for e^x;
(b) a calculator; or
(c) tables of exponential functions.

(a) The value of e^x can be calculated to any required degree of accuracy since it is defined in terms of the following power series:

$$e^x = 1 + x + \frac{x^2}{2!} + \frac{x^3}{3!} +$$

which is valid for all values of x,   (1)

(where $3! = 3 \times 2 \times 1$ and is called 'factorial 3' – see Chapter 1).
This series is said to **converge**, that is, if all the terms are added an actual
value for e^x is obtained, where x is a real number. The more terms that
are taken, the closer will be the value of e^x to its actual value.
The value of the exponent e, correct to say 4 decimal places, may be
determined by substituting $x = 1$ in the power series of equation (1).

$$\text{Thus } e^1 = 1 + 1 + \frac{(1)^2}{2!} + \frac{(1)^3}{3!} + \frac{(1)^4}{4!} + \frac{(1)^5}{5!} + \frac{(1)^6}{6!} + \frac{(1)^7}{7!} + \frac{(1)^8}{8!}$$

$$= 1 + 1 + 0.5 + 0.166\,67 + 0.041\,67 + 0.008\,33 + 0.001\,39$$
$$+ 0.000\,20 + 0.000\,02$$
$$= 2.718\,28$$

i.e., $e = 2.718\,3$, **correct to 4 decimal places.**

The value of $e^{0.01}$, correct to, say, 9 significant figures is found by
substituting $x = 0.01$ in the power series for e^x.

$$\text{Thus: } e^{0.01} = 1 + 0.01 + \frac{(0.01)^2}{2!} + \frac{(0.01)^3}{3!} + \frac{(0.01)^4}{4!} + \dots$$

$$= 1 + 0.01 + 0.000\,05 + 0.000\,000\,167 + 0.000\,000\,000\,4$$

and by adding, $e^{0.01} = 1.010\,050\,17$, correct to 9 significant figures.
In this example, successive terms in the series grow smaller very rapidly
and it is relatively easy to determine the value of $e^{0.01}$ to a high degree of
accuracy. However, when x is near to unity or larger than unity, a very
large number of terms are required for an accurate result.

If, in the series of equation (1), x is replaced by $-x$,

$$\text{then } e^{-x} = 1 + (-x) + \frac{(-x)^2}{2!} + \frac{(-x)^3}{3!} + \dots$$

$$\text{i.e., } e^{-x} = 1 - x + \frac{x^2}{2!} - \frac{x^3}{3!} + \dots$$

In a similar manner the power series for e^x may be used to evaluate any
exponential function of the form ae^{kx}, where a and k are constants. In
the series of equation (1), let x be replaced by kx, then:

$$ae^{kx} = a \left\{ 1 + (kx) + \frac{(kx)^2}{2!} + \frac{(kx)^3}{3!} + \dots \right\}$$

$$\text{Thus } 3e^{2x} = 3 \left\{ 1 + (2x) + \frac{(2x)^2}{2!} + \frac{(2x)^3}{3!} + \dots \right\}$$

$$= 3 \left\{ 1 + (2x) + \frac{4x^2}{2 \times 1} + \frac{8x^3}{3 \times 2 \times 1} + \dots \right\}$$

$$= 3 \left\{ 1 + 2x + 2x^2 + \frac{4}{3}x^3 + \dots \right\}$$

(b) Most **scientific notation calculators** contain an 'e^x' function which enables all practical values of e^x and e^{-x} to be determined, correct to 8 or 9 significant figures.

For example, $\quad e^1 = 2.718\ 281\ 83$,
$$e^{2.5} = 12.182\ 494\ 0,$$
and $\quad\quad e^{-1.732} = 0.176\ 930\ 20$, correct to 9 significant figures.

In practical situations the degree of accuracy given by a calculator is often far greater than is appropriate. The accepted convention is that the final result is stated to one significant figure greater than the least significant measured value.

(c) For many purposes, an accuracy of four or five significant figures is sufficient and most books of **mathematical tables** contain tables of the values of exponential functions. One such table is shown in Table 1 on page 20.

This table enables the values of e^x or e^{-x} to be read over a range of x from 0.02 to 6.0 in discrete steps of 0.01 over most of the range.

For example, $\quad e^{0.38} = 1.462\ 3, e^{-0.38} = 0.683\ 9$,
$$e^{4.3} = 73.700 \text{ and } e^{-5.9} = 0.002\ 74$$

Some intermediate values can be obtained by using the laws of indices.

For example, $\quad e^{0.74} = e^{(0.7\ +\ 0.04)}$
$$= (e^{0.7})(e^{0.04})$$
$$= (2.013\ 8)(1.040\ 8)$$
$$= 2.095\ 963$$
$$= \mathbf{2.096\ 0}\text{, allowing for rounding off errors in the}$$
original data. The relationship between the tabular values of e^x are **not** linear and a correct result will not be obtained by methods of interpolation between the given values.

Worked problems on evaluating exponential functions

Problem 1. Determine the value of $2e^{0.3}$ correct to 5 significant figures by using the power series for e^x

Substituting $x = 0.3$ in the power series

$$e^x = 1 + x + \frac{x^2}{2!} + \frac{x^3}{3!} + \ldots \text{ gives}$$

$$e^{0.3} = 1 + 0.3 + \frac{(0.3)^2}{(2)(1)} + \frac{(0.3)^3}{(3)(2)(1)} + \frac{(0.3)^4}{(4)(3)(2)(1)} + \frac{(0.3)^5}{(5)(4)(3)(2)(1)}$$

$$= 1 + 0.3 + 0.045 + 0.004\ 5 + 0.000\ 338 + 0.000\ 020$$

$$= 1.349\ 86 \text{ correct to 6 significant figures.}$$

Hence $2e^{0.3} = \mathbf{2.699\ 7}$, correct to 5 significant figures.

Table 1 Exponential functions

x	e^x	e^{-x}	x	e^x	e^{-x}
.02	1.0202	.9802	1.0	2.7183	.3679
.04	1.0408	.9608	1.1	3.0042	.3329
.06	1.0618	.9418	1.2	3.3201	.3012
.08	1.0833	.9231	1.3	3.6693	.2725
			1.4	4.0552	.2466
.10	1.1052	.9048			
.11	1.1163	.8958	1.5	4.4817	.2231
.12	1.1275	.8869	1.6	4.9530	.2019
.13	1.1388	.8781	1.7	5.4739	.1827
.14	1.1503	.8694	1.8	6.0497	.1653
			1.9	6.6859	.1496
.15	1.1618	.8607			
.16	1.1735	.8521	2.0	7.3891	.1353
.17	1.1853	.8437	2.1	8.1662	.1225
.18	1.1972	.8353	2.2	9.0250	.1108
.19	1.2092	.8270	2.3	9.9742	.1003
			2.4	11.023	.0907
.20	1.2214	.8187			
.21	1.2337	.8106	2.5	12.182	.0821
22	1.2461	.8025	2.6	13.464	.0743
.23	1.2586	.7945	2.7	14.880	.0672
24	1.2712	.7866	2.8	16.445	.0608
			2.9	18.174	.0550
.25	1.2840	.7788			
.26	1.2696	.7711	3.0	20.085	.0498
.27	1.3100	.7634	3.1	22.198	.0450
.28	1.3231	.7558	3.2	24.532	.0408
.29	1.3364	.7483	3.3	27.113	.0369
			3.4	29.964	.0334
.30	1.3499	.7408			
.31	1.3634	.7335	3.5	33.115	.0302
.32	1.3771	.7261	3.6	36.598	.0273
.33	1.3910	.7189	3.7	40.447	.0247
.34	1.4050	.7118	3.8	44.701	.0224
			3.9	49.402	.0202
.35	1.4191	.7047			
.36	1.4333	.6977	4.0	54.598	.0183
.37	1.4477	.6907	4.1	60.340	.0166
.38	1.4623	.6839	4.2	66.686	.0150
.39	1.4770	.6771	4.3	73.700	.0136
			4.4	81.451	.0123
.40	1.4918	.6703			
.41	1.5068	.6636	4.5	90.017	.0111
.42	1.5220	.6570	4.6	99.484	.0100
.43	1.5373	.6505	4.7	109.95	.00910
.44	1.5527	.6440	4.8	121.51	.00823
			4.9	134.29	.00745
.45	1.5683	.6376			
.46	1.5841	.6313	5.0	148.41	.00674
.47	1.6000	.6250	5.1	164.02	.00610
.48	1.6161	.6188	5.2	181.27	.00552
.49	1.6323	.6126	5.3	200.34	.00499
			5.4	221.41	.00452
.50	1.6487	.6065			
.6	1.8221	.5488	5.5	244.69	.00409
.7	2.0138	.4966	5.6	270.43	.00370
.8	2.2255	.4493	5.7	298.87	.00335
.9	2.4596	.4066	5.8	330.30	.00303
			5.9	365.04	.00274
			6.0	403.43	.00248

Problem 2. Determine the value of $-4e^{-1}$ correct to 4 decimal places using the power series for e^x.

Substituting $x = -1$ in the power series

$$e^x = 1 + x + \frac{x^2}{2!} + \frac{x^3}{3!} + \ldots \text{ gives}$$

$$e^{-1} = 1 + (-1) + \frac{(-1)^2}{(2)(1)} + \frac{(-1)^3}{(3)(2)(1)} + \frac{(-1)^4}{(4)(3)(2)(1)} + \ldots$$

$$= 1 - 1 + 0.5 - 0.166\,667 + 0.041\,667 - 0.008\,333$$
$$+ 0.001\,389 - 0.000\,198 + \ldots$$

$$= 0.367\,858, \text{ correct to 6 decimal places.}$$

Hence, $-4e^{-1} = (-4)(0.367\,858) = -1.471\,4$, correct to 4 decimal places.

Problem 3. Use exponential tables to determine the values of:

(a) $e^{0.14}$, (b) $e^{-2.6}$, (c) $2e^{-0.66}$, and (d) $4e^{10}$, correct to 4 significant figures.

(a) Using a table of exponential values, when $x = 0.14$

$$e^x = e^{0.14} = 1.1503 = \mathbf{1.150}, \text{ correct to 4 significant figures.}$$

(b) From exponential tables, when $x = 2.6$,

$$e^{-x} = e^{-2.6} = \mathbf{0.074\,3}, \text{ correct to 4 significant figures.}$$

(c) $e^{-0.66} = e^{(-0.7 + 0.04)}$ and using the laws of indices,

$$e^{-0.66} = (e^{-0.7})(e^{0.04}).$$

Using exponential tables gives:

$$\text{when } x = 0.7, e^{-x} = e^{-0.7} = 0.496\,6$$

$$\text{and when } x = 0.04, e^x = e^{0.04} = 1.040\,8$$

Hence $e^{-0.66} = (0.496\,6)(1.040\,8) = 0.516\,86$

Thus $2e^{-0.66} = (2)(0.516\,86) = \mathbf{1.034}$, correct to 4 significant figures.

(d) $e^{10} = e^{(5 + 5)} = (e^5)(e^5)$

and when $x = 5$, using exponential tables gives:

$$e^x = e^5 = 148.41$$

Thus $e^{10} = (148.41)^2$

$$= 22\,026.$$

Then $4e^{10} = 4(22\,026) = \mathbf{88\,100}$, correct to 4 significant figures.

Problem 4. Expand $e^x (x^2 + 1)$, as far as the term in x^5.

The power series for e^x is $1 + x + \dfrac{x^2}{2!} + \dfrac{x^3}{3!} + \dfrac{x^4}{4!} + \ldots$

Hence $e^x (x^2 + 1) = (1 + x + \dfrac{x^2}{2!} + \dfrac{x^3}{3!} + \dfrac{x^4}{4!} + \ldots)(x^2 + 1)$

i.e., $e^x (x^2 + 1) = (x^2 + x^3 + \dfrac{x^4}{2!} + \dfrac{x^5}{3!}) + (1 + x + \dfrac{x^2}{2!} + \dfrac{x^3}{3!} + \dfrac{x^4}{4!} + \dfrac{x^5}{5!} + \ldots)$

Grouping like terms gives:

$$e^x (x^2 + 1) = 1 + x + (1 + \dfrac{1}{2!}) x^2 + (1 + \dfrac{1}{3!}) x^3 + (\dfrac{1}{2!} + \dfrac{1}{4!}) x^4$$

$$+ (\dfrac{1}{3!} + \dfrac{1}{5!}) x^5 \ldots$$

i.e., $e^x (x^2 + 1) = 1 + x + \dfrac{3}{2} x^2 + \dfrac{7}{6} x^3 + \dfrac{13}{24} x^4 + \dfrac{7}{40} x^5$

when expanded as far as the term in x^5.

Further problems on exponential functions may be found in Section 5, (Problems 1–7), p. 31.

3 Naperian logarithms

A logarithm of a number is defined as the power to which a base has to be raised to be equal to the number. Thus if $y = a^x$, then $x = \log_a y$. When using logarithms as an aid to calculations, a base of 10 is usually selected because the characteristic of the logarithm can be readily obtained. A more logical base when using calculus and when dealing with problems involving the natural growth or decay laws is the exponent 'e'. Logarithms to a base of 'e' are called **Hyperbolic**, **Naperian** or **Natural logarithms** and the Naperian logarithm of x is written as '$\log_e x$' or more commonly, '$\ln x$'.

4 Evaluating Naperian logarithms

The value of a Naperian logarithm may be determined by using:

(a) a relationship between common and natural logarithms;
(b) a calculator; or
(c) four-figure Naperian logarithm tables.

(a) Let $x = \log_a y$

then $a^x = y$, from the definition of a logarithm.

Taking logarithms to a base of b of both sides gives:

$$\log_b a^x = \log_b y$$

i.e. $x \log_b a = \log_b y$, from the laws of logarithms.

from which, $x = \dfrac{\log_b y}{\log_b a}$

Hence a general rule of logarithms used when changing a base states:

$$\log_a y = \frac{\log_b y}{\log_b a}$$

Substituting e for a and 10 for b gives:

$$\ln y = \frac{\lg y}{\lg e}$$

But $\lg e = \lg 2.718 = 0.434\ 3$

Hence $\ln y = \dfrac{\lg y}{0.434\ 3}$ or $2.302\ 6 \lg y$.

Thus, the Naperian logarithm of a number is obtained by multiplying the logarithm of the number which has a base of 10 by 2.302 6

Thus $\ln 100 = 2.302\ 6\ \lg 100 = 2.302\ 6 \times 2 = 4.605\ 2$
and $\ln 31.68 = 2.302\ 6\ \lg 31.68 = 2.302\ 6 \times 1.500\ 8 = 3.455\ 7$

(b) Most scientific notation calculators contain a '$\ln x$' function which gives the value of a Naperian logarithm of a number displayed when the appropriate key is pressed.

Using a calculator, $\ln 5.321 = 1.671\ 661\ 26 = 1.671\ 7$, correct to 4 decimal places,

and $\ln 21.43 = 3.064\ 791\ 81 = 3.064\ 8$, correct to 4 decimal places.

(c) **Using Naperian logarithm tables**

For numbers from 1 to 10, the tables of Naperian logarithms are used in the same way as tables of logarithms to a base of 10. With reference to Table 2 care should be taken to see that the correct characteristic has been taken from the first column of the tables, as this is 1 for numbers between 2.718 and 7.388 and 2 for numbers between 7.389 and 10.0.

Numbers larger than 10 are expressed in standard form and the supplementary table of Naperian logarithms of 10^{+n} used. Thus, the Naperian logarithm of, say, 70, is obtained as follows:

$$\begin{aligned}
\ln 70 &= \ln (7 \times 10^1) \\
&= \ln 7 + \ln 10^1 \\
&= 1.945\ 9 + 2.302\ 6 \\
&= 4.248\ 5
\end{aligned}$$

Numbers smaller than 1 are also expressed in standard form and the supplementary table of Naperian logarithms of 10^{-n} used. The Naperian

Table 2 Hyperbolic or Naperian logarithms

	0	1	2	3	4	5	6	7	8	9	Mean Differences		
											1 2 3	4 5 6	7 8 9
1.0	0.0000	0099	0198	0296	0392	0488	0583	0677	0770	0862	10 19 29	38 48 57	67 76 86
1.1	.0953	1044	1133	1222	1310	1398	1484	1570	1655	1740	9 17 26	35 44 52	61 70 78
1.2	.1823	1906	1989	2070	2151	2231	2311	2390	2469	2546	8 16 24	32 40 48	56 64 72
1.3	.2624	2700	2776	2852	2927	3001	3075	3148	3221	3293	7 15 22	30 37 44	52 59 67
1.4	.3365	3436	3507	3577	3646	3716	3784	3853	3920	3988	7 14 21	28 35 41	48 55 62
1.5	.4055	4121	4187	4253	4318	4383	4447	4511	4574	4637	6 13 19	26 32 39	45 52 58
1.6	.4700	4762	4824	4886	4947	5008	5068	5128	5188	5247	6 12 18	24 30 36	42 48 55
1.7	.5306	5365	5423	5481	5539	5596	5653	5710	5766	5822	6 11 17	24 29 34	40 46 51
1.8	.5878	5933	5988	6043	6098	6152	6206	6259	6313	6366	5 11 16	22 27 32	38 43 49
1.9	.6419	6471	6523	6575	6627	6678	6729	6780	6831	6881	5 10 15	20 26 31	36 41 46
2.0	.6931	6981	7031	7080	7129	7178	7227	7275	7324	7372	5 10 15	20 24 29	34 39 44
2.1	.7419	7467	7514	7561	7608	7655	7701	7747	7793	7839	5 9 14	18 23 28	33 37 42
2.2	.7885	7930	7975	8020	8065	8109	8154	8198	8242	8286	4 9 13	18 22 27	31 36 40
2.3	.8329	8372	8416	8459	8502	8544	8587	8629	8671	8713	4 9 13	17 21 26	30 34 38
2.4	.8755	8796	8838	8879	8920	8961	9002	9042	9083	9123	4 8 12	16 20 24	29 33 37
2.5	.9163	9203	9243	9282	9322	9361	9400	9439	9478	9517	4 8 12	16 20 24	27 31 35
2.6	.9555	9594	9632	9670	9708	9746	9783	9821	9858	9895	4 8 11	15 19 23	26 30 34
2.7	.9933	9969	1.0006	0043	0080	0116	0152	0188	0225	0260	4 7 11	15 18 22	25 29 33
2.8	1.0296	0332	0367	0403	0438	0473	0508	0543	0578	0613	4 7 11	14 18 21	25 28 32
2.9	1.0647	0682	0716	0750	0784	0818	0852	0886	0919	0953	3 7 10	14 17 20	24 27 31
3.0	1.0986	1019	1053	1086	1119	1151	1184	1217	1249	1282	3 7 10	13 16 20	23 26 30
3.1	1.1314	1346	1378	1410	1442	1474	1506	1537	1569	1600	3 6 10	13 16 19	22 25 29
3.2	1.1632	1663	1694	1725	1756	1787	1817	1848	1878	1909	3 6 9	12 15 18	22 25 28
3.3	1.1939	1969	1.2000	2030	2060	2090	2119	2149	2179	2208	3 6 9	12 15 18	21 24 27
3.4	1.2238	2267	2296	2326	2355	2384	2413	2442	2470	2499	3 6 9	12 15 17	20 23 26
3.5	1.2528	2556	2585	2613	2641	2669	2698	2726	2754	2782	3 6 8	11 14 17	20 23 25
3.6	1.2809	2837	2865	2892	2920	2947	2975	3002	3029	3056	3 5 8	11 14 16	19 22 25
3.7	1.3083	3110	3137	3164	3191	3218	3244	3271	3297	3324	3 5 8	11 13 16	19 21 24
3.8	1.3350	3376	3403	3429	3455	3481	3507	3533	3558	3584	3 5 8	10 13 16	18 21 23
3.9	1.3610	3635	3661	3686	3712	3737	3762	3788	3813	3838	3 5 8	10 13 15	18 20 23
4.0	1.3863	3888	3913	3938	3962	3987	4012	4036	4061	4085	2 5 7	10 12 15	17 20 22
4.1	1.4110	4134	4159	4183	4207	4231	4255	4279	4303	4327	2 5 7	10 12 14	17 19 22
4.2	1.4351	4375	4398	4422	4446	4469	4493	4516	4540	4563	2 5 7	9 12 14	16 19 21
4.3	1.4586	4609	4633	4656	4679	4702	4725	4748	4770	4793	2 5 7	9 12 14	16 18 21
4.4	1.4816	4839	4861	4884	4907	4929	4951	4974	4996	5019	2 5 7	9 11 14	16 18 20
4.5	1.5041	5063	5085	5107	5129	5151	5173	5195	5217	5239	2 4 7	9 11 13	15 18 20
4.6	1.5261	5282	5304	5326	5347	5369	5390	5412	5433	5454	2 4 6	9 11 13	15 17 19
4.7	1.5476	5497	5518	5539	5560	5581	5602	5623	5644	5665	2 4 6	8 11 13	15 17 19
4.8	1.5686	5707	5728	5748	5769	5790	5810	5831	5851	5872	2 4 6	8 10 12	14 16 19
4.9	1.5892	5913	5933	5953	5974	5994	6014	6034	6054	6074	2 4 6	8 10 12	14 16 18
5.0	1.6094	6114	6134	6154	6174	6194	6214	6233	6253	6273	2 4 6	8 10 12	14 16 18
5.1	1.6292	6312	6332	6351	6371	6390	6409	6429	6448	6467	2 4 6	8 10 12	14 16 18
5.2	1.6487	6506	6525	6544	6563	6582	6601	6620	6639	6658	2 4 6	8 10 11	13 15 17
5.3	1.6677	6696	6715	6734	6752	6771	6790	6808	6827	6845	2 4 6	7 9 11	13 15 17
5.4	1.6864	6882	6901	6919	6938	6956	6974	6993	7011	7029	2 4 5	7 9 11	13 15 17

Hyperbolic or Naperian logarithms of 10^{+n}

n	1	2	3	4	5	6	7	8	9
$\log_e 10^n$	2.3026	4.6052	6.9078	9.2103	11.5129	13.8155	16.1181	18.4207	20.7233

Table 2 *(cont'd)* Hyperbolic or Naperian Logarithms

	0	1	2	3	4	5	6	7	8	9	Mean Differences 1	2	3	4	5	6	7	8	9
5.5	1.7047	7066	7084	7102	7120	7138	7156	7174	7192	7210	2	4	5	7	9	11	13	14	16
5.6	1.7228	7246	7263	7281	7299	7317	7334	7352	7370	7387	2	4	5	7	9	11	12	14	16
5.7	1.7405	7422	7440	7457	7475	7492	7509	7527	7544	7561	2	3	5	7	9	10	12	14	16
5.8	1.7579	7596	7613	7630	7647	7664	7681	7699	7716	7733	2	3	5	7	9	10	12	14	15
5.9	1.7750	7766	7783	7800	7817	7834	7851	7867	7884	7901	2	3	5	7	8	10	12	13	15
6.0	1.7918	7934	7951	7967	7984	8001	8017	8034	8050	8066	2	3	5	7	8	10	12	13	15
6.1	1.8083	8099	8116	8132	8148	8165	8181	8197	8213	8229	2	3	5	6	8	10	11	13	15
6.2	1.8245	8262	8278	8294	8310	8326	8342	8358	8374	8390	2	3	5	6	8	10	11	13	14
6.3	1.8405	8421	8437	8453	8469	8485	8500	8516	8532	8547	2	3	5	6	8	9	11	13	14
6.4	1.8563	8579	8594	8610	8625	8641	8656	8672	8687	8703	2	3	5	6	8	9	11	12	14
6.5	1.8718	8733	8749	8764	8779	8795	8810	8825	8840	8856	2	3	5	6	8	9	11	12	14
6.6	1.8871	8886	8901	8916	8931	8946	8961	8976	8991	9006	2	3	5	6	8	9	11	12	14
6.7	1.9021	9036	9051	9066	9081	9095	9110	9125	9140	9155	1	3	4	6	7	9	10	12	13
6.8	1.9169	9184	9199	9213	9228	9242	9257	9272	9286	9301	1	3	4	6	7	9	10	12	13
6.9	1.9315	9330	9344	9359	9373	9387	9402	9416	9430	9445	1	3	4	6	7	9	10	12	13
7.0	1.9459	9473	9488	9502	9516	9530	9544	9559	9573	9587	1	3	4	6	7	9	10	11	13
7.1	1.9601	9615	9629	9643	9657	9671	9685	9699	9713	9727	1	3	4	6	7	8	10	11	13
7.2	1.9741	9755	9769	9782	9796	9810	9824	9838	9851	9865	1	3	4	6	7	8	10	11	12
7.3	1.9879	9892	9906	9920	9933	9947	9961	9974	9988	2.0001	1	3	4	5	7	8	10	11	12
7.4	2.0015	0028	0042	0055	0069	0082	0096	0109	0122	0136	1	3	4	5	7	8	9	11	12
7.5	2.0149	0162	0176	0189	0202	0215	0229	0242	0255	0268	1	3	4	5	7	8	9	11	12
7.6	2.0281	0259	0308	0321	0334	0347	0360	0373	0386	0399	1	3	4	5	7	8	9	10	12
7.7	2.0412	0425	0438	0451	0464	0477	0490	0503	0516	0528	1	3	4	5	6	8	9	10	12
7.8	2.0541	0554	0567	0580	0592	0605	0618	0631	0643	0656	1	3	4	5	6	8	9	10	11
7.9	2.0669	0681	0694	0707	0719	0732	0744	0757	0769	0782	1	3	4	5	6	8	9	10	11
8.0	2.0794	0807	0819	0832	0844	0857	0869	0882	0894	0906	1	2	4	5	6	7	9	10	11
8.1	2.0919	0931	0943	0956	0968	0980	0992	1005	1017	1029	1	2	4	5	6	7	9	10	11
8.2	2.1041	1054	1066	1078	1090	1102	1114	1126	1138	1150	1	2	4	5	6	7	9	10	11
8.3	2.1163	1175	1187	1199	1211	1223	1235	1247	1258	1270	1	2	4	5	6	7	8	10	11
8.4	2.1282	1294	1306	1318	1330	1342	1353	1365	1377	1389	1	2	4	5	6	7	8	9	11
8.5	2.1401	1412	1424	1436	1448	1459	1471	1483	1494	1506	1	2	4	5	6	7	8	9	11
8.6	2.1518	1529	1541	1552	1564	1576	1587	1599	1610	1622	1	2	3	5	6	7	8	9	10
8.7	2.1633	1645	1656	1668	1679	1691	1702	1713	1725	1736	1	2	3	5	6	7	8	9	10
8.8	2.1748	1759	1770	1782	1793	1804	1815	1827	1838	1849	1	2	3	5	6	7	8	9	10
8.9	2.1861	1872	1883	1894	1905	1917	1928	1939	1950	1961	1	2	3	4	6	7	8	9	10
9.0	2.1972	1983	1994	2006	2017	2028	2039	2050	2061	2072	1	2	3	4	6	7	8	9	10
9.1	2.2083	2094	2105	2116	2127	2138	2148	2159	2170	2181	1	2	3	4	5	7	8	9	10
9.2	2.2192	2203	2214	2225	2235	2246	2257	2268	2279	2289	1	2	3	4	5	6	8	9	10
9.3	2.2300	2311	2322	2332	2343	2354	2364	2375	2386	2396	1	2	3	4	5	6	7	9	10
9.4	2.2407	2418	2428	2439	2450	2460	2471	2481	2492	2502	1	2	3	4	5	6	7	8	10
9.5	2.2513	2523	2534	2544	2555	2565	2576	2586	2597	2607	1	2	3	4	5	6	7	8	9
9.6	2.2618	2628	2638	2649	2659	2670	2680	2690	2701	2711	1	2	3	4	5	6	7	8	9
9.7	2.2721	2732	2742	2752	2762	2773	2783	2793	2803	2814	1	2	3	4	5	6	7	8	9
9.8	2.2824	2834	2844	2854	2865	2875	2885	2895	2905	2915	1	2	3	4	5	6	7	8	9
9.9	2.2925	2935	2946	2956	2966	2976	2986	2996	3006	3016	1	2	3	4	5	6	7	8	9
10.0	2.3026																		

Hyperbolic or Naperian logarithms of 10^{-n}

n	1	2	3	4	5	6	7	8	9
$\log_e 10^{-n}$	3.6974	5.3948	7.0922	10.7897	12.4871	14.1845	17.8819	19.5793	21.2767

logarithm of 0.07 is obtained as follows:

$$\begin{aligned}
\ln 0.07 &= \ln (7 \times 10^{-2}) \\
&= \ln 7 + \ln 10^{-2} \\
&= 1.945\,9 + \bar{5}.394\,8 \\
&= \bar{3}.340\,7 = -3 + 0.340\,7 \text{ or } -2.659\,3.
\end{aligned}$$

Tables of antilogarithms are not normally given for Naperian logarithms. The antilogarithm of a number between 0 and 2.302 6 is obtained by finding the value of the logarithm within the table and the antilogarithm is then obtained from the corresponding row and columns. For example, when $\ln x = 1.234\,6$, the nearest value lower than the logarithm within the table is 1.232 6 and corresponds to the row 3.4 and column 3. The mean difference is 1.234 6 − 1.232 6, that is 20 when these numbers are treated as integer values and gives a mean difference column value of 7. Hence, when $\ln x = 1.234\,6$, then $x = 3.437$.

For logarithms larger than 2.302 6, the value of the logarithm is expressed in the form:

$A + B =$ the value of the logarithm,

where A is the nearest **lower** number to $A + B$ in the supplementary table of Naperian logarithms of 10^{+n} and B is the number required to make the equation correct. Thus, the value of x, when $\ln x = 6.774\,3$, is obtained as follows:

$$6.774\,3 = \quad 4.605\,2 \quad + \quad (6.774\,3 - 4.605\,2)$$

The ln 10^{+n} value	The value to make the equation correct

Thus, $6.774\,3 = 4.605\,2 + 2.169\,1$
i.e., $\qquad \ln x = 4.605\,2 + 2.169\,1$

When determining an antilogarithm, addition becomes multiplication.

Hence, $\quad x = 10^2 \times 8.750$
$\qquad\quad = 875$

[If, when determining the antilogarithm of a number in this way, the B number, i.e., the value to make the equation correct, is not between 0 and 2.302 6, then the wrong supplementary table value of A has been chosen. A check should be made to make sure that the value of A is the nearest lower number to $A + B$.]

When the logarithm has a negative characteristic, it is expressed in the form: $A + B =$ the value of the logarithm, where A is the nearest **more negative** number to $A + B$ in the supplementary tables of $\ln 10^{-n}$ and B is the number required to make the equation correct. The value of x, when $\ln x = \bar{4}.567\,1$, is obtained as follows:

$$\overline{4}.567\ 1 = \overline{5}.394\ 8 \quad + \quad (\overline{4}.567\ 1 - \overline{5}.394\ 8)$$

The ln 10^{-n} value	The value to make the equation correct

Thus $\overline{4}.567\ 1 = \overline{5}.394\ 8 + 1.172\ 3$

i.e. $\qquad \ln x = \overline{5}.394\ 8 + 1.172\ 3$

When determining an antilogarithm, addition becomes multiplication.

Hence $x = 10^{-2} \times 3.229$

$\qquad = 0.032\ 29$

[If, when determing the antilogarithm of a number in this way, the B number, i.e., the value to make the equation correct, is not between 0 and 2.302 6, then the wrong supplementary table value of A has been chosen. A check should be made to make sure that the value of A is the nearest more negative number to $A + B$.]

The method of determining the value of e^x using tables of exponential functions is shown in Section 2. However, only certain discrete values of e^x can be found by this method. Using tables of Naperian logarithms, values of e^x for all values of x (within the accuracy limits outlined) can be determined. The way of doing this is to express e^x in logarithmic form. Let e^x be equal to y, then by taking Naperian logarithms of each side of the equation

$$\ln e^x = \ln y$$

or $x \ln e = \ln y$

But $\ln e$ is $\log_e e$ or unity, since if $\log_e e = x$, then $e = e^x$ or $x = 1$, by the definition of a logarithm.

Hence, $x = \ln y$.

Thus, to determine the value of y when $y = e^{1.234\ 6}$, take Naperian logarithms of each side.

Hence, $\ln y = \ln e^{1.234\ 6}$

or $\qquad \ln y = 1.234\ 6 \ln e = 1.234\ 6$ since $\ln e = 1$.

Determining the antilogarithm gives:

$y = 3.437$, i.e., $e^{1.234\ 6} = \mathbf{3.437}$

Worked problems on Naperian logarithms

Problem 1. Use common logarithms to evaluate ln 43.28, correct to 4 significant figures.

From the change of base rule, $\ln y = 2.302\ 6 \lg y$

When $y = 43.28$, $\quad \ln 43.28 = 2.302\ 6 \lg 43.28$

$\qquad\qquad\qquad\qquad = 2.302\ 6 \times 1.6363$

$\qquad\qquad\qquad\qquad = 3.767\ 7$ or $\mathbf{3.768}$, **correct to 4 significant figures.**

Problem 2. Use tables to determine the value of ln x when x is:

(a) 2.019,   (b) 371.4, and   (c) 0.000 837.

(a) Since 2.019 lies between 0 and 2.302 6, its value can be obtained directly from tables of Naperian logarithms. The row is 2.0 and column 1, giving a matrix number of 0.698 1. The mean difference column headed 9 gives a mean difference of 44 and adding this to the matrix number, treating both numbers as integers, gives 6 981 + 44 or 7 025.

Thus when x is 2.019, ln x is 0.702 5

(b) Expressing 371.4 in standard form gives:

$$371.4 = 3.714 \times 10^2$$
$$\text{Hence, } \ln 371.4 = \ln (3.714 \times 10^2)$$
$$= \ln 3.714 + \ln 10^2$$

Using the main tables to find the value of ln 3.714 and the supplementary table of ln 10^{+n} to find ln 10^2 gives:

$$\ln 371.4 = 1.312\,1 + 4.605\,2$$
$$= 5.917\,3.$$

i.e., **when x is 371.4, ln x is 5.917 3**

(c) Expressing 0.000 837 in standard form gives:

$$0.000\,837 = 8.37 \times 10^{-4}$$
$$\text{Hence ln } 0.000\,837 = \ln (8.37 \times 10^{-4})$$
$$= \ln 8.37 + \ln 10^{-4}$$

The main table is used to evaluate ln 8.37 and the supplementary table of ln 10^{-n} to find the value of 10^{-4}. This gives:

$$\ln 0.000\,837 = 2.124\,7 + \overline{10}.789\,7$$
$$= \overline{8}.914\,4$$

i.e., **when $x = 0.000\,837$, then ln $x = \overline{8}.914\,4$ or $-7.085\,6$**

Problem 3. Use tables to determine the value of x when ln x is

(a) 2.1720,   (b) 9.5713 and   (c) $\overline{7}$.3714.

(a) Since ln 2.172 0 lies between 0 and 2.302 6, its antilogarithm is found by using the main tables of Naperian logarithms only. The row 8.7 and column 7 give a matrix number of 2.171 3. The mean difference is 21 720 − 21 713, treating the matrix number as integers, giving a mean difference of 7. Thus the fourth significant figure in the result is 6, the number at the top of the appropriate mean difference column.

Thus, when ln $x = 2.172\,0, x = 8.776$

(b) Expressing 9.571 3 in the form: 9.571 3 = $A + B$ where A is the nearest smaller number to 9.571 3 in the supplementary table of ln 10^{+n} and B

is the number needed to make the equation correct gives:

9.571 3 = 9.210 3 + (9.571 3 − 9.210 3)
i.e. $\ln x$ = 9.571 3 = 9.210 3 + 0.361 0.

Finding the antilogarithms and changing the addition to multiplication gives:

x = 10^4 × 1.435
  = 14 350
i.e., **when $\ln x$ = 9.571 3, x = 14 350.**

(c) As for part (b), expressing $\overline{7}$.371 4 in the form: $\overline{7}$.371 4 = $A + B$, where A is the nearest more negative number in the supplementary table of $\ln 10^{-n}$ and B is the number to make the equation correct, gives:

$\overline{7}$.371 4 = $\overline{7}$.092 2 + ($\overline{7}$.371 4 − $\overline{7}$.092 2)

[At first sight, $\overline{7}$.092 2 does not appear to be more negative than $\overline{7}$.371 4. However, since $\overline{7}$.092 2 = −7 + 0.092 2 = −6.907 8 and $\overline{7}$.371 4 = −7 + 0.371 4 = −6.628 6, it can be seen that $\overline{7}$.092 2 is more negative than $\overline{7}$.371.4]

Then, $\ln x$ = $\overline{7}$.371 4 = $\overline{7}$.092 2 + 0.279 2

and taking the antilogarithm of each side gives:

$x = 10^{-3}$ × 1.322
i.e., **when $\ln x$ = $\overline{7}$.371 4, x = 0.001 322**

Problem 4. Use tables to determine the values of y, when

(a) $y = e^{3.173}$, (b) $y = -7.6\, e^{0.017\,3}$ and (c) $y = \dfrac{7}{4} e^{-8.721}$

(a) $y = e^{3.173}$, and taking Naperian logarithms of each side of the equation gives:

$$\ln y = \ln e^{3.173}$$
$$= 3.173 \ln e$$
$$= 3.173, \text{ since } \ln e = 1.$$

Then, $\ln y$ = 2.302 6 + (3.173 − 2.302 6)
i.e. $\ln y$ = 2.302 6 + 0.870 4.

Determining the antilogarithm of each side of the equation gives:

y = 10 × 2.388
y = **23.88**

(b) Let, u, say, = $e^{0.017\,3}$. Then $\ln u$ = 0.017 3.
Since 0.017 3 is a number between 0 and 2.302 6, its antilogarithm is found directly from the tables of Naperian logarithms.
Determining the antilogarithm of each side of the equation gives:

$$u = 1.018$$

Hence $y = -7.6 \times 1.018$

$$= -7.74$$

(c) As for part (b), let $u = e^{-8.721}$

$$\ln u = -8.721$$

To determine the antilogarithm of a negative number, it is expressed as having a negative characteristic and a positive mantissa.

Thus $-8.721 = \bar{9}.279\,0$

Now, $\bar{9}.279\,0 = \bar{10}.789\,7 + (\bar{9}.279\,0 - \bar{10}.789\,7)$

i.e., $\ln u = \bar{10}.789\,7 + 0.489\,3$

i.e., $u = 10^{-4} \times 1.631,$

and $y = \dfrac{7}{4} \times 10^{-4} \times 1.631$

$$= 2.854 \times 10^{-4}$$

Problem 5. Solve the equation $5 = 3\,e^{-2x}$ to find x correct to 4 significant figures.

Rearranging $5 = 3\,e^{-2x}$ gives: $\dfrac{5}{3} = e^{-2x}$

Taking the reciprocal of both sides gives: $\dfrac{3}{5} = \dfrac{1}{e^{-2x}} = e^{2x}$

i.e., $0.60 = e^{2x}$

Taking Naperian logarithms of both sides gives: $\ln 0.60 = \ln e^{2x} = 2x$

Hence $x = \dfrac{1}{2} \ln 0.60 = \dfrac{1}{2}(-0.510\,83)$

i.e., $x = -0.255\,4.$

Problem 6. Given $36 = 72\,(1 - e^{-t/3})$ determine t, correct to 3 significant figures.

Rearranging $36 = 72\,(1 - e^{-t/3})$ gives: $\dfrac{36}{72} = 1 - e^{-t/3}$

and $e^{-t/3} = 1 - \dfrac{36}{72} = 0.50$

Taking the reciprocal of both sides gives: $e^{t/3} = \dfrac{1}{0.50} = 2.0$

Taking Naperian logarithms of both sides gives: $\dfrac{t}{3} = \ln 2.0$

from which, $t = 3 \ln 2.0 = 3(0.693\,1)$

i.e., $t = 2.079\,3$ or **2.08**, correct to 3 significant figures.

Problem 7. Solve the equation $2.58 = \ln\left(\dfrac{4.92}{x}\right)$ to find x.

From the definition of a logarithm, since $2.58 = \ln\left(\dfrac{4.92}{x}\right)$ then

$$e^{2.58} = \dfrac{4.92}{x}$$

Rearranging gives: $x = \dfrac{4.92}{e^{2.58}} = 4.92\,e^{-2.58} = (4.92)(0.075\,774)$

i.e., $x = 0.372\,8$, correct to 4 significant figures.

Practical applications of equations involving $\ln x$ and e^x are numerous and some typical examples are highlighted in Chapter 3.

Further problems on Naperian logarithms may be found in the following section (5) (problems 8–27).

5 Further problems

Exponential functions
In problems 1 to 3 use the power series for e^x to determine the values of y, correct to 4 significant figures.

1. (a) $y = e^2$ (b) $y = e^{0.4}$ (c) $y = e^{0.1}$
   (a) [7.389]   (b) [1.492]   (c) [1.105]
2. (a) $y = e^{-0.3}$ (b) $y = e^{-0.1}$ (c) $y = e^{-2}$
   (a) [0.740 8]   (b) [0.904 8]   (c) [0.135 3]
3. (a) $y = 3e^4$ (b) $y = 0.86e^{-0.4}$ (c) $y = -5e^{-0.75}$
   (a) [163.8]   (b) [0.576 5]   (c) [−2.362]

In Problems 4 and 5, use exponential tables to evaluate the functions given, correct to 4 significant figures.

4. (a) $e^{5.2}$ (b) $e^{-0.37}$ (c) $e^{0.86}$
   (a) [181.3]   (b) [0.690 7]   (c) [2.363]
5. (a) $e^{-0.58}$ (b) $e^{-0.17}$ (c) e^{12}
   (a) [0.559 9]   (b) [0.843 7]   (c) [162 800]

6. Expand $e^{2x}(1 - 2x)$ to the term in x^4.

$$\left[1 - 4x^2 - \frac{8x^3}{3} - 2x^4\right]$$

7. Expand $(3e^{x^2})(x^{1/2})$ to six terms.

$$\left[3x^{1/2} + 3x^{5/2} + \frac{3}{2}x^{9/2} + \frac{1}{2}x^{13/2} + \frac{1}{8}x^{17/2} + \frac{1}{40}x^{21/2}\right]$$

Naperian logarithms

In Problems 8 to 13, determine the values of $\ln x$ when x has the values shown.

8. (a) 2.614   (b) 6.775   (c) 9.213
   (a) [0.960 9]   (b) [1.913 2]   (c) [2.220 6]

9. (a) $3\frac{9}{17}$ (b) $\frac{127}{19}$ (c) $8\frac{4}{7}$

   (a) [1.261 1]   (b) [1.899 7]   (c) [2.148 4]

10. (a) 77.34   (b) 190   (c) 2377
   (a) [4.348 2]   (b) [5.247 0]   (c) [7.773 6]

11. (a) 23.2   (b) 17 140   (c) 7601
   (a) [3.144 2]   (b) [9.749 2]   (c) [8.936 0]

12. (a) 0.171   (b) 0.005 35   (c) 0.877 4
   (a) [$\bar{2}$.233 9]   (b) [$\bar{6}$.769 3]   (c) [$\bar{1}$.869 2]
   or   (a) [−1.766 1]   (b) [−5.270 7]   (c) [−0.130 8]

13. (a) 3.74×10^{-3} (b) 7.818×10^{-2} (c) 9.671×10^{-4}
   (a) [$\bar{6}$.411 3]   (b) [$\bar{3}$.451 3]   (c) [$\bar{7}$.058 8]
   or   (a) [−5.588 7]   (b) [−2.548 7]   (c) [−6.841 2]

In problems 14 to 19 determine the values of x when $\ln x$ has the values shown.

14. (a) 0.277 4   (b) 1.308 9   (c) 2.101 3
   (a) [1.320]   (b) [3.702]   (c) [8.177]

15. (a) 0.871 5   (b) 1.001 7   (c) 2.277 3
   (a) [2.390]   (b) [2.723]   (c) [9.750]

16. (a) 2.917 4   (b) 7.173 8   (c) 14.207 4
   (a) [18.49]   (b) [1 305]   (c) [1.480×10^6]

17. (a) 4.61   (b) 10.371   (c) 17.214
   (a) [100.5]   (b) [31 920]   (c) [2.992×10^7]

18. (a) $\bar{1}$.172 9   (b) $\bar{5}$.217 3   (c) $\bar{10}$.027 1
   (a) [0.437 3]   (b) [8.373×10^{-3}]   (c) [4.665×10^{-5}]

19. (a) $\bar{2}$.367 5   (b) $\bar{6}$.007 7   (c) $\bar{15}$.381 4
   (a) [0.195 4]   (b) [2.498×10^{-3}]   (c) [4.479×10^{-7}]

20. Find the value of:

   (a) $e^{2.173}$ (b) $e^{4.179}$ (c) $e^{6.71}$
   (a) [8.785]   (b) [65.30]   (c) [820.6]

21. Calculate the value of $2.7\,e^{0.1x}$ when the value of x is

   (a) 0.0174   (b) 14   (c) $\dfrac{7}{16}$.

           (a) [2.705]   (b) [10.95]   (c) [2.821]

22. Determine the value of $-0.371e^{-2x/3}$ when the value of x is:

   (a) -1.84 (b) 3.716   (c) 12

      (a) [-1.265]   (b) [-3.115×10^{-2}] (c) [-1.245×10^{-4}]

In Problems 23 to 27, solve the given equations, each correct to 4 significant figures.

23. $2 = 4e^{5t}$ [$-0.138\,6$]

24. $5.36 = 2.81e^{-3.2x}$ [$-0.201\,8$]

25. $21 = 33\,(1 - e^{-x/2})$ [2.023]

26. $6.48 = \ln\left(\dfrac{x}{3.9}\right)$ [2 543]

27. $2.48 = 3.62\ln\left(\dfrac{1.46}{x}\right)$ [0.735 9]

Chapter 3

Curves of exponential growth and decay and the use of log-linear graph paper

1. Graphs of exponential functions

A graph of the curves $y = e^x$ and $y = e^{-x}$ over the range $x = -3$ to $x = 3$ is shown in Fig. 1. The values of e^x and e^{-x}, correct to 2 decimal places, are obtained from tables of exponential functions or by calculator, and are shown below.

x	−3.0	−2.5	−2.0	−1.5	−1.0	−0.5	0	0.5	1.0	1.5	2.0	2.5	3.0
e^x	0.05	0.08	0.14	0.22	0.37	0.61	1	1.65	2.72	4.48	7.39	12.18	20.09
e^{-x}	20.09	12.18	7.39	4.48	2.72	1.65	1	0.61	0.37	0.22	0.14	0.08	0.05

A graph of $y = 1 - e^{-x}$ over the range $x = 0$ to $x = 3.5$ is shown in Fig. 2. A table of values is shown below.

x	0	0.5	1.0	1.5	2.0	2.5	3.0	3.5
e^{-x}	1	0.61	0.37	0.22	0.14	0.08	0.05	0.03
$1 - e^{-x}$	0	0.39	0.63	0.78	0.86	0.92	0.95	0.97

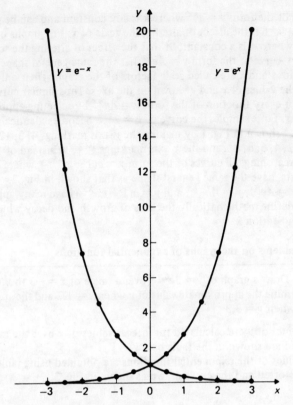

Figure 1 Graph depicting $y = e^x$ and $y = e^{-x}$

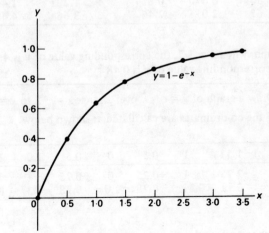

Figure 2 Graph depicting $y = 1 - e^{-x}$

For graphs of the form $y = e^{kx}$ where k is any constant and can be positive or negative, 'k' has the effect of altering the scale of x. For graphs of the form $y = Ae^{kx}$, where A is a constant, 'A' has the effect of altering the scale of y. Hence every curve of the form $y = Ae^{kx}$ has the same general shape as shown in Fig. 1 and A and k are called **scale factors** of the graph. Their only function is to alter the values of x and y shown on the axes. Thus similar curves can be obtained for every function of the form $y = Ae^{kx}$ by selecting appropriate scale factors. For example, the curve of $y = 2e^{3x}$ becomes identical to the curve $y = e^x$ shown in Fig. 1 by making the y-axis markings 4, 8, 12, 16, ... instead of 2, 4, 6, 8, ... and the x-axis markings $\frac{1}{3}, \frac{2}{3}, 1$, instead of 1, 2, 3. By similar reasoning, all curves of the form $y = a(1 - e^{-kx})$, where a and k are constants, have the same general shape as that shown in Fig. 2.
Curves of $y = Ae^{kx}$, $y = Ae^{-kx}$ and $y = a(1 - e^{-kx})$ have many applications since they define mathematically the laws of growth and decay which are discussed in Section 2.

Worked problems on the graphs of exponential functions

Problem 1. Draw a graph of $y = 3e^{0.2x}$ over a range of $x = -3$ to $x = 3$ and hence determine the approximate value of y when $x = 1.7$ and the approximate value of x when $y = 3.3$

The values of y are calculated for integer values of x over the range required and are shown in the table below.
The values of the exponential functions are obtained using tables. The points are plotted and the curve drawn as shown in Fig. 3.

x	-3	-2	-1	0	1	2	3
$0.2x$	-0.6	-0.4	-0.2	0	0.2	0.4	0.6
$e^{0.2x}$	0.549	0.670	0.819	1	1.221	1.492	1.822
$3e^{0.2x}$	1.65	2.01	2.46	3	3.66	4.48	5.47

From the graph, when $x = 1.7$, the corresponding value of y is **4.2** and when y is 3.3, the corresponding value of x is **0.48**

Problem 2. Draw a graph of $y = e^{-x^2}$ over a range $x = -2$ to $x = 2$.
The values of the co-ordinates are calculated as shown below:

x	-2	-1.5	-1	0.5	0	0.5	1.0	1.5	2.0
$-x^2$	-4	-2.25	-1	-0.25	0	-0.25	-1	-2.25	-4
e^{-x^2}	0.02	0.11	0.37	0.78	1.0	0.78	0.37	0.11	0.02

The graph is shown plotted in Fig. 4.

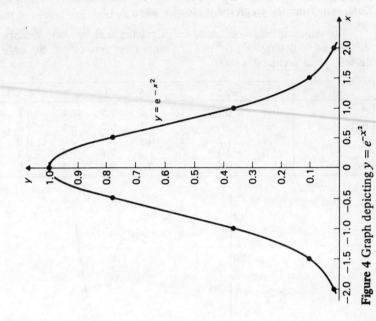

Figure 4 Graph depicting $y = e^{-x^2}$

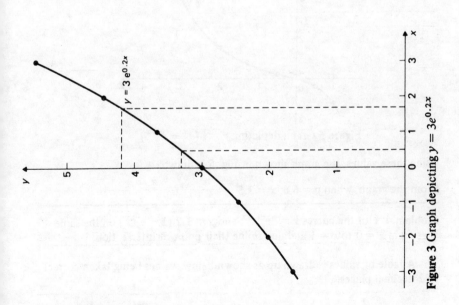

Figure 3 Graph depicting $y = 3e^{0.2x}$

Problem 3. Draw a graph of $y = \frac{1}{5}(e^x - e^{-2x})$ over a range $x = -1$ to $x = 4$. Determine from the graph the value of x when $y = 6.6$

The values of the co-ordinates are calculated as shown below. Since the values used to determine $\frac{1}{5}(e^x - e^{-2x})$ range from zero to over 50, only 1 decimal place accuracy is taken.

x	-1	-0.5	0	0.5	1	2	3	4
e^x	0.4	0.6	1	1.6	2.7	7.4	20.1	54.6
$-e^{-2x}$	2	1	0	-1	-2	-4	-6	-8
e^{-2x}	7.4	2.7	1	0.4	0.1	0.0	0.0	0.0
$e^x - e^{-2x}$	-7.0	-2.1	0	1.2	2.6	7.4	20.1	54.6
$\frac{1}{5}(e^x - e^{-2x})$	-1.4	-0.4	0	0.2	0.5	1.5	4.0	10.9

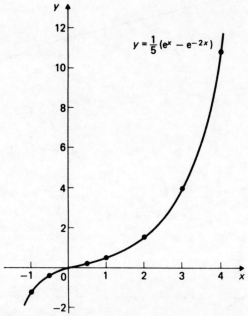

Figure 5 Graph depicting $y = \frac{1}{5}(e^x - e^{-2x})$

Using these values, the graph shown in Fig. 5 is drawn.

From the graph, when $y = 6.6$, $x = 3.5$

Problem 4. Plot the curves $y = 2e^{-1.5x}$ and $y = 1.2(1 - e^{-2x})$ on the same axes from $x = 0$ to $x = 1$ and determine their point of intersection.

A table of values is drawn up as shown below, values being taken correct to 2 decimal places.

x	0	0.2	0.4	0.6	0.8	1.0
$2e^{-1.5x}$	2.00	1.48	1.10	0.81	0.60	0.45
$1.2(1 - e^{-2x})$	0	0.40	0.66	0.84	0.96	1.04

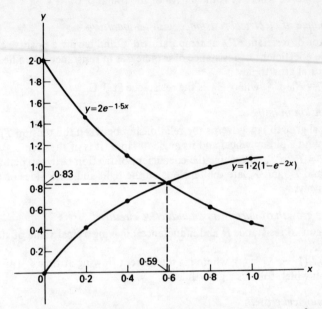

Figure 6 Graph depicting $y = 2e^{-1.5x}$ and $y = 1.2(1 - e^{-2x})$

The curves are shown in Fig. 6 and are seen to intersect at (0.59, 0.83). (Hence the solution of the simultaneous equations $y = 2e^{-1.5x}$ and $y = 1.2(1 - e^{-2x})$ is $x = 0.59$ and $y = 0.83$).

Further problems on graphs of exponential functions may be found in Section 5 (Problems 1 to 9) p. 53.

2. Laws of growth and decay

The laws of exponential growth or decay occur frequently in engineering and science and are always of the form $y = Ae^{kx}$ and $y = A(1 - e^{kx})$, where A and k are constants and can be either positive or negative. The natural law $y = Ae^{kx}$ relates quantities in which the rate of increase of y is proportional to y itself for the growth law, or in which the rate of decrease of y is proportional to y itself for the decay law. Some of the quantities following exponential laws are given below.

(a) Linear expansion

A rod of length l at temperature $\theta°C$ and having a positive coefficient of linear expansion of α will get longer when heated. The natural growth law is:

$l = l_0\, e^{\alpha\theta}$, where l_0 is the length of the rod at $0°C$.

(b) Change of electrical resistance with temperature

A resistor of resistance R_θ at temperature $\theta°C$ and having a positive temperature coefficient of resistance of α increases in resistance when heated. The natural growth law is

$R_\theta = R_0\, e^{\alpha\theta}$, where R_0 is the resistance at $0°C$.

(c) Tension in belts

A natural growth law governs the relationship between the tension T_1 in a belt around a pulley wheel and its angle of lap α. It is of the form

$T_1 = T_0\, e^{\mu\alpha}$, where μ is the coefficient of friction between belt and pulley and T_1 and T_0 are the tensions on the tight and slack sides of the belt respectively.

(d) The growth of current in an inductive circuit

In a circuit of resistance R and inductance L having a final value of steady current I,

$i = I\,(1 - e^{-Rt/L})$, where i is the current flowing at time t. This is an equation which follows a growth law.

(e) Biological growth

The rate of growth of bacteria is proportional to the amount present. When y is the number of bacteria present at time t and y_0 the number present at time $t = 0$ then

$y = y_0\, e^{kt}$, where k is the growth constant.

(f) Newton's law of cooling

The rate at which a body cools is proportional to the excess of its temperature above that of its surroundings. The law is: $\theta = \theta_0 e^{-kt}$, where the excess of temperature at time $t = 0$ is θ_0 and at time t is θ. The negative power of the exponent indicates a decay curve when k is positive.

(g) Discharge of a capacitor

When a capacitor of capacitance C, having an initial charge of Q is discharged through a resistor R, then

$q = Q\, e^{-\frac{t}{CR}}$, where q is the charge after time t.

(h) Atmospheric pressure

The pressure p at height h above ground level is given by

$p = p_0\, e^{-h/c}$, where p_0 is the pressure at ground level and c is a constant.

(i) The decay of current in an inductive circuit
When a circuit having a resistance R, inductance L and initial current I is allowed to decay, it follows a natural law of the form
$i = I e^{-Rt/L}$, where i is the current flowing after time t.

(j) Radioactive decay
The rate of disintegration of a radioactive nucleus having 'N_0' radioactive atoms present and a decay constant of λ is given by:
$$N = N_0 e^{-\lambda t},$$
where N is the number of radioactive atoms present after time t.

These are just some of the relationships which exist which follow the natural laws of growth or decay.

Worked problems on the laws of growth and decay

Problem 1. A belt is in contact with a pulley for a sector of $\theta = 1.073$ radians and the coefficient of friction between these two surfaces is $\mu = 0.27$. Determine the tension on the taut side of the belt, T newtons, when the tension on the slack side is given by $T_0 = 23.8$ newtons, given that these quantities are related by the law $T = T_0 e^{\mu\theta}$. If we require the transmitted force $(T - T_0)$ to be increased to 25.0 newtons, assuming that T_0 remains at 23.8 newtons and θ at 1.073 radians, determine the coefficient of friction.

$$T = T_0 \ e^{\mu\theta} = 23.8 \ e^{(0.27 \times 1.073)}$$
$$= 23.8 \ e^{0.290}$$

Let, u, say equal $e^{0.290}$, then $\ln u = 0.290$
and using tables of Naperian logarithms to find the antilogarithm, gives:
$$u = 1.336$$
Hence $T = 23.8 \times 1.336$
$$= \textbf{31.80 newtons.}$$

For the transmitted force to be 25 newtons, T becomes $23.8 + 25$, or 48.8 newtons.
Then $48.8 = 23.8 \ e^{\mu \times 1.073}$
$$\frac{48.8}{23.8} = e^{1.073\mu}$$
or $2.050 = e^{1.073\mu}$
Taking Naperian logarithms of each side of this equation, gives:
$$\ln 2.050 = 1.073\mu$$
$$0.7178 = 1.073\mu$$
i.e., **the coefficient of friction,** $\mu = \textbf{0.669 0}$

Problem 2. The instantaneous current, i amperes at time t seconds is given by:
$i = 6.0 \ e^{-t/CR}$, when a capacitor is being charged. The capacitance C is 8.3×10^{-6} farads and the resistance R has a value of 0.24×10^6 ohms. Determine the instantaneous current when t is 3.0 seconds. Also determine

the time for the instantaneous current to fall to 4.2 amperes. Sketch a curve of current against time from $t = 0$ to $t = 6$ s.

$$i = 6.0 \, e^{[-3/(8.3 \times 10^{-6} \times 0.24 \times 10^{6})]}$$

$$= 6.0 \, e^{[-3/(8.3 \times 0.24)]}$$

$$= 6.0 \, e^{-1.5060}$$

Letting, u, say, equal $e^{-1.5060}$ and taking Naperian logarithms of each side of this equation, gives:

$$\ln u = -1.5060$$
$$\text{or } \ln u = \bar{2}.4940$$

Taking antilogarithms gives, $u = 0.2218$

Hence $i = 6 \times 0.2218$
$$= 1.33 \text{ amperes.}$$

That is, the current flowing when t is 3.0 seconds is 1.33 amperes.

It is usually easier to transpose and make t the subject of the formula before evaluation. Thus, since $i = 6.0 \, e^{-t/CR}$,

$$\frac{i}{6.0} = e^{-t/CR}$$

$$e^{t/CR} = \frac{6.0}{i}$$

$$\ln e^{t/CR} = \ln \left(\frac{6.0}{i} \right)$$

$$\frac{t}{CR} = \ln \left(\frac{6.0}{i} \right)$$

$$\text{or } t = CR \ln \left(\frac{6.0}{i} \right)$$

Substituting the values of C, R and i gives:

$$t = 8.3 \times 10^{-6} \times 0.24 \times 10^{6} \ln \frac{6.0}{4.2}$$
$$= 1.992 \ln 1.428 \, 6$$
$$= 1.992 \times 0.356 \, 7$$
$$= 0.71 \text{ seconds.}$$

i.e., **the time for the current to fall to 4.2 amperes is 0.71 seconds.**
Since $i = 6.0 \, e^{-t/CR}$ and $C = 8.3 \times 10^{-6}$ and $R = 0.24 \times 10^{6}$
then $i = 6.0 \, e^{-0.502t}$. At $t = 0$, $i = 6.0 \, e^{0} = 6.0$, (since $e^{0} = 1$)
and when $t = \infty$, $i = 6.0 \, e^{(-0.502)\infty} = 6.0 \, (0) = 0$.
A decay curve representing $i = 6.0 \, e^{-0.502t}$ is shown in Fig. 7.

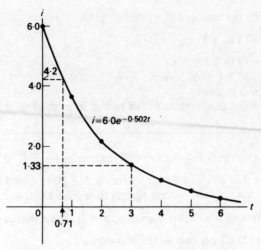

Figure 7 Decay curve of current against time

Problem 3. The temperature θ_2 degrees Celsius of a winding which is being heated electrically, at time t seconds, is given by:

$\theta_2 = \theta_1 (1 - e^{-t/T})$, where θ_1 is the temperature at time $t = 0$ seconds and T seconds is a constant. Calculate (a) θ_1 in degrees Celsius when θ_2 is $45°C$, t is 28 s and T is 73 s, and (b) the time t seconds for θ_2 to be half the value of θ_1.

(a) Transposing the formulae to make θ_1 the subject gives:

$$\theta_1 = \frac{\theta_2}{1 - e^{-t/T}}$$

Substituting the values of θ_2, t and T gives:

$$\theta_1 = \frac{45}{1 - e^{-28/73}} = \frac{45}{1 - e^{-0.3836}}$$

i.e., $\theta_1 = \dfrac{45}{1 - 0.6814} = \dfrac{45}{0.3186}$

$\theta_1 = 141.24°C$.

That is, the initial temperature is 141°C, correct to the nearest degree.

(b) Transposing to make t the subject of the formula:

$$\frac{\theta_2}{\theta_1} = 1 - e^{-t/T}$$

$$e^{-t/T} = 1 - \frac{\theta_2}{\theta_1}$$

Hence $-\dfrac{t}{T} = \ln\left(1 - \dfrac{\theta_2}{\theta_1}\right)$

i.e., $t = -T\ln\left(1 - \dfrac{\theta_2}{\theta_1}\right)$

Substituting the values of T, θ_1 and θ_2 gives:

$$t = -73 \ln \left(1 - \frac{1}{2}\right)$$
$$= -73 \ln 0.5$$
$$= -73 \times (-0.693\ 1)$$
$$= 50.6 \text{ seconds.}$$

i.e., **the time for the temperature to fall to half its original value is 50.6 seconds.**

Problem 4. The current i flowing in a coil is given by $i = \frac{E}{R}(1 - e^{-Rt/L})$ amperes, where R is 10 ohms, L is 2.5 henry's, E is 20 volts and t is the time in seconds. Draw a graph of current against time from $t = 0$ to $t = 1$ second. The time constant of the circuit is given by $\tau = \frac{L}{R}$. Show that in a time τ s the current rises to 63 per cent of its final value.

Since $R = 10$, $L = 2.5$ and $E = 20$ then $i = \frac{20}{10}(1 - e^{-10t/2.5})$,

i.e., $i = 2(1 - e^{-4t})$.

A table of values is drawn up as shown below.

t	0	0.05	0.10	0.15	0.20	0.30	0.40	0.60	0.80	1.00
i	0	0.36	0.66	0.90	1.10	1.40	1.60	1.82	1.92	1.96

A graph of current i against time t is shown in Fig. 8.

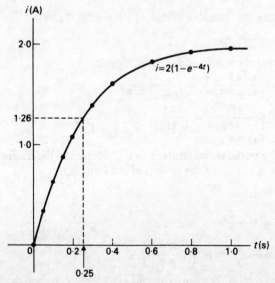

Figure 8

When $t = \infty$, $i = 2\,(1 - e^{-4\infty}) = 2\,(1 - 0) = 2$ A.

Thus the curve is tending towards a final value of $i = 2$A (i.e., $\dfrac{E}{R}$).

Time constant $\tau = \dfrac{L}{R} = \dfrac{2.5}{10} = 0.25$ s. From Fig. 8, when $t = 0.25$ s,

$i = 1.26$ A which is the same as 63 per cent of 2A.

Hence in time $\tau = \dfrac{L}{R}$ the current rises to 63 per cent of its final value.

Further problems on the laws of growth and decay may be found in Section 5 (Problems 10 to 21), p. 54.

3. Reducing equations of the form $y = ab^x$ to linear form using log-linear graph paper

Much of the tedium involved in the work carried out so far in this chapter can be eliminated by converting $y = ae^{kx}$ to the form of a straight line law and using log-linear graph paper as shown later in this chapter. However, it is pertinent to consider another form of equation, $y = ab^x$, at this time, and this is dealt with first. Taking logarithms to a base of 10 of each side of the equation

$y = ab^x$ gives

$\lg y = \lg (ab^x)$

$\quad = \lg a + \lg b^x$, by the laws of logarithms

$\quad = x\lg b + \lg a$, where a and b are constants.

Comparing this equation with the straight line equation $Y = mX + c$ gives:

$$\begin{array}{ccccc} \lg y & = & (\lg b) & x & + \lg a \\ Y & = & m & X & + c \end{array}$$

This shows that by plotting $\lg y$ against x, the slope of the resultant straight line graph is $\lg b$ and the y-axis intercept value is $\lg a$. In this case, graph paper which has a linear scale on one axis (x) and a logarithmic scale on the other axis $(\lg y)$ can be used. This type of graph paper is called **log-linear graph paper**.

Examination of the scale markings on a logarithmic axis shows that the scales do not have equal divisions. They are marked from 1 to 9 and this pattern of markings can be repeated several times since

$\lg 1 - \lg 0.1 = 0 - \overline{1} = 0 - (-1) = 1$, $\lg 10 - \lg 1 = 1 - 0 = 1$ and

$\lg 100 - \lg 10 = 2 - 1 = 1$, and so on.

The number of times the pattern of markings is repeated signifies the number of cycles, the distance each cycle occupies on a logarithmic scale being the same. Thus, one cycle can be used to signify values from 0.1 to 1, or from 1 to 10, or from 10 to 100 and so on. Paper having three cycles on the logarithmic scale is called 'log 3 cycle X linear' graph paper (see Fig. 9.).

To depict a set of numbers from 0.6 to 174, say, on the logarithmic axis of log-linear graph paper, 4 cycles will be required, (0.1 to 1, 1 to 10, 10 − 100 and 100 − 1000) and the start of each cycle is marked 0.1, 1, 10 and 100 or 10^{-1}, 10^0, 10^1 and 10^2. The divisions within a cycle are proportional to the logarithms of the numbers 1 to 10 and the distance from, say, the 1 to 2 marks is 0.301 0, (i.e. lg 2.000 0 − lg 1.000 0), of the total distance in the cycle. Similarly, the distance from the 9 to 10 marks is 0.045 76 of the total distance in the cycle, i.e. the distance between marks decreases logarithmically within the cycle.

The method of determining the constants a and b in the equation $y = ab^x$ is shown in the worked problem following.

Worked problem using log-linear graph paper to reduce an equation of the form $y = ab^x$ to linear form.

Problem 1. Quantities x and y are believed to be related by a law of the form $y = ab^x$. The values of x and corresponding values of y are as shown.

x	0	0.5	1.0	1.5	2.0	2.5	3.0
y	1	3.2	10	31.6	100	316.2	1000

Verify the law is as stated, find the approximate values of a and b and comment on the significance of the graph drawn.

Since $y = ab^x$, then $\lg y = \lg b . x + \lg a$. Comparing this equation with the straight line equation $Y = mX + c$ gives:

$$\boxed{\lg y} = \lg b \; \boxed{x} + \lg a$$
$$\boxed{Y} = m \; \boxed{X} + c$$

Thus $\lg y$ is plotted against x to verify that the law is as stated. Using log-linear graph paper, values of x are selected on the linear scale over a range 0 to 3. Values of y have a range from 1 to 1 000 and 3 cycles are needed to span this range. The graph is shown in Fig. 9.

A straight line can be drawn through the points so the law is verified. Since there is a mixture of linear values on the x-axis and logarithmic values on the y-axis, direct measurement of the slope of the graph is not possible to determine $\lg b$. Selecting any two points on the graph, say A and B, having co-ordinates $(2, 10^2)$ and $(1, 10^1)$ gives:

$$\text{slope} = \frac{\text{AC}}{\text{BC}} = \frac{\lg 10^2 - \lg 10^1}{2 - 1} = \frac{2 - 1}{2 - 1} = 1$$

Hence, slope = $\lg b$ = 1, giving $b = 10$.
Also, when $x = 0, y = 10^0 = 1$
i.e., $a = 1$.

That is, the constants a and b have values of 1 and 10 respectively.

The significance of the graph is that the relationship is $y = 10^x$ and by

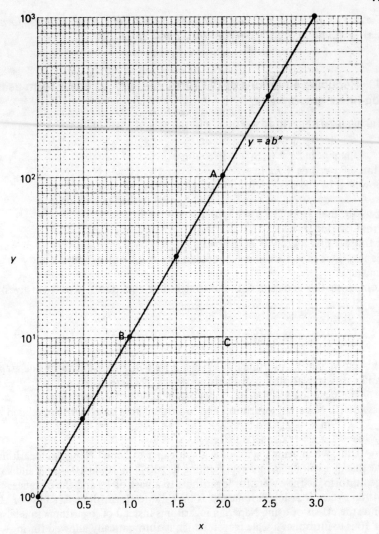

Figure 9 Graph to verify a law of the form $y = ab^x$

the definition of a logarithm, when $y = 10^x$, $x = \lg y$. Hence the graph may be used to determine the approximate value of any logarithm between $y = 1$ and $y = 1\ 000$. Also the approximate value of any antilogarithm between $x = 0$ and $x = 3$ can be found by finding the corresponding value of y. For example, when $y = 500$, from the graph, $x = 2.7$, i.e., the value of $\lg 500$ is approximately 2.7.

By drawing a graph of $y = a^x$, where a is any positive number, the values of logarithms to a base of 'a' can be obtained, and this is one of the principal uses of equations of the form $y = ab^x$.

Further problems on reducing equations of the form $y = ab^x$ *to linear form may be found in Section 5 (Problems 22 and 23), p. 55.*

4. Reducing equations of the form $y = ae^{kx}$ to linear form using log-linear graph paper

Taking logarithms to a base of 'e' of each side of the equation
$y = ae^{kx}$ gives:
$\ln y = \ln ae^{kx}$ or $\ln y = \ln a + \ln e^{kx}$
Thus $\ln y = \ln a + kx \ln e$.
However, by the basic definition of a logarithm, when $y = a^x$ (1)
then $x = \log_a y$ (2)
If $y = a$, then from (1), $a = a^x$, or $x = 1$.
From (2), $\log_a a = 1$.
It follows that $\log_e e = 1$ or $\ln e = 1$.
Hence, since $\ln y = kx \ln e + \ln a$, then $\ln y = kx + \ln a$, where a and k are constants.
Comparing this equation with the straight line equation $Y = mX + c$ gives:

$$
\begin{array}{ccc}
\boxed{\ln y} & = k & \boxed{x} & + \ln a \\
\boxed{Y} & = m & \boxed{X} & + c
\end{array}
$$

This shows that by plotting $\ln y$ against x we will obtain a straight line graph (and verify a relationship of the form $y = ae^{kx}$ where it exists).

The same log-linear graph paper can be used as for logarithms to a base of 10. Naperian logarithms and logarithms to a base of 10 are related by:
$\ln x = 2.3026 \lg x$
i.e. $\ln x = $ (a constant) $(\lg x)$

Thus, when using logarithmic graph paper to depict Naperian logarithms, the distances along an axis representing $\ln 100 - \ln 10, \ln 10 - \ln 1$ and so on are uniform, as they were for logarithms to a base of 10 and the distances within cycles alter logarithmically as they did for logarithms to a base of 10. Thus the effect of using Naperian logarithms instead of logarithms to a base of 10 is to introduce a scale factor, which is automatically allowed for in subsequent calculations and measurements, as shown in the worked problems. When log-linear graph paper is used, it is not necessary to determine the values of $\ln y$, since values of y are plotted directly on the logarithmic axis.

In Section 1, graphs of $y = e^x$ and $y = e^{-x}$ are plotted for values of x, from -3.0 to $+3.0$ with the resulting curves shown in Fig. 1. Graphs of $y = e^x$ and $y = e^{-x}$ may be plotted on log-linear graph paper as follows:

Taking Naperian logarithms of both sides of $y = e^x$ gives $\ln y = x$. From the table of values shown on page 34, values of y range from 0.05 to 20.09 which requires 4 cycles on a logarithmic scale (i.e. 0.01 to 0.1, 0.1 to 1, 1 to 10 and 10 to 100). Thus 'log 4 cycle $\times$ linear' graph paper is required as shown in Fig. 10. When the graph is plotted a straight line results.

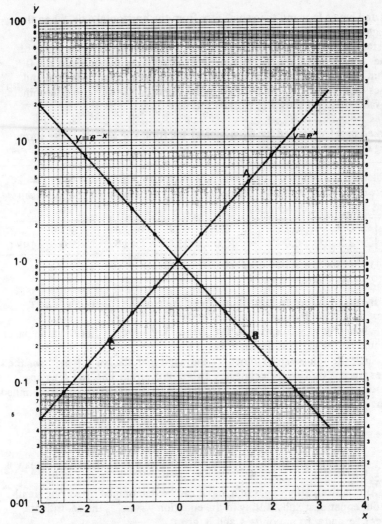

Figure 10 Graphs of $y = e^x$ and $y = e^{-x}$

Gradient of straight line $= \dfrac{AB}{BC} = \dfrac{\ln 4.48 - \ln 0.22}{1.5 - (-1.5)} = 1$

The y-axis intercept value at $x = 0$ is $y = 1$.

When $y = e^{-x}$ is plotted on log-linear graph paper a straight line also results and has a gradient of -1 as shown in Fig. 10.

The graphs of the form $y = ae^{kx}$ in the worked problems following show that the slope of the graph, 'k' is given by $\dfrac{\ln y}{x}$ and is obtained by selecting two points on the curve and determining the values of y from the vertical axis and hence ln y and the values of x from the horizontal axis. When the straight line graph cuts the ordinate $x = 0$, the intercept value gives the constant 'a' (as shown in worked Problem 1). However, when the range of values is such that the straight line graph does not cut the ordinate $x = 0$ within the scale selected, a point is selected on the straight line graph and values of x, y and k are substituted in the equation $y = ae^{kx}$, to determine the value of 'a' (as shown in worked Problem 2).

Worked problems to reduce equations of the form $y = ae^{kx}$ to linear form using log-linear graph paper

Problem 1. It is believed that x and y are related by a law of the form $y = ae^{kx}$ where a and k are constants. Values of x and y are measured and the results are as shown:

x	−0.9	0.25	0.9	2.1	2.8	3.7	4.8
y	2.5	6.0	10.0	25.0	42.5	85.0	198.0

Verify that the law stated does relate these quantities and determine the approximate values of a and k.

By taking Naperian logarithms of each side of the equation $y = ae^{kx}$ gives: $\ln y = kx + \ln a$.
The values of y vary from 2.5 to 198, hence 'log 3 cycle × linear' graph paper is required. The graph is shown in Fig. 11.
Since the points can be joined by a straight line, **the law $y = ae^{kx}$ for the values given is verified**. Selecting any two points on the line, say A having co-ordinates (3, 50) and B, having co-ordinates (0, 5), the slope k is determined from:

$$\text{slope} = k = \frac{\ln y}{x} = \frac{\ln 50 - \ln 5}{3 - 0} = \frac{2.302\,6}{3} = 0.768$$

The y-axis intercept value at $x = 0$ is $y = 5$, hence $a = 5$. Therefore the law is $y = 5e^{0.768x}$.
Alternatively, the values of a and k can be determined by solving simultaneous equations. Substituting in the equation $y = ae^{kx}$, the co-ordinate values of x and y from points A and B, gives:

$$50 = ae^{3k} \tag{1}$$
$$5 = ae^{0k} \tag{2}$$

Since $e^{0k} = e^0 = 1$, $a = 5$ from equation (2).
Substituting $a = 5$ in equation (1) gives:

$$50 = 5e^{3k}$$
$$\text{or } e^{3k} = 10$$
$$3k = \ln 10 = 2.302\,6$$
$$k = 0.768, \text{ as previously obtained.}$$

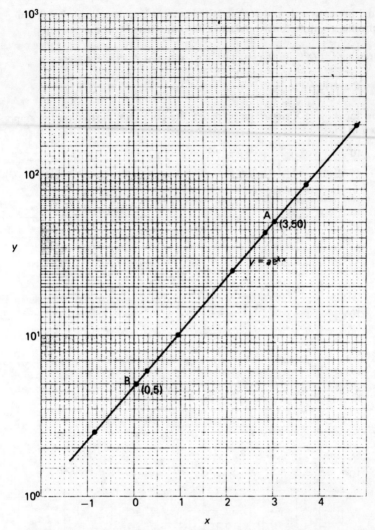

Figure 11 Graph to verify a law of the form $y = ae^{kx}$ (Problem 1)

Problem 2. The current i (in milliamperes) flowing at an 8.3 microfarad capacitor, which is being discharged, varies with time t (in milliseconds), as shown:

i milliamperes	50.0	17.0	5.8	1.7	0.58	0.24
t milliseconds	200	255	310	375	425	475

Show that these results are connected by the law of the form $i = Ie^{t/T}$, (where

I and T are constants and I is the initial current flow in milliamperes) and determine the approximate values of the constants I and T.

Expressing $i = Ie^{t/T}$ in the straight line form of $Y = mX + c$ gives:

$$\ln i = \frac{1}{T}\, t + \ln I$$

Using 'log 3 cycle × linear' graph paper, the points are plotted on the graph shown in Fig. 12.

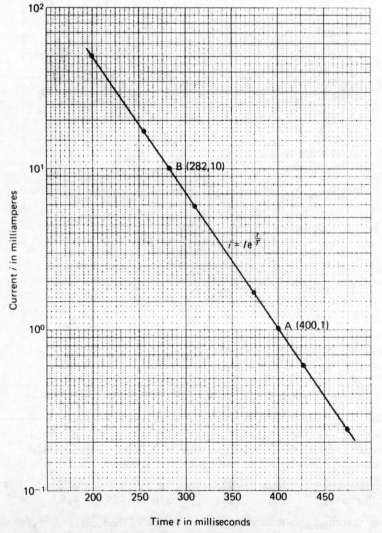

Figure 12 Variation of current with time (Problem 2)

Since these points can be joined by a straight line, **the law** $i = Ie^{t/T}$ **is verified.**
Selecting any two points on the line, say A (400, 1) and B (282, 10), the

slope, $\dfrac{1}{T}$ is determined from $\dfrac{\ln i}{t} = \dfrac{\ln 1 - \ln 10}{400 - 282}$

i.e., $\dfrac{1}{T} = \dfrac{-2.302\,6}{118} = -0.019\,5$

Hence $T = \dfrac{1}{-0.019\,5} = -51.3$, correct to 3 significant figures.

Since the line does not cross the i-axis at $t = 0$, the value of I is found by
selecting a point on the line and using the co-ordinates of this point, together
with the value of T in the equation $i = Ie^{t/T}$. Using the co-ordinates of point
A gives:

$1 = Ie^{(-400/51.3)}$

$I = e^{(400/51.3)}$

$\quad = 2\,430 \text{ mA}$

Hence the law is $i = 2\,430e^{-t/51.3}$**, i.e., the values of** I **and** T **are 2 430 mA**
and -51.3 **respectively.**

Further problems on reducing equations of the form $y = ae^{kx}$ *to linear form*
may be found in the following Section (5) (Problems 24 to 29), p. 55.

5. Further problems

Graphs of exponential functions
In problems 1 to 8, draw the graphs of the exponential functions given and
use the graphs to determine the approximate values of x and y required.

1. $y = 5e^{0.4x}$ over a range $x = -3$ to $x = 3$ and determine the value of y
   when $x = 2.7$ and the value of x when $y = 10$.   [14.7, 1.7]

2. $y = 0.35e^{2.5x}$ over a range $x = -2$ to $x = 2$ and determine the value of y
   when $x = 1.8$ and the value of x when $y = 40$.   [31.5, 1.9]

3. $y = \dfrac{1}{3}\, e^{-2x}$ over a range $x = -2$ to $x = 2$ and determine the value of
   y when $x = -1.75$ and the value of x when $y = 5$.   [11, −1.35]

4. $y = 0.46e^{-0.27x}$ over a range $x = -10$ to $x = 10$ and determine the value
   of y when $x = -8.5$ and the value of x when $y = 6.1$.   [4.6, −9.6]

5. $y = 4e^{-2x^2}$ over a range $x = -1.5$ to $x = 1.5$ and determine the value of
   y when $x = -1.2$ and the value of x when $y = 2.9$.   [0.22, ± 0.4]

6. $y = 100e^{x^2/3}$ over a range $x = -3$ to $x = 3$ and determine the value of y
   when $x = \dfrac{7}{3}$ and the value of x when $y = 250$.   [614, ± 1.66]

7. $y = \dfrac{1}{2}\, (e^x - e^{-x})$ over a range $x = -3$ to $x = 3$ and determine the value
   of y when $x = -2.3$ and the value of x when $y = 5$.   [−4.94, 2.31]

8. $y = 3 (e^{2x} - 4e^{-x})$ over a range $x = 2$ to $x = -2$ and determine the value of y when $x = -1.6$ and the value of x when $y = 35$.   [−59, 1.28]

9. Plot the curves $y = 3.2e^{-1.4x}$ and $y = 1.7 (1 - e^{-2x})$ on the same axes from $x = 0$ to $x = 1$ and determine their point of intersection.

$$[(0.67, 1.25)]$$

Laws of growth and decay

10. The instantaneous voltage v in a capacitive circuit is related to time t by the equation $v = Ve^{-t/CR}$, where V, C and R are constants. Determine v when $t = 27 \times 10^{-3}$, $C = 8.0 \times 10^{-6}$, $R = 57 \times 10^3$ and $V = 100$. Also determine R when $v = 83$, $t = 9.0 \times 10^{-3}$, $C = 8.0 \times 10^{-6}$ and $V = 100$. Sketch a curve of v against t.   [94.3, 6.04×10^3]

11. The length of a bar, l, at temperature θ is given by $l = l_0 e^{\alpha\theta}$, where l_0 and α are constants. Determine α when $l = 2.738$, $l_0 = 2.631$ and $\theta = 315.7$. Also determine l_0 when l and θ are as for the first part of the problem but $\alpha = 1.771 \times 10^{-4}$.   [$1.263 \times 10^{-4}$, 2.589]

12. Two quantities x and y are found to be related by the equation $y = ae^{-kx}$, where a and k are constants.
    (a) Determine y when $a = 1.671 \times 10^4$, $k = -4.60$ and $x = 1.537$.
    (b) Determine x when $y = 76.31$, $a = 15.3$ and $k = 4.77$
        [(a) 1.966×10^7 (b) −0.3369]

13. Quantities p and q are related by the equation $p = 7.413 (1 - e^{kq/t})$, where k and t are constants. Determine p when $k = 3.7 \times 10^{-2}$, $q = 712.8$ and $t = 5.747$. Also determine t when $p = -98.3$ and q and k are as for the first part of the problem.   [−722, 9.92]

14. When quantities I and C are related by the equation $I = BT^2 e^{-C/T}$, and B and T are constants, determine I when $B = 14.3$, $T = 1.27$ and $C = 8.15$. Also determine C when $I = 7.47 \times 10^{-2}$ and B and T are as for the first part of the problem.   [0.037 66, 7.280]

15. In an experiment involving Newton's law of cooling, the temperature θ after a time t of 73.0 seconds is found to be $51.8°C$. Using the relationship $\theta = \theta_0 e^{-kt}$, determine k when $\theta_0 = 15.0°C$.   [−0.016 98]

16. The pressure p at height h above ground level is given by $p = p_0 e^{-h/c}$, where p_0 is the pressure at ground level and c is a constant. When p_0 is 1.013×10^5 pascals and the pressure at a height of 1 570 metres is 9.871×10^4 pascals, determine the value of c.   [60 620]

17. The current i amperes flowing in a capacitor at time t seconds is given by $i = 7.51 (1 - e^{-t/CR})$, where the circuit resistance R is 27.4 kilohms and the capacitance C is 14.71 microfarads. Determine: (a) the time for the current to reach 6.37 amperes, and (b) the current flow after 0.458 seconds.   (a) [0.759 8 s] (b) [5.099 A]

18. The voltage drop, V volts, across an inductor of L henrys at time t seconds is given by $V = 125e^{-Rt/L}$. Determine: (a) the time for the voltage to reach 98.0 volts, and (b) the voltage when t is 14.7 microseconds, given that the circuit resistance R is 128 ohms and its inductance is 10.3 millihenrys.   (a) [0.019 58 ms] (b) [104.1 V]

19. The resistance R_t of an electrical conductor at temperature t degrees Celsius is given by $R_t = R_0 e^{\alpha t}$, where α is a constant and R_0 is 3.41 kilohms. Calculate the value of α when R_t is 3.72 kilohms, and $t = 1\,710$ degrees Celsius. For this conductor, at what temperature will the resistance be 3.50 kilohms?   [5.088×10^{-5}, 512°C]

20. The amount A after n years of a sum invested P, is given by the compound interest law $A = Pe^{rn/100}$ when the interest rate r is added continuously. Determine the amount after 10 years for a sum of £1 000 invested if the interest rate is 4 per cent per annum.   [£1 491.82]

21. The amount of product (x in mol cm^{-3}) formed in a chemical reaction starting with 3 mol cm^{-3} of reactant is given by $x = 3(1 - e^{-4t})$ where $t = $ time for form x in minutes. Plot a graph at 30 second intervals up to 3 minutes of this equation and determine x after one minute.
   [2.945 mol cm^{-3}]

Reduction of $y = ab^x$ into linear form.

22. Values of p and q are believed to be related by a law of the form $p = ab^q$ where a and b are constants. The values of p and corresponding values of q are:

p	4.5	7.4	11.2	15.8	39.0	68.0	271.5
q	0.6	1.3	1.9	2.4	3.7	4.5	6.5

Verify that the law relating p and q is correct and determine the approximate values of a and b.   [3, 2]

23. The values of k and corresponding values of l are:

l	0.2	0.7	1.3	1.9	2.4	3.6
k	6.0	14.2	39.4	109.7	257.2	1990.0

The law relating these quantities is of the form $k = mn^l$. Determine the approximate values of m and n.   [4.3, 5.5]

Reduction of $y = ae^{kx}$ into linear form.

24. Determine the law of the form $y = ae^{kx}$ which relates the following values:

y	0.015	0.08	0.17	0.30	0.96	3.0
x	−6.0	8.5	15.0	20.0	30.0	40.0

[$y = 0.03e^{0.115x}$]

25. The voltage drop across an inductor, v volts, is believed to be related to time, t milliseconds, by the relationship $v = Ve^{t/T}$, where V and T are constants. The variation of voltage with time for this inductor is:

v volts	700	400	190	100	50	17
t milliseconds	27.3	31.7	37.5	42.5	47.8	56.3

Show that the law relating these quantities is as stated and determine the approximate values of V and T.   [24.1 kV, −7.75 ms]

26. The tension in two sides of a belt, T and T_0 newtons, passing round a pulley wheel and in contact with the pulley over an angle of θ radians, is given by $T = T_0 e^{\mu\theta}$ where T_0 and μ are constants. Determine the approximate values of T_0 and the coefficient of friction μ, from the following observations:

T newtons	67.3	76.4	90.0	107.4	117.6	125.5
θ radians	1.13	1.54	2.07	2.64	2.93	3.14

$$[47.4, 0.31]$$

27. A liquid which is cooling is believed to follow a law of the form $\theta = \theta_0 e^{kt}$ where θ_0 and k are constants and θ is the temperature of the body at time t. Measurements are made of the temperature and time and the results are:

θ°C	83	58	41.5	32	26
t minutes	16.7	25	32.5	37	43.5

Show that these quantities are related by this law and determine the approximate values of θ_0 and k.   [174°C, −0.044]

28. The mass (m) of a given substance is believed to dissolve in one litre of water at temperature $(t^\circ C)$ according to the law $m = ae^{kt}$. m was measured at various temperatures and the following results obtained:

t°C	10	20	30	40	50
m kg	35.5	39.1	43.2	47.7	52.8

Show that the law is true and find approximate values for a and k.

$$[a = 32.1, k = 0.009\ 90]$$

29. The following results were obtained when measuring the growth of duck-weed:

Weeks (t)	0	1	2	3	4	5
No. of fronds (n)	20	30	52	77	135	211

It is thought the measurements are connected by the equation $n = Ae^{kt}$. Verify that this is so and obtain approximate values of A and k.

$$[A = 18.4, k = 0.49]$$

Chapter 4

Partial fractions

1 Introduction

Consider the following addition of algebraic fractions:

$$\frac{1}{x+1} + \frac{1}{x+2} = \frac{(x+2)+(x+1)}{(x+1)(x+2)} = \frac{2x+3}{x^2+3x+2}$$

If we start with the expression $\frac{2x+3}{x^2+3x+2}$, and find the fractions whose

sum gives this result, the two fractions obtained (i.e. $\frac{1}{x+1}$ and $\frac{1}{x+2}$) are

called the **partial fractions** of $\frac{2x+3}{x^2+3x+2}$.

This process of expressing a fraction in terms of simpler fractions, called resolving into partial fractions, is used as a preliminary to integrating certain functions and the techniques used are explained by example later in this chapter. However, before attempting to resolve an algebraic expression into partial fractions, the following points must be considered and appreciated:

(a) **The denominator of the algebraic expression** must **factorise.** In the above example the denominator $x^2 + 3x + 2$ factorises as $(x+1)(x+2)$.

(b) In the above example, the numerator, $2x + 3$, is said to be of degree one since the highest powered x term is x^1. The denominator, $x^2 + 3x + 2$, is said to be of degree two since the highest powered x term is x^2. **In order to resolve an algebraic expression into partial fractions, the**

numerator must be at least one degree less than the denominator. When the degree of the numerator is equal to or higher than the degree of the denominator, the denominator must be divided into the numerator until the remainder is of lower degree than the denominator. For example,

$\dfrac{x^2 + x - 5}{x^2 - 2x - 3}$ cannot be resolved into partial fractions as it stands, since

the numerator and denominator are of the same degree. Dividing $x^2 + x - 5$ by $x^2 - 2x - 3$ gives:

$$
\begin{array}{r}
1 \\
x^2 - 2x - 3 \overline{\smash{\big)}\, x^2 + x - 5} \\
\underline{x^2 - 2x - 3} \\
3x - 2
\end{array}
$$

Thus: $\dfrac{x^2 + x - 5}{x^2 - 2x - 3} = 1 + \dfrac{3x - 2}{x^2 - 2x - 3}$

Since $x^2 - 2x - 3$ factorises as $(x + 1)(x - 3)$ then $\dfrac{3x - 2}{x^2 - 2x - 3}$ may be

resolved into partial fractions (see Type 1, Section 2).

(c) Given an identity such as:

$$5x^2 - 3x + 2 \equiv Ax^2 + Bx + C$$

(note: $\equiv$ means 'identically equal to'), then $A = 5, B = -3$ and $C = 2$, since the identity is true for all values of x and the coefficients of x^n (where $n = 0, 1, 2 \ldots$) on the left-hand side of the identity are equal to the coefficients of x^n on the right-hand side of the identity. Similarly, if $ax^3 + bx^2 - cx + d \equiv 2x^3 + 5x - 7$ then $a = 2, b = 0, c = -5$ and $d = -7$.

2 Type 1. Denominator containing linear factors

The corresponding partial fractions of an algebraic expression $\dfrac{f(x)}{(x - a)(x - b)}$

are of the form $\dfrac{A}{(x - a)} + \dfrac{B}{(x - b)}$, where $f(x)$ is a polynomial of degree less

than 2. Similarly, the corresponding partial fractions of $\dfrac{f(x)}{(x + a)(x - b)(x - c)}$

are of the form $\dfrac{A}{(x + a)} + \dfrac{B}{(x - b)} + \dfrac{C}{(x - c)}$, where $f(x)$ is a polynomial of

degree less than 3, and so on.

Problem 1. Resolve $\dfrac{x - 8}{x^2 - x - 2}$ into partial fractions.

The denominator factorises as $(x + 1)(x - 2)$ and the numerator is of less degree than the denominator. Thus $\dfrac{x-8}{x^2-x-2}$ may be resolved into partial fractions.

Let $\dfrac{x-8}{x^2-x-2} = \dfrac{x-8}{(x+1)(x-2)} \equiv \dfrac{A}{x+1} + \dfrac{B}{x-2}$ where A and B are constants to be determined.

Adding the two fractions on the right-hand side gives:

$$\dfrac{x-8}{(x+1)(x-2)} \equiv \dfrac{A(x-2)+B(x+1)}{(x+1)(x-2)}$$

Since the denominators are the same on each side of the identity then the numerators must be equal to each other.

Hence $x - 8 \equiv A(x-2) + B(x+1)$

There are two methods whereby A and B may be determined using the properties of identities introduced in Section 1.

Method 1.

Since an identity is true for all real values of x, substitute into the identity a value of x to reduce one of the unknown constants to zero.

Let $x = 2$. Then $\quad 2 - 8 = A(0) + B(3)$
i.e. $\qquad\qquad -6 = 3B$
$\qquad\qquad\qquad B = -2$

Let $x = -1$. Then $-1 - 8 = A(-3) + B(0)$
$\qquad\qquad\qquad -9 = -3A$
$\qquad\qquad\qquad A = 3$

Method 2.

Since the coefficients of x^n $(n = 0, 1, 2 \ldots)$ on the left-hand side of an identity equal the coefficients of x^n on the right-hand side, equate the respective coefficients on each side of the identity.

Since $\quad x - 8 \equiv A(x-2) + B(x+1)$
then $\quad x - 8 \equiv Ax - 2A + Bx + B = (A+B)x + (-2A+B)$
Thus $\qquad 1 = A + B$ (by equating the coefficients of x) $\qquad\qquad$ (1)
and $\qquad -8 = -2A + B$ (by equating the constants) $\qquad\qquad$ (2)

Solving the two simultaneous equations gives $A = 3$ and $B = -2$ as before.

Thus $\dfrac{x-8}{x^2-x-2} \equiv \dfrac{3}{x+1} + \dfrac{-2}{x-2} \equiv \dfrac{3}{x+1} - \dfrac{2}{x-2}$

It is usually quicker and easier to adopt the first method as far as possible although with other types of partial fractions a combination of the two methods is necessary.

Problem 2. Express $\dfrac{6x^2 + 7x - 25}{(x - 1)(x + 2)(x - 3)}$ in partial fractions.

Let $\dfrac{6x^2 + 7x - 25}{(x - 1)(x + 2)(x - 3)} \equiv \dfrac{A}{(x - 1)} + \dfrac{B}{(x + 2)} + \dfrac{C}{(x - 3)}$

$$\equiv \frac{A(x + 2)(x - 3) + B(x - 1)(x - 3) + C(x - 1)(x + 2)}{(x - 1)(x + 2)(x - 3)}$$

Equating the numerators gives:

$$6x^2 + 7x - 25 \equiv A(x + 2)(x - 3) + B(x - 1)(x - 3) + C(x - 1)(x + 2)$$

Let $x = 1$. Then $6 + 7 - 25 = A(3)(-2) + B(0)(-2) + C(0)(3)$

i.e. $\qquad -12 = -6A$

$\qquad\qquad A = 2$

Let $x = -2$. Then $6(-2)^2 + 7(-2) - 25 = A(0)(-5) + B(-3)(-5) + C(-3)(0)$

i.e. $\qquad\qquad\qquad -15 = 15B$

$\qquad\qquad\qquad B = -1$

Let $x = 3$. Then $6(3)^2 + 7(3) - 25 = A(5)(0) + B(2)(0) + C(2)(5)$

i.e $\qquad\qquad\qquad 50 = 10C$

$\qquad\qquad\qquad C = 5$

Thus: $\dfrac{6x^2 + 7x - 25}{(x - 1)(x + 2)(x - 3)} \equiv \dfrac{2}{(x - 1)} - \dfrac{1}{(x + 2)} + \dfrac{5}{(x - 3)}$

Problem 3. Convert $\dfrac{x^3 - x^2 - 5x}{x^2 - 3x + 2}$ into partial fractions.

The numerator is of higher degree than the denominator, thus dividing gives:

$$
\begin{array}{r}
x + 2 \\
x^2 - 3x + 2 \overline{\big)\; x^3 - x^2 - 5x } \\
x^3 - 3x^2 + 2x \\
\hline
2x^2 - 7x \\
2x^2 - 6x + 4 \\
\hline
-x - 4
\end{array}
$$

Thus $\dfrac{x^3 - x^2 - 5x}{x^2 - 3x + 2} = x + 2 + \dfrac{-x - 4}{x^2 - 3x + 2} = x + 2 - \dfrac{x + 4}{(x - 1)(x - 2)}$

Let $\dfrac{x + 4}{(x - 1)(x - 2)} \equiv \dfrac{A}{x - 1} + \dfrac{B}{x - 2} \equiv \dfrac{A(x - 2) + B(x - 1)}{(x - 1)(x - 2)}$

Equating the numerators gives:

$$x + 4 \equiv A(x - 2) + B(x - 1)$$

Let $x = 1$. Then $\qquad 5 = -A$

$\qquad\qquad\qquad A = -5$

Let $x = 2$. Then $\qquad 6 = B$

Thus $\dfrac{x+4}{(x-1)(x-2)} \equiv \dfrac{-5}{(x-1)} + \dfrac{6}{(x-2)}$

Thus $\dfrac{x^3 - x^2 - 5x}{x^2 - 3x + 2} \equiv x + 2 - \dfrac{-5}{(x-1)} + \dfrac{6}{(x-2)}$

$\equiv x + 2 + \dfrac{5}{(x-1)} - \dfrac{6}{(x-2)}$

---

3 Type 2. Denominator containing repeated linear factors

When the denominator of an algebraic expression has a factor $(x-a)^n$ then the corresponding partial fractions are $\dfrac{A}{(x-a)} + \dfrac{B}{(x-a)^2} + \ldots + \dfrac{C}{(x-a)^n}$, since $(x-a)^n$ is assumed to hide the factors $(x-a)^{n-1}$, $(x-a)^{n-2} \ldots (x-a)$.

Problem 1. Express $\dfrac{x+5}{(x+3)^2}$ in partial fractions.

Let $\dfrac{x+5}{(x+3)^2} \equiv \dfrac{A}{(x+3)} + \dfrac{B}{(x+3)^2} \equiv \dfrac{A(x+3)+B}{(x+3)^2}$

Equating the numerators gives:

$$x + 5 \equiv A(x+3) + B$$

Let $x = -3$. Then $-3 + 5 = A(0) + B$

i.e. $B = 2$

Equating the coefficient of x gives $A = 1$.
(Check by equating constant terms gives: $5 = 3A + B$ which is true when $A = 1$ and $B = 2$.)

Thus $\dfrac{x+5}{(x+3)^2} \equiv \dfrac{1}{(x+3)} + \dfrac{2}{(x+3)^2}$

Problem 2. Resolve $\dfrac{5x^2 - 19x + 3}{(x-2)^2(x+1)}$ into partial fractions.

The given denominator is a combination of the linear factor type and repeated factor type.

Let $\dfrac{5x^2 - 19x + 3}{(x-2)^2(x+1)} \equiv \dfrac{A}{(x-2)} + \dfrac{B}{(x-2)^2} + \dfrac{C}{(x+1)}$

$\equiv \dfrac{A(x-2)(x+1) + B(x+1) + C(x-2)^2}{(x-2)^2(x+1)}$

Equating the numerators gives:

$$5x^2 - 19x + 3 \equiv A(x-2)(x+1) + B(x+1) + C(x-2)^2$$

Let $x = 2$. Then $5(2)^2 - 19(2) + 3 \quad = A(0)(3) + B(3) + C(0)^2$
i.e. $\qquad\qquad -15 \quad = 3B$
$$B \quad = -5$$

Let $x = -1$. Then $5(-1)^2 - 19(-1) + 3 = A(-3)(0) + B(0) + C(-3)^2$
i.e. $\qquad\qquad\qquad 27 = 9C$
$$C = 3$$

$$\begin{aligned}
5x^2 - 19x + 3 &\equiv A(x-2)(x+1) + B(x+1) + C(x-2)^2 \\
&\equiv A(x^2 - x - 2) + B(x+1) + C(x^2 - 4x + 4) \\
&\equiv (A + C)x^2 + (-A + B - 4C)x + (-2A + B + 4C)
\end{aligned}$$

Equating the coefficients of x^2 gives:
$$5 = A + C$$

Since $C = 3$ then $A = 2$

[Check: Equating the coefficients of x gives: $\qquad -19 \quad = -A + B - 4C$.
If $A = 2, B = -5$ and $C = 3$ then $-A + B - 4C \quad = -19 = $ L.H.S.
Equating the constant terms gives: $\qquad 3 \quad = -2A + B + 4C$.
If $A = 2, B = -5$ and $C = 3$ then $-2A + B + 4C \quad = 3 = $ L.H.S.]

Thus $\dfrac{5x^2 - 19x + 3}{(x-2)^2(x+1)} \equiv \dfrac{2}{(x-2)} - \dfrac{5}{(x-2)^2} + \dfrac{3}{(x+1)}$

Problem 3. Convert $\dfrac{2x^2 - 13x + 13}{(x-4)^3}$ into partial fractions.

Let $\dfrac{2x^2 - 13x + 13}{(x-4)^3} \equiv \dfrac{A}{(x-4)} + \dfrac{B}{(x-4)^2} + \dfrac{C}{(x-4)^3}$

$$\equiv \dfrac{A(x-4)^2 + B(x-4) + C}{(x-4)^3}$$

Equating the numerators gives:

$$2x^2 - 13x + 13 \equiv A(x-4)^2 + B(x-4) + C$$

Let $x = 4$. Then $2(4)^2 - 13(4) + 13 \quad = A(0)^2 + B(0) + C$
i.e. $\qquad\qquad\qquad -7 = C$

Also $2x^2 - 13x + 13 \equiv A(x^2 - 8x + 16) + B(x-4) + C$
$$\equiv Ax^2 + (-8A + B)x + (16A - 4B + C)$$

Equating the coefficients of x^2 gives: $2 = A$
Equating the coefficients of x gives: $-13 = -8A + B$, from which $B = 3$.

(Check: Equating the constant terms gives: $13 = 16A - 4B + C$.
If $A = 2, B = 3$ and $C = -7$
then R.H.S. $= 16(2) - 4(3) - 7 = 13 = $ L.H.S.)

Thus $\dfrac{2x^2 - 13x + 13}{(x-4)^3} \equiv \dfrac{2}{(x-4)} + \dfrac{3}{(x-4)^2} - \dfrac{7}{(x-4)^3}$

---

4 Type 3. Denominator containing a quadratic factor

When the denominator contains a quadratic factor of the form $px^2 + qx + r$ (where p, q and r are constants), which does not factorise without containing surds or imaginary values, then the corresponding partial fraction is of the form $\dfrac{Ax + B}{px^2 + qx + r}$, i.e. the numerator is assumed to be a polynomial of degree one less than the denominator. Hence the corresponding partial fractions of an algebraic expression $\dfrac{f(x)}{(px^2 + qx + r)(x-a)}$ are of the form

$\dfrac{Ax + B}{px^2 + qx + r} + \dfrac{C}{x-a}$.

Problem 1. Resolve $\dfrac{8x^2 - 3x + 19}{(x^2 + 3)(x-1)}$ into partial fractions.

Let $\dfrac{8x^2 - 3x + 19}{(x^2 + 3)(x-1)} \equiv \dfrac{Ax + B}{(x^2 + 3)} + \dfrac{C}{(x-1)}$

$$\equiv \dfrac{(Ax + B)(x-1) + C(x^2 + 3)}{(x^2 + 3)(x-1)}$$

Equating the numerators gives:

$8x^2 - 3x + 19 \equiv (Ax + B)(x-1) + C(x^2 + 3)$

Let $x = 1$. Then $8(1)^2 - 3(1) + 19 = (A + B)(0) + C(4)$

i.e. $24 = 4C$

$C = 6$

$8x^2 - 3x + 19 \equiv (Ax + B)(x-1) + C(x^2 + 3)$
$\equiv Ax^2 - Ax + Bx - B + Cx^2 + 3C$
$\equiv (A + C)x^2 + (-A + B)x + (-B + 3C)$

Equating the coefficients of the x^2 terms gives:

$8 = A + C$

Since $C = 6$, $A = 2$

Equating the coefficients of the x terms gives:

$-3 = -A + B$

Since $A = 2$, $B = -1$

(Check: Equating the constant terms gives: $19 = -B + 3C$
R.H.S. $= -B + 3C = -(-1) + 3(6) = 19 = $ L.H.S.)

Hence $\dfrac{8x^2 - 3x + 19}{(x^2 + 3)(x - 1)} \equiv \dfrac{2x - 1}{(x^2 + 3)} + \dfrac{6}{(x - 1)}$

Problem 2. Resolve $\dfrac{2 + x + 6x^2 - 2x^3}{x^2 (x^2 + 1)}$ into partial fractions.

Terms such as x^2 may be treated as $(x + 0)^2$, i.e. it is a repeated linear factor type.

Let $\dfrac{2 + x + 6x^2 - 2x^3}{x^2 (x^2 + 1)} \equiv \dfrac{A}{x} + \dfrac{B}{x^2} + \dfrac{Cx + D}{(x^2 + 1)}$

$$\equiv \dfrac{Ax (x^2 + 1) + B(x^2 + 1) + (Cx + D) x^2}{x^2 (x^2 + 1)}$$

Equating the numerators gives:

$$2 + x + 6x^2 - 2x^3 \equiv Ax(x^2 + 1) + B(x^2 + 1) + (Cx + D) x^2$$

$$\equiv (A + C)x^3 + (B + D)x^2 + Ax + B$$

Let $x = 0$. Then $2 = B$

Equating the coefficients of x^3 gives:

$$-2 = A + C \tag{1}$$

Equating the coefficients of x^2 gives:

$$6 = B + D$$

Since $B = 2$, $\qquad D = 4$

Equating the coefficients of x gives:

$$1 = A$$

From equation (1), $C = -3$

(Check: Equating the constant terms: $2 = B$ as before.)

Hence $\dfrac{2 + x + 6x^2 - 2x^3}{x^2(x^2 + 1)} \equiv \dfrac{1}{x} + \dfrac{2}{x^2} + \dfrac{4 - 3x}{x^2 + 1}$

5 Summary

Type. Denominator containing	Expression	Form of partial fractions
1. Linear factors	$\dfrac{f(x)}{(x+a)(x+b)(x+c)}$	$\dfrac{A}{(x+a)} + \dfrac{B}{(x+b)} + \dfrac{C}{(x+c)}$
2. Repeated linear factors	$\dfrac{f(x)}{(x-a)^3}$	$\dfrac{A}{(x-a)} + \dfrac{B}{(x-a)^2} + \dfrac{C}{(x-a)^3}$
3. Quadratic factors	$\dfrac{f(x)}{(ax^2+bx+c)(x-d)}$	$\dfrac{Ax+B}{(ax^2+bx+c)} + \dfrac{C}{(x-d)}$
General Example:	$\dfrac{f(x)}{(x^2+a)(x+b)^2(x+c)}$	$\dfrac{Ax+B}{(x^2+a)} + \dfrac{C}{(x+b)} + \dfrac{D}{(x+b)^2} + \dfrac{E}{(x+c)}$

In each of the above cases $f(x)$ must be of less degree than the relevant denominator. If it is not, then the denominator must be divided into the numerator. For every possible factor of the denominator there is a corresponding partial fraction.

6 Further problems

Resolve the following into partial fractions:

1. $\dfrac{8}{x^2-4}$ $\qquad \left[\dfrac{2}{(x-2)} - \dfrac{2}{(x+2)} \right]$

2. $\dfrac{3x+5}{x^2+2x-3}$ $\qquad \left[\dfrac{2}{(x-1)} + \dfrac{1}{(x+3)} \right]$

3. $\dfrac{y-13}{y^2-y-6}$ $\qquad \left[\dfrac{3}{(y+2)} + \dfrac{2}{(y-3)} \right]$

4. $\dfrac{17x^2-21x-6}{x(x+1)(x-3)}$ $\qquad \left[\dfrac{2}{x} + \dfrac{8}{(x+1)} + \dfrac{7}{(x-3)} \right]$

5. $\dfrac{6x^2+7x-49}{(x-4)(x+1)(2x-3)}$ $\qquad \left[\dfrac{3}{(x-4)} - \dfrac{2}{(x+1)} + \dfrac{4}{(2x-3)} \right]$

6. $\dfrac{x^2+2}{(x+4)(x-2)}$ $\qquad \left[1 - \dfrac{3}{(x+4)} + \dfrac{1}{(x-2)} \right]$

7. $\dfrac{2x^2 + 4x + 19}{2(x-3)(x+4)}$ $\quad \left[1 + \dfrac{7}{2(x-3)} - \dfrac{5}{2(x+4)}\right]$

8. $\dfrac{2x^3 + 7x^2 - 2x - 27}{(x-1)(x+4)}$ $\quad \left[2x + 1 - \dfrac{4}{(x-1)} + \dfrac{7}{(x+4)}\right]$

9. $\dfrac{2t-1}{(t+1)^2}$ $\quad \left[\dfrac{2}{(t+1)} - \dfrac{3}{(t+1)^2}\right]$

10. $\dfrac{8x^2 + 12x - 3}{(x+2)^3}$ $\quad \left[\dfrac{8}{(x+2)} - \dfrac{20}{(x+2)^2} + \dfrac{5}{(x+2)^3}\right]$

11. $\dfrac{6x+1}{(2x+1)^2}$ $\quad \left[\dfrac{3}{(2x+1)} - \dfrac{2}{(2x+1)^2}\right]$

12. $\dfrac{1}{x^2(x+2)}$ $\quad \left[\dfrac{1}{2x^2} - \dfrac{1}{4x} + \dfrac{1}{4(x+2)}\right]$

13. $\dfrac{9x^2 - 73x + 150}{(x-7)(x-3)^2}$ $\quad \left[\dfrac{5}{(x-7)} + \dfrac{4}{(x-3)} - \dfrac{3}{(x-3)^2}\right]$

14. $\dfrac{-(9x^2 + 4x + 4)}{x^2(x^2-4)}$ $\quad \left[\dfrac{1}{x} + \dfrac{1}{x^2} + \dfrac{2}{(x+2)} - \dfrac{3}{(x-2)}\right]$

15. $\dfrac{-(a^2 + 5a + 13)}{(a^2+5)(a-2)}$ $\quad \left[\dfrac{2a-1}{(a^2+5)} - \dfrac{3}{(a-2)}\right]$

16. $\dfrac{3-x}{(x^2+3)(x+3)}$ $\quad \left[\dfrac{1-x}{2(x^2+3)} + \dfrac{1}{2(x+3)}\right]$

17. $\dfrac{12 - 2x - 5x^2}{(x^2+x+1)(3-x)}$ $\quad \left[\dfrac{2x+5}{(x^2+x+1)} - \dfrac{3}{(3-x)}\right]$

18. $\dfrac{x^3 + 7x^2 + 8x + 10}{x(x^2 + 2x + 5)}$ $\quad \left[1 + \dfrac{2}{x} + \dfrac{3x-1}{(x^2+2x+5)}\right]$

19. $\dfrac{5x^3 - 3x^2 + 41x - 64}{(x^2+6)(x-1)^2}$ $\quad \left[\dfrac{2-3x}{(x^2+6)} + \dfrac{8}{(x-1)} - \dfrac{3}{(x-1)^2}\right]$

20. $\dfrac{6x^3 + 5x^2 + 4x + 3}{(x^2+x+1)(x^2-1)}$ $\quad \left[\dfrac{2x-1}{(x^2+x+1)} + \dfrac{3}{(x-1)} + \dfrac{1}{(x+1)}\right]$

Chapter 5

Trigonometry (1) — Graphs of trigonometric functions

1 Graphs of trigonometric ratios

One method of plotting graphs of trigonometric ratios is to initially draw up a table of values. This is achieved by using 4 figure tables and a knowledge of angle of any magnitude or by using a calculator. In the graphs plotted below, 15° intervals have been used and values in the tables are taken correct to 3 decimal places.

(i) $y = \sin A$.

$A°$	0	15	30	45	60	75	90	105	120	135	150
$\sin A$	0	0.259	0.500	0.707	0.866	0.966	1.000	0.966	0.866	0.707	0.500

$A°$	165	180	195	210	225	240	255	270	285
$\sin A$	0.259	0	−0.259	−0.500	−0.707	−0.866	−0.966	−1.000	−0.966

$A°$	300	315	330	345	360
$\sin A$	−0.866	−0.707	−0.500	−0.259	0

(ii) $y = \sin 2A$

$A°$	0	15	30	45	60	75	90	105	120	135
$2A$	0	30	60	90	120	150	180	210	240	270
$\sin 2A$	0	0.500	0.866	1.000	0.866	0.500	0	−0.500	−0.866	−1.000

$A°$	150	165	180	195	210	225	240	255	270	285
$2A$	300	330	360	390	420	450	480	510	540	570
sin $2A$	-0.866	-0.500	0	0.500	0.866	1.000	0.866	0.500	0	-0.500

$A°$	300	315	330	345	360
$2A$	600	630	660	690	720
sin $2A$	-0.866	-1.000	-0.866	-0.500	0

(iii) $y = \sin \tfrac{1}{2}A$

$A°$	0	15	30	45	60	75	90	105	120	125	150
$\tfrac{1}{2}A$	0	7½	15	22½	30	37½	45	52½	60	67½	75
sin $\tfrac{1}{2}A$	0	0.131	0.259	0.383	0.500	0.609	0.707	0.793	0.866	0.924	0.966

$A°$	165	180	195	210	225	240	255	270	285	300	315
$\tfrac{1}{2}A$	82½	90	97½	105	112½	120	127½	135	142½	150	157½
sin $\tfrac{1}{2}A$	0.991	1.000	0.991	0.966	0.924	0.866	0.793	0.707	0.609	0.500	0.383

$A°$	330	345	360
$\tfrac{1}{2}A$	165	172½	180
sin $\tfrac{1}{2}A$	0.259	0.131	0

Graphs of $y = \sin A$, $y = \sin 2A$ and $y = \sin \tfrac{1}{2}A$ are shown plotted in Fig. 1.

(iv) $y = \cos A$

$A°$	0	15	30	45	60	75	90	105	120	135
cos A	1.000	0.966	0.866	0.707	0.500	0.259	0	-0.259	-0.500	-0.707

$A°$	150	165	180	195	210	225	240	255	270
cos A	-0.866	-0.966	-1.000	-0.966	-0.866	-0.707	-0.500	-0.259	0

$A°$	285	300	315	330	345	360
cos A	0.259	0.500	0.707	0.866	0.966	1.000

(v) $y = \cos 2A$

$A°$	0	15	30	45	60	75	90	105	120	135
$2A$	0	30	60	90	120	150	180	210	240	270
cos $2A$	1.000	0.866	0.500	0	-0.500	-0.866	-1.000	-0.866	-0.500	0

$A°$	150	165	180	195	210	225	240	255	270	285
$2A$	300	330	360	390	420	450	480	510	540	570
cos $2A$	0.500	0.866	1.000	0.866	0.500	0	-0.500	-0.866	-1.000	-0.866

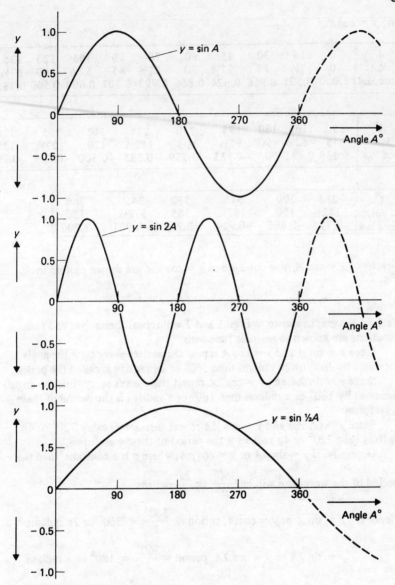

Figure 1 Graphs of sin A, sin $2A$, and sin $\frac{1}{2}A$

$A°$	300	315	330	345	360
$2A$	600	630	660	690	720
cos $2A$	−0.500	0	0.500	0.866	1.000

(vi) $y = \cos \frac{1}{2}A$

$A^°$	0	15	30	45	60	75	90	105	120	135
$\frac{1}{2}A$	0	7½	15	22½	30	37½	45	52½	60	67½
$\cos \frac{1}{2}A$	1.000	0.991	0.966	0.924	0.866	0.793	0.707	0.609	0.500	0.383

$A^°$	150	165	180	195	210	225	240	255	270
$\frac{1}{2}A$	75	82½	90	97½	105	112½	120	127½	135
$\cos \frac{1}{2}A$	0.259	0.131	0	−0.131	−0.259	−0.383	−0.500	−0.609	−0.707

$A^°$	285	300	315	330	345	360
$\frac{1}{2}A$	142½	150	157½	165	172½	180
$\cos \frac{1}{2}A$	−0.793	−0.866	−0.924	−0.966	−0.991	−1.000

Graphs of $y = \cos A$, $y = \cos 2A$ and $y = \cos \frac{1}{2}A$ are shown plotted in Fig. 2.

Period

Each of the graphs shown in Figs. 1 and 2 will repeat themselves and such functions are known as **periodic functions**.

Since $y = \sin A$ and $y = \cos A$ repeat themselves every time the angle increases by 360° or 2π radians then 360° or 2π radians is called the period.

Since $y = \sin 2A$ and $y = \cos 2A$ repeat themselves every time the angle increases by 180° or π radians then 180° or π radians is the period of these waveforms.

Since $y = \sin \frac{1}{2}A$ and $y = \cos \frac{1}{2}A$ repeat themselves every 720° or 4π radians then 720° or 4π radians is the period of these waveforms.

Generally, if $y = \sin pA$ or $y = \cos pA$, where p is a constant, then the period of the waveform will be $\dfrac{360°}{p}$ or $\dfrac{2\pi}{p}$ radians.

Hence if $y = \sin A$ or $y = \cos A$, period $= \dfrac{360°}{1} = 360°$ or 2π radians

$y = \sin 2A$ or $y = \cos 2A$, period $= \dfrac{360°}{2} = 180°$ or π radians

$y = \sin \frac{1}{2}A$ or $y = \cos \frac{1}{2}A$, period $= \dfrac{360°}{\frac{1}{2}} = 720°$ or 4π radians

$y = \sin 6A$ or $y = \cos 6A$, period $= \dfrac{360°}{6} = 60°$ or $\dfrac{\pi}{3}$ radians

$y = \sin \frac{1}{5}A$ or $y = \cos \frac{1}{5}A$, period $= \dfrac{360°}{\frac{1}{5}} = 1800°$ or 10π radians

and so on.

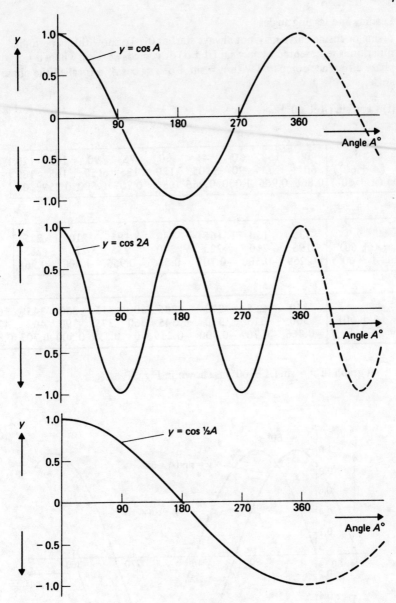

Figure 2 Graphs of cos A, cos $2A$ and cos $\frac{1}{2}A$

Leading and lagging angles

A sine or cosine curve may not always start at $0°$. To show this, a periodic function is represented by $y = \sin (A \pm \alpha)$ or $y = \cos (A \pm \alpha)$, where α is a phase difference compared with $y = \sin A$ or $y = \cos A$. α is called the **phase angle**.

(i) $y = \sin (A + 60°)$

$A°$	0	15	30	45	60	75	90	105	120
$(A + 60°)$	60	75	90	105	120	135	150	165	180
$\sin (A + 60°)$	0.866	0.966	1.000	0.966	0.866	0.707	0.500	0.259	0

$A°$	135	150	165	180	195	210	225
$(A + 60)°$	195	210	225	240	255	270	285
$\sin (A + 60°)$	−0.259	−0.500	−0.707	−0.866	−0.966	−1.000	−0.966

$A°$	240	255	270	285	300	315	330	345	360
$(A + 60)°$	300	315	330	345	360	375	390	405	420
$\sin (A + 60°)$	−0.866	−0.707	−0.500	−0.259	0	0.259	0.500	0.707	0.866

A graph of $y = \sin (A + 60°)$ is shown in Fig. 3.

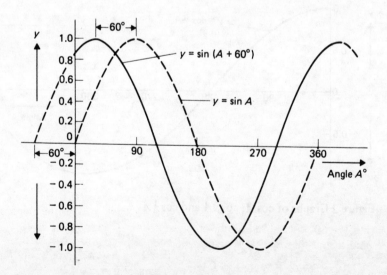

Figure 3 Graph of $y = \sin (A + 60°)$

(ii) $y = \cos (A - 45°)$

$A°$	0	15	30	45	60	75	90	105	120
$(A - 45)°$	−45	−30	−15	0	15	30	45	90	75
$\cos (A - 45°)$	0.707	0.866	0.966	1.000	0.966	0.866	0.707	0.500	0.259

$A°$	135	150	165	180	195	210	225
$(A - 45)°$	90	105	120	135	150	165	180
$\cos (A - 45°)$	0	−0.259	−0.500	−0.707	−0.866	−0.966	−1.000

$A°$	240	255	270	285	300	315	330	345	360
$(A - 45)°$	195	210	225	240	255	270	285	300	315
$\cos (A - 45°)$	−0.966	−0.866	−0.707	−0.500	−0.259	0	0.259	0.500	0.707

A graph of $y = \cos (A - 45°)$ is shown in Fig. 4.

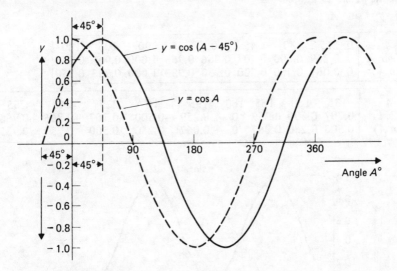

Figure 4 Graph of $y = \cos (A - 45°)$

If the graph of $y = \sin A$ is assumed to commence at $0°$ then the graph of $y = \sin (A + 60°)$ from Fig. 3 is seen to start $60°$ earlier. Thus the graph of $y = \sin (A + 60°)$ is said to **lead** the graph of $y = \sin A$ by $60°$.

Similarly, if the graph of $y = \cos A$ is assumed to commence at $0°$ then the graph of $y = \cos (A - 45°)$ from Fig. 4 is seen to start $45°$ later. Thus the graph of $y = \cos (A - 45°)$ is said to **lag** the graph of $y = \cos A$ by $45°$.

In each of the above two examples the angle of lead or lag may also be seen on the graphs by comparing the positions of the maximum values.

Generally, a graph of $y = \sin(A + \alpha)$ leads $y = \sin A$ by angle α. A graph of $y = \sin(A - \alpha)$ lags $y = \sin A$ by angle α.

It may be seen from Figs. 1 and 2 that a cosine curve is the same shape as a sine curve, except that it starts 90° earlier, i.e., leads by 90°.

Hence $\cos A = \sin(A + 90°)$.

Since sine and cosine curves are of the same shape both are referred to generally as 'sine waves'.

Note that $y = \sin(2t + 60°)$ leads $y = \sin 2t$ by $\dfrac{60°}{2}$, i.e., 30°.

Similarly, $y = \cos(3t - 45°)$ lags $y = \cos 3t$ by $\dfrac{45°}{3}$, i.e., 15°, and so on.

Generally, $y = \sin(pt + \alpha°)$ leads $y = \sin pt$ by $\dfrac{\alpha°}{p}$ and $y = \sin(pt - \alpha°)$

lags $y = \sin pt$ by $\dfrac{\alpha°}{p}$.

Graphs of $\sin^2 A$ and $\cos^2 A$

(i) $y = \sin^2 A$.

$A°$	0	15	30	45	60	75	90	105	120
$\sin A$	0	0.259	0.500	0.707	0.866	0.966	1.000	0.966	0.866
$(\sin A)^2$	0	0.067	0.250	0.500	0.750	0.933	1.000	0.933	0.750

$A°$	135	150	165	180	195	210	225	240	255
$\sin A$	0.707	0.500	0.259	0	−0.259	−0.500	−0.707	−0.866	−0.966
$(\sin A)^2$	0.500	0.250	0.067	0	0.067	0.250	0.500	0.750	0.933

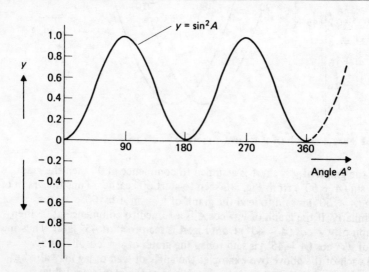

Figure 5 Graph of $y = \sin^2 A$

$A°$	270	285	300	315	330	345	360
$\sin A$	−1.000	−0.966	−0.866	−0.707	−0.500	−0.259	0
$(\sin A)^2$	1.000	0.933	0.750	0.500	0.250	0.067	0

A graph of $y = \sin^2 A$ is shown in Fig. 5.

(ii) $y = \cos^2 A$

$A°$	0	15	30	45	60	75	90	105	120
$\cos A$	1.000	0.966	0.866	0.707	0.500	0.259	0	−0.259	−0.500
$(\cos A)^2$	1.000	0.933	0.750	0.500	0.250	0.067	0	0.067	0.250

$A°$	135	150	165	180	195	210	225
$\cos A$	−0.707	−0.866	−0.966	−1.000	−0.966	−0.866	−0.707
$(\cos A)^2$	0.500	0.750	0.933	1.000	0.933	0.750	0.500

$A°$	240	255	270	285	300	315	330	345	360
$\cos A$	−0.500	−0.259	0	0.259	0.500	0.707	0.866	0.966	1.000
$(\cos A)^2$	0.250	0.067	0	0.067	0.250	0.500	0.750	0.933	1.000

A graph of $y = \cos^2 A$ is shown in Fig. 6.

The graphs of $y = \sin^2 A$ and $y = \cos^2 A$ shown in Figs. 5 and 6 are periodic functions of period 180° or π radians. Both graphs display only positive values.

A graph of $y = \sin^2 2A$ would have a period of $\dfrac{180°}{2}$ i.e., 90° or $\dfrac{\pi}{2}$

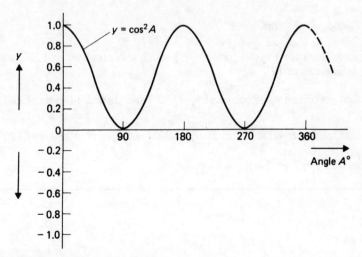

Figure 6 Graph of $y = \cos^2 A$

radians. Similarly, a graph of $y = \cos^2 5A$ would have a period of $\dfrac{180°}{5}$ i.e.,

$36°$ or $\dfrac{\pi}{5}$ radians and so on.

Amplitude

Amplitude is the name given to the maximum value of a sine wave. For each of the sine waves shown in Figs. 1 to 4 the maximum value is $+1$ (and hence -1 in the negative direction). Thus for $y = \sin A$, $y = \cos A$ and so on, the amplitude is 1.

However, if $y = 3 \sin A$, then each of the values in the table is multiplied by 3 and the maximum value, and thus the amplitude is 3. Similarly, if $y = 7 \cos 2A$ then the amplitude is 7 and if $y = 4 \sin (A - 30°)$ the amplitude is 4. In each of these examples, the period of the graph is unaffected by the amplitude.

Sketching graphs of trigonometric ratios

It is often useful to be able to sketch waveforms. This can be achieved reasonably accurately without the time consuming process of drawing up a table. If the amplitude and period of a function are known then a graph of that function may be sketched.
(A 'sketch' is assumed to mean 'the general outline showing important points on the axes'.)

Worked problems on sketching graphs of trigonometrical ratios

Problem 1. Sketch $y = 2 \sin 3A$ from $A = 0$ to $A = 2\pi$ radians.

Amplitude $= 2$, hence the maximum value is $+2$ and the minimum value is -2.

Period $= \dfrac{2\pi}{3}$ radians $= 120°$.

Therefore there are 3 cycles (sine waves) which are completed at $120°$, and then at intervals of $120°$.

The first maximum value occurs at $\dfrac{1}{4}$ $(120°)$ and then at intervals of $120°$.

The first minimum value occurs at $\dfrac{3}{4}$ $(120°)$ and then at intervals of $120°$.

A sketch of $y = 2 \sin 3A$ is shown in Fig. 7.

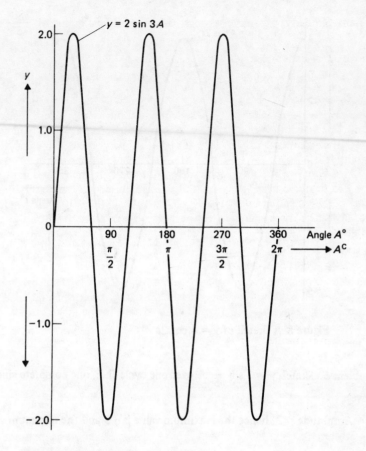

Figure 7 A sketch of $y = 2 \sin 3A$

Problem 2. Sketch $y = 4 \cos 2t$.

Amplitude $= 4$, hence the maximum value is $+4$ and the minimum value is -4.

Period $= \dfrac{360°}{2} = 180°$ (or π radians).

Two cycles are completed between $0°$ and $360°$, at $180°$ and $360°$.
Maximum values occur at $0°$ and $180°$ ($\cos 2t = 1$).
Minimum values occur at $90°$ and $270°$ ($\cos 2t = -1$).
A sketch of $y = 4 \cos 2t$ is shown in Fig. 8.

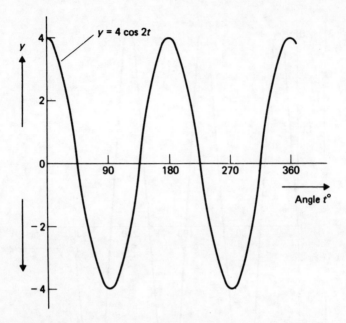

Figure 8 A sketch of $y = 4 \cos 2t$

Problem 3. Sketch $y = 3 \sin \dfrac{2}{5} A$ over one cycle (i.e., one complete sine wave).

Amplitude $= 3$, hence the maximum value is $+3$ and the minimum value is -3.

$$\text{Period} = \frac{360°}{\frac{2}{5}} = 360° \times \frac{5}{2} = 900°, \text{ i.e, one cycle is completed}$$

between $0°$ and $900°$ (and half a cycle is completed after $450°$).

The maximum value is at $\dfrac{450°}{2} = 225°$ and the minimum value is at $225° + 450° = 675°$.

A sketch of $y = 3 \sin \frac{2}{5}A$ is shown in Fig. 9.

Problem 4. Sketch the following graphs from $t = 0$ to $t = 2\pi$ seconds showing relevant details:

(a) $y = 2 \sin 2t$ (b) $y = 5 \cos 3t$

(c) $y = 4 \sin \left(t - \dfrac{\pi}{4}\right)$ (d) $y = 3 \cos \left(t + \dfrac{\pi}{3}\right)$

(e) $y = 4 \sin^2 t$ (f) $y = 3 \cos^2 2t$.

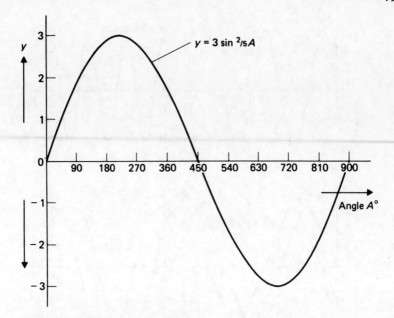

Figure 9 A sketch of $y = 3 \sin \frac{2}{5}A$

(a) $y = 2 \sin 2t$ has an amplitude of 2 and a period of $\frac{2\pi}{2}$, i.e., π radians, as shown in Fig. 10(a).

(b) $y = 5 \cos 3t$ has an amplitude of 5 and a period of $\frac{2\pi}{3}$ radians, as shown in Fig. 10(b).

(c) $y = 4 \sin (t - \frac{\pi}{4})$ has an amplitude of 4, a period of $\frac{2\pi}{1}$, i.e., 2π radians, and lags $y = 4 \sin t$ by $\frac{\pi}{4}$ radians, as shown in Fig. 10(c).

(d) $y = 3 \cos (t + \frac{\pi}{3})$ has a amplitude of 3, a period of 2π radians and leads $y = 3 \cos t$ by $\frac{\pi}{3}$ radians, as shown in Fig. 10(d).

(e) $y = 4 \sin^2 t$ has an amplitude of 4 and a period of $\frac{\pi}{1}$, i.e., π radians, as shown in Fig. 10(e).

(f) $y = 3 \cos^2 2t$ has an amplitude of 3 and a period of $\frac{\pi}{2}$ rads, radians, as shown in Fig. 10(f).

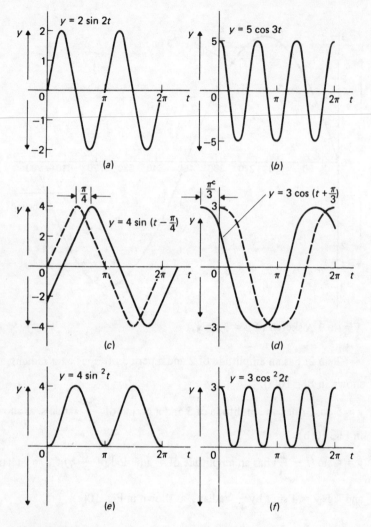

Figure 10

Problem 5. Sketch $y = 5 \cos (2t + 30°)$.

Amplitude $= 5$

Period $= \dfrac{360°}{2} = 180°$

The graph of $y = 5 \cos (2t + 30°)$ **leads** the graph of $y = 5 \cos 2t$ by $\dfrac{30°}{2}$, i.e., $15°$ (i.e., the waveform starts $15°$ earlier).

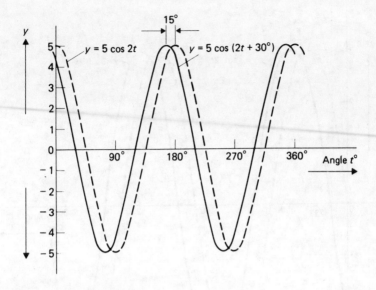

Figure 11 A sketch of $y = 5 \cos (2t + 30°)$

$y = 5 \cos 2t$ is sketched as shown in Fig. 11 and then $y = 5 \cos (2t + 30°)$ is sketched, leading $5 \cos 2t$ by $15°$.

Problem 6. Sketch $y = 3 \sin (2t - \frac{\pi}{4})$.

Amplitude $= 3$

Period $= \frac{2\pi}{2} = \pi$ radians.

The graph of $y = 3 \sin (2t - \frac{\pi}{4})$ lags the graph of $y = 3 \sin 2t$ by $\frac{\pi/4}{2}$, i.e., $\frac{\pi}{8}$ radians (i.e., the waveform starts $\frac{\pi}{8}$ radians or $22\frac{1}{2}°$ later).

$y = 3 \sin 2t$ is sketched as shown in Fig. 12, and then $y = 3 \sin (2t - \frac{\pi}{4})$

is sketched, lagging $3 \sin 2t$ by $\frac{\pi}{8}$ radians.

Further problems on sketching trigonometric ratios may be found in Section 4 (Problems 1–5), p. 87.

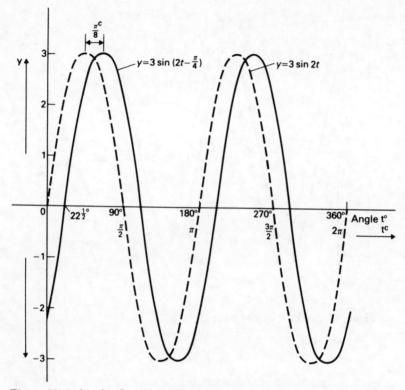

Figure 12 A sketch of $y = 3 \sin (2t - \frac{\pi}{4})$

2 Phasors, periodic time and frequency

In Fig. 13 let OA represent a vector that is free to rotate anti-clockwise about O at a velocity of ω radians per second. A rotating vector is known as a **phasor**.

After a time t seconds the vector OA will turn through an angle ωt radians (shown as angle AOB in Fig. 13). If the line BC is constructed perpendicular to OA as shown then:

$$\sin \omega t = \frac{BC}{OB}$$

i.e., $BC = OB \sin \omega t$.

If all such vertical components are projected on to a graph of y against angle ωt in radians a sine curve results of amplitude OA. This method of producing a sine wave provides an alternative to that discussed in section 1.

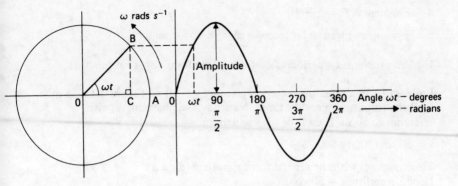

Figure 13 Production of sine curve by rotating vector

Periodic Time

Let T seconds be the time for the rotating vector OA to make one revolution (i.e., 2π radians, which is one period).

Then: $2\pi = \omega T$

or $T = \dfrac{2\pi}{\omega}$ seconds.

Time T is known as the **periodic time**. Thus the base of a sine curve (i.e. the horizontal axis) has a time scale as well as an angular scale.

Frequency

The number of complete waveforms (or cycles) occurring per second is called the frequency, f. (The electrical unit of frequency is the herts (Hz)).

Frequency $= \dfrac{\text{Number of cycles}}{\text{second}} = \dfrac{1}{T} = \dfrac{\omega}{2\pi}$ Hz

i.e., $f = \dfrac{\omega}{2\pi}$ **Hz.**

Angular velocity $\omega = 2\pi f.$

General equation of a periodic function

Given the general sinusoidal periodic function

$y = A \sin(\omega t \pm \alpha)$

the following information can be obtained.

1. Amplitude $= A$
2. Angular velocity $= \omega$ radians per second
3. Periodic time, T $= \dfrac{2\pi}{\omega}$ seconds.

4. Frequency, $f = \dfrac{\omega}{2\pi}$ Hz

5. α = angle of lead or lag (compared with $y = A \sin \omega t$).

Worked problems on periodic functions of the form $y = A \sin (\omega t \pm \alpha)$.

Problem 1. An alternating voltage is given by $v = 50 \sin (200\pi t - 0.25)$ volts. Find the amplitude, periodic time, frequency and phase angle (with reference to $50 \sin 200\pi t$) of the oscillation.

$v = 50 \sin (200\pi t - 0.25)$.

This compares with the general form $y = A \sin (\omega t \pm \alpha)$
Hence, **Amplitude = 50 volts.**

Angular velocity $\omega = 200\pi$

Therefore **periodic time**, $T = \dfrac{2\pi}{\omega} = \dfrac{2\pi}{200\pi}$

$$= \dfrac{1}{100} = \textbf{0.01s.}$$

Frequency, $f = \dfrac{1}{T} = \dfrac{1}{0.01} = \textbf{100 Hz.}$

Phase angle $\alpha = 0.25$ radians (or $14°\ 19'$) lagging $\sin 200\pi\ t$.

Problem 2. The current in an alternating current circuit at any time t seconds is given by:

$i = 75.0 \sin (100\pi\ t + 0.320)$ amperes.

Find (a) the amplitude, periodic time, frequency and phase angle (with reference to $75.0 \sin 100\pi\ t$),
 (b) the value of the current when $t = 0$,
 (c) the value of the current when $t = 0.006$ s,
 (d) the time when the current first reaches 50.0 amperes,
and (e) the time when the current is maximum.
Sketch one cycle of the oscillation.

(a) **Amplitude = 75.0 amperes.**

Periodic time, $T = \dfrac{2\pi}{\omega} = \dfrac{2\pi}{100\pi}$ (since $\omega = 100\pi$)

$$= \dfrac{1}{50}\ \text{or}\ \textbf{0.02 s.}$$

Frequency, $f = \dfrac{1}{T} = \dfrac{1}{0.02} = \textbf{50 Hz.}$

Phase angle $\alpha = 0.320$ radians (or $18°\ 20'$) leading $75.0 \sin 100\pi\ t$.

(b) When $t = 0, i$ $= 75.0 \sin (0 + 0.320)$
$= 75.0 \sin 18° \, 20'$
$= 75.0 \, (0.3146)$
Hence i $= $ **23.60 amperes.**

(c) When $t = 0.006$ s, i $= 75.0 \sin [100 \, \pi \, (0.006) + 0.320]$
$= 75.0 \sin (0.6 \, \pi + 0.320)$
$= 75.0 \sin (2.205)$
$= 75.0 \sin (126.34)°$
$= 75.0 \, (0.8055)$
Hence i $= $ **60.41 amperes.**

(d) When $i = 50.0$ amperes, $50.0 = 75.0 \sin (100 \, \pi \, t + 0.320)$

$$\frac{50.0}{75.0} = \sin (100 \, \pi \, t + 0.320)$$

0.6667 $= \sin (100 \, \pi \, t + 0.320)$
$100 \, \pi \, t + 0.320$ $= \arcsin 0.666 \, 7$
$= 41° \, 49'$ or 0.7298 radians
$100 \, \pi \, t + 0.320$ $= 0.7298$
$100 \, \pi \, t$ $= 0.7298 - 0.320$
$= 0.4098$

Hence t $= \dfrac{0.4098}{100 \, \pi} = $ **0.00130 s.**

(e) When the current is a maximum, $i = $ amplitude $= 75.0$ amperes.
$75.0 = 75.0 \sin (100 \, \pi \, t + 0.320)$
$1 = \sin (100 \, \pi \, t + 0.320)$

$100 \, \pi \, t + 0.320$ $= \arcsin 1 = 90°$ or $\dfrac{\pi}{2}$ radians

$100 \, \pi \, t + 0.320$ $= 1.570 \, 8$
$100 \, \pi \, t$ $= 1.570 \, 8 - 0.320$
$= 1.250 \, 8$

Hence t $= \dfrac{1.250 \, 8}{100 \, \pi}$ s $= $ **0.004 0 s**

A sketch of $i = 75.0 \sin (100 \, \pi \, t + 0.320)$ amperes is shown in Fig. 14.

Further problems on periodic functions of the form $y = A \sin (\omega t \pm \alpha)$ may be found in Section 4 (Problems 6–15), p. 87.

3. Trigonometric approximations for small angles

If angle x is a **small angle** (i.e., less than about $5°$) and is expressed in **radians** then the following trigonometric approximations may be shown to be true:

(a) $\sin x \triangleq x$
(b) $\tan x \triangleq x$
(c) $\cos x \triangleq 1 - \dfrac{x^2}{2}$

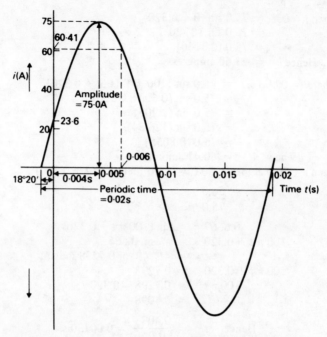

Figure 14 Graph of $i = 75.0 \sin (100\pi t + 0.320)$ amperes

For example, let $x = 1°$ which is $(1 \times \dfrac{\pi}{180})$ radians, i.e. 0.017 5 radians, correct to 4 decimal places (since 2π radians $= 360°$). From tables or calculator, $\sin 1° = 0.017\ 5$ and $\tan 1° = 0.017\ 5$, showing that $\sin x = \tan x = x$ when $x = 0.017\ 5$ radians. Also, $\cos 1° = 0.999\ 8$.

When $x = 1°$, i.e., 0.017 5 radians, $1 - \dfrac{x^2}{2} = 1 - \dfrac{0.017\ 5^2}{2} = 0.999\ 8$ correct to four decimal places, showing that $\cos x = 1 - \dfrac{x^2}{2}$ when $x = 0.017\ 5$ rads.

Similarly, let $x = 5°$ which is $(5 \times \dfrac{\pi}{180})$ radians, i.e., 0.087 3 radians, correct to 4 decimal places.
From tables or calculator, $\sin 5° = 0.087\ 2$, thus $\sin x \eqsim x$,
$\tan 5° = 0.087\ 5$, thus $\tan x \eqsim x$,
and $\cos 5° = 0.996\ 2$.

Since $x = 0.087\ 3$ radians, $1 - \dfrac{x^2}{2} = 1 - \dfrac{0.087\ 3^2}{2} = 0.996\ 2$, showing that $\cos x = 1 - \dfrac{x^2}{2}$ when $x = 0.087\ 3$ radians.

If $\sin x \simeq x$ for small angles then $\dfrac{\sin x}{x} \simeq 1$ and this relationship can be used when determining the differential coefficients of $\sin x$ and $\cos x$.

4. Further problems

Graphs of trigonometrical ratios

In problems 1 to 4, find the amplitude and period of the wave (in degrees) and sketch the curves between $0°$ and $360°$.

1. (a) $y = 2 \sin 3A$. (b) $y = \sin \dfrac{5A}{2}$. (c) $y = 3 \sin 8x$.

(a) $[2, 120°]$ (b) $[1, 144°]$ (c) $[3, 45°]$

2. (a) $y = 4 \cos \dfrac{\phi}{2}$. (b) $y = \dfrac{5}{2} \cos \dfrac{3\phi}{8}$. (c) $y = 9 \cos \dfrac{7t}{3}$.

(a) $[4, 720°]$ (b) $[\dfrac{5}{2}, 960°]$ (c) $[9, 154° \, 17']$.

3. (a) $y = 5 \sin^2 4A$. (b) $y = 2.4 \cos^2 \dfrac{2A}{3}$. (c) $y = \dfrac{1}{3} [7 \cos^2 \dfrac{5A}{6}]$.

(a) $[5, 45°]$ (b) $[2.4, 270°]$ (c) $[\dfrac{7}{3}, 216°]$.

4. (a) $y = 3.6 \cos (4x - 30°)$. (b) $y = 5 \sin (\dfrac{4t}{9} + \dfrac{\pi}{4})$.

(c) $y = 8 \sin^2 (\dfrac{2\phi}{3} - \dfrac{\pi}{3})$. (a) $[3.6, 90°]$ (b) $[5, 810°]$ (c) $[8, 270°]$

5. Sketch the following graphs from $t = 0$ to $t = 2\pi$ seconds showing relevant details:
   (a) $y = 5 \sin 3t$
   (b) $y = 7 \cos 2t$
   (c) $y = 2 \sin (t + \dfrac{4\pi}{9})$
   (d) $y = 4 \cos (t - \dfrac{\pi}{5})$
   (e) $y = 6 \sin^2 2t$
   (f) $y = 1.5 \cos^2 t$
   (the graphs are shown in Fig. 15.)

Periodic functions of the form $y = A \sin (\omega t \pm \alpha)$

In problems 6 to 9 find the amplitude, periodic time, frequency and phase angle (stating whether it is leading or lagging $\sin \omega t$) of the alternating quantities given.

6. $i = 60 \sin (50 \pi t + 0.36)$

$[60, 0.04\text{s}, 25 \text{ Hz}, 20° \, 38' \text{ leading } \sin 50 \pi t.]$

7. $v = 25 \sin (400 \pi t - 0.231)$

$[25, 0.005\text{s}, 200 \text{ Hz}, 13° \, 14' \text{ lagging } \sin 400 \pi t]$

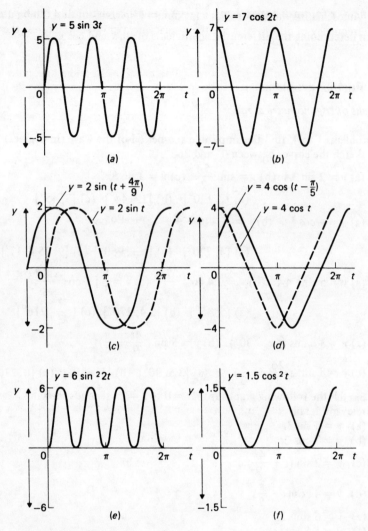

Figure 15 Solution to problem 5

8. $y = 35 \sin (40t - 0.6)$

$$[35, 0.157s, 6.37 \text{ Hz}, 34° 23' \text{ lagging } \sin 40t]$$

9. $x = 10 \sin (314.2t + 0.468)$

$$[10, 0.02s, 50 \text{ Hz}, 26° 49' \text{ leading } \sin 314.2t]$$

10. A sinusoidal current has a maximum value of 25A and a frequency of 60 Hz. At $t = 0$, the current is zero. Express the instantaneous current i, in the form $i = A \sin \omega t$. $\qquad [i = 25 \sin (120 \pi t)]$

11. An oscillating mechanism has a maximum displacement of 4.0 m and a frequency of 50 Hz. At $t = 0$ the displacement is 120 cm. Express the displacement in the general form $A \sin (\omega t \pm \alpha)$.
$$[4.0 \sin (100 \, \pi \, t + 0.305)]$$

12. An alternating voltage v has a periodic time of 0.01 s and a maximum value of 30 volts. When $t = 0$, $v = -20$ V. Express the instantaneous voltage in the form $v = A \sin (\omega t \pm \alpha)$. $\qquad$ [30 sin (200 $\pi \, t - 0.73$)]

13. The voltage in an alternating current circuit at any time t seconds is given by $e = 45.0 \sin 50 \, t$. Find the first two times when the voltage is (a) 10.0V and (b) 25.0V.
(a) [0.00448 s and 0.0583 s] (b) [0.0118 s and 0.0511 s]

14. The current in an a.c. circuit at any time t seconds is given by:
$i = 55.0 \sin (100\pi t + 0.410)$ amperes.
Find (a) the value of the current when $t = 0$,
(b) the value of the current when $t = 0.005$ s,
(c) the time when the current first reaches 32.0 A,
(d) the time when the current is first maximum.
Sketch one cycle of the oscillation showing important points.
(a) [21.92 A] (b) [50.44 A] (c) [0.0006 72 s] (d) [0.00369 s]

15. The instantaneous value of voltage in an a.c. circuit at any time t seconds is given by:
$v = 200.0 \sin (50 \, \pi \, t - 0.683)$ volts.
Find (a) the amplitude, periodic time, frequency and phase angle (with reference to 200.0 sin 50 π t) of the function,
(b) the voltage when $t = 0$,
(c) the voltage when $t = 0.01$ s,
(d) the times in the first cycle when the voltage is 100.0 V,
(e) the times in the first cycle when the voltage is -58.0 V,
(f) the first times when the voltage is a maximum.
Sketch the curve showing important points.
(a) [200 V, 0.04 s, 25 Hz, 39° 8' lag,] (b) [−126.2 V] (c) [155.1 V]
(d) [0;007681 s and 0.02101 s] (e) [0.02622 s and 0.00248 s]
(f) [0.01435 s]

Trigonometric approximations for small angles

16. Show that if x is expressed in radians then:
$\sin x \backsimeq \tan x \backsimeq x$ and $\cos x \backsimeq 1 - \dfrac{x^2}{2}$
when (a) $x = 0.5°$ (b) $x = 1.7°$ (c) $x = 4° \, 20'$.

Chapter 6

Trigonometry (2) – Combining sinusoidal waveforms

1. Combination of two periodic functions

It is often necessary (especially in electrical alternating current theory and also when adding forces and other vectors in mechanics) to find the single phasor which could replace two or more separate phasors. The resulting single phasor is known as the resultant and there are a number of methods by which this may be found. Two such methods are:

(a) by plotting the periodic functions graphically, or
(b) by using phasors.

(a) Combination of two periodic functions by sketching and plotting graphs
One method of obtaining the resultant waveform is by sketching the separate functions on the same axes using the same scales and then adding (or subtracting) ordinates at regular intervals. This method is shown in Problems 1 and 2.

Another method of obtaining the resultant waveform is by drawing up a table of values before plotting the resultant waveform. This method is shown in Problems 3 and 4. If sine waves of the same frequency (and hence period) are combined then a sine wave will result, this resultant having the same frequency as the single phasors. If, however, sine waves of different frequencies are combined then a sine wave will not result. The resultant will, however, be a periodic function although asymmetric.

Worked problems on combination of periodic functions by sketching and plotting graphs

Problem 1. Sketch the graph of $y = 2 \sin A$ from $A = 0°$ to $A = 360°$. On the same axes sketch $y = 3 \cos A$. By adding ordinates sketch $y_R = 2 \sin A + 3 \cos A$ and obtain a sinusoidal expression for this resultant waveform.

$y = 2 \sin A$, $y = 3 \cos A$ and $y_R = 2 \sin A + 3 \cos A$ are shown in Fig. 1.

When adding ordinates at every 15° interval a pair of dividers is useful.

The resultant waveform has the same period, i.e. 360°, as the single phasors. The amplitude of the resultant (i.e. the maximum value) is 3.65. The resultant waveform leads the graph of $y = 2 \sin A$ by 57°. Hence the sinusoidal expression describing the resultant waveform is:

$$y_R = \textbf{3.65} \sin (A + 57°)$$

or $y_R = \textbf{3.65} \sin (A + \textbf{0.995}).$

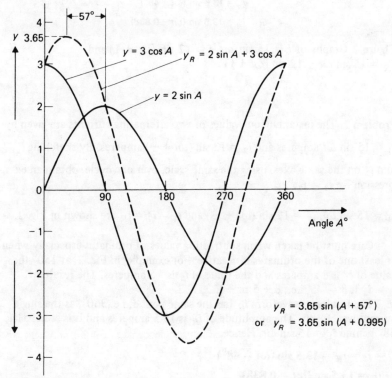

Figure 1 Graphs of $y = 2 \sin A$, $y = 3 \cos A$ and $y = 2 \sin A + 3 \cos A$

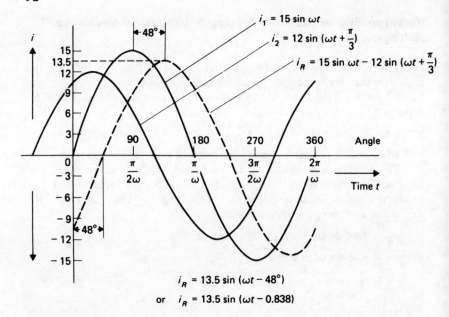

$i_R = 13.5 \sin (\omega t - 48°)$

or $i_R = 13.5 \sin (\omega t - 0.838)$

Figure 2 Graphs of $i = 15 \sin \omega t$, $i = 12 \sin (\omega t + \frac{\pi}{3})$ and $i_R = 15 \sin \omega t - 12 \sin (\omega t + \frac{\pi}{3})$

Problem 2. The instantaneous values of two alternating currents are given by $i_1 = 15 \sin \omega t$ amperes and $i_2 = 12 \sin (\omega t + \frac{\pi}{3})$ amperes. By sketching i_1 and i_2 on the same axes, using the same scale, over one cycle, obtain an expression for $i_1 - i_2$.

$i_1 = 15 \sin \omega t$, $i_2 = 12 \sin (\omega t + \frac{\pi}{3})$ and $i_1 - i_2 = i_R$ are shown in Fig. 2.

Care must be taken when subtracting values of ordinates especially when at least one of the ordinates is negative. For example, in Fig. 2, at 150° the value of i_1 is 8 amperes and the value of i_2 is −5 amperes. The resultant $i_1 - i_2$ is 8 − −5, i.e., 8 + 5 or +13.

The resultant waveform i_R has the same period, i.e. 360°, as the single current waveforms. The amplitude of i_R is 13.5 amperes and it is seen to lag 48° behind $i_1 = 15 \sin \omega t$. Hence:

$i_1 - i_2 = i_R = 13.5 \sin (\omega t - 48°)$

or $i_R = 13.5 \sin (\omega t - 0.838)$.

Problem 3. By drawing up a table plot the waveform $y = 3 \sin 2x - \cos 3x$.

x	0	15	30	45	60	75	90	105	120
$2x$	0	30	60	90	120	150	180	210	240
$\sin 2x$	0	0.500	0.866	1.00	0.866	0.500	0	-0.500	-0.866
$3 \sin 2x$	0	1.50	2.60	3.00	2.60	1.50	0	-1.50	-2.60
$3x$	0	45	90	135	180	225	270	315	360
$\cos 3x$	1.00	0.707	0	-0.707	-1.00	-0.707	0	0.707	1.00
$(3 \sin 2x - \cos 3x)$	-1.00	0.79	2.60	3.71	3.60	2.21	0	-2.21	-3.60

x	135	150	165	180	195	210	225	240	255
$2x$	270	300	330	360	390	420	450	480	510
$\sin 2x$	-1.00	-0.866	-0.500	0	0.500	0.866	1.00	0.866	0.500
$3 \sin 2x$	-3.00	-2.60	-1.50	0	1.50	2.60	3.00	2.60	1.50
$3x$	405	450	495	540	585	630	675	720	765
$\cos 3x$	0.707	0	-0.707	-1.00	-0.707	0	0.707	1.00	0.707
$(3 \sin 2x - \cos 3x)$	-3.71	-2.60	-0.79	1.00	2.21	2.60	2.29	1.60	0.79

x	270	285	300	315	330	345	360
$2x$	540	570	600	630	660	690	720
$\sin 2x$	0	-0.500	-0.866	-1.00	-0.866	-0.500	0
$3 \sin 2x$	0	-1.50	-2.60	-3.00	-2.60	-1.50	0
$3x$	810	855	900	945	990	1035	1080
$\cos 3x$	0	-0.707	-1.00	-0.707	0	0.707	1.00
$(3 \sin 2x - \cos 3x)$	0	-0.79	-1.60	-2.29	-2.60	-2.21	-1.00

The waveform $y = 3 \sin 2x - \cos 3x$ is shown in Fig. 3.

The waveform is not sinusoidal since the components forming it have different frequencies (and thus periods). The waveform has a period of $360°$ or 2π radians. When two sine waves of different periods are combined the resultant sine wave will always have a period equal to the lowest common multiple (L.C.M.) of the two component periods.

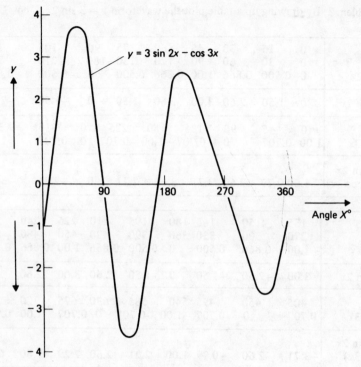

Figure 3 Graph of $y = 3 \sin 2x - \cos 3x$

In the above example the period of $3 \sin 2x$ is $180°$ and the period of $\cos 3x$ is $120°$. The L.C.M. of $180°$ and $120°$ is $360°$. Hence the period of $y = 3 \sin 2x - \cos 3x$ is $360°$.

Problem 4. Draw to scale a graph representing:

$$v = 3 \sin \omega t + 2 \cos \left(\omega t - \frac{5\pi}{18}\right).$$

Express v in the general form, $v = A \sin(\omega t \pm \alpha)$.

A table of values must first be produced.

$-\dfrac{5\pi}{18}$ radians is the same as $-\dfrac{5\pi}{18} \times \dfrac{180°}{\pi} = -50°$.

ωt (degrees)	0	15	30	45	60	75	90	105
$\sin \omega t$	0	0.259	0.500	0.707	0.866	0.966	1.00	0.966
$3 \sin \omega t$	0	0.78	1.50	2.12	2.60	2.90	3.00	2.90
$\omega t - 50°$	−50	−35	−20	−5	10	25	40	55
$\cos (\omega t - 50°)$	0.64	0.82	0.94	0.996	0.98	0.91	0.77	0.57
$2 \cos (\omega t - 50°)$	1.28	1.64	1.88	1.99	1.96	1.82	1.54	1.14
$3 \sin \omega t + 2(\omega t - 50°)$	1.28	2.42	3.38	4.11	4.56	4.72	4.54	4.04

ωt (degrees)	120	135	150	165	180	195	210	225
$\sin \omega t$	0.866	0.707	0.500	0.259	0	−0.259	−0.500	−0.707
$3 \sin \omega t$	2.60	2.12	1.50	0.78	0	−0.78	−1.50	−2.12
$\omega t - 50°$	70	85	100	115	130	145	160	175
$\cos (\omega t - 50°)$	0.34	0.087	−0.17	−0.42	−0.64	−0.82	−0.94	−0.996
$2 \cos (\omega t - 50°)$	0.68	0.17	−0.34	−0.84	−1.28	−1.64	−1.88	−1.99
$3 \sin \omega t + 2 \cos (\omega t - 50°)$	3.28	2.29	1.16	−0.06	−1.28	−2.42	−3.38	−4.11

ωt (degrees)	240	255	270	285	300	315	330	345	360
$\sin \omega t$	−0.866	−0.966	−1.00	−0.966	−0.866	−0.707	−0.500	−0.259	0
$3 \sin \omega t$	−2.60	−2.90	−3.00	−2.90	−2.60	−2.12	−1.50	−0.78	0
$\omega t - 50°$	190	205	220	235	250	265	280	295	310
$\cos (\omega t - 50°)$	−0.98	−0.91	−0.77	−0.57	−0.34	−0.087	0.17	0.42	0.64
$2 \cos (\omega t - 50°)$	−1.96	−1.82	−1.54	−1.14	−0.68	−0.17	0.34	0.84	1.28
$3 \sin \omega t + 2 \cos (\omega t - 50°)$	−4.56	−4.72	−4.54	−4.04	−3.28	−2.29	−1.16	0.06	1.28

A graph of $v = 3 \sin \omega t + 2 \cos \left(\omega t - \dfrac{5\pi}{18}\right)$ is shown in Fig. 4.

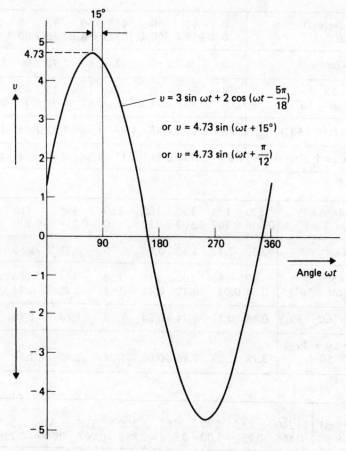

Figure 4 Graph of $v = 3 \sin \omega t + 2 \cos (\omega t - \frac{5\pi}{18})$

The maximum value of the resultant sine wave, i.e., the amplitude is 4.73. The resultant wave is $15°$ or $\frac{\pi}{12}$ radians ahead of a sine wave which starts at $0°$.

Hence: $v = 3 \sin \omega t + 2 \cos (\omega t - \frac{5\pi}{18}) = 4.73 \sin (\omega t + \frac{\pi}{12})$.

(b) Combination of two periodic functions of the same frequency by using phasors

The resultant of two periodic functions of the same frequency may be found from their relative positions when the time is zero. For example, if

$y_1 = 3 \sin \omega t$ and $y_2 = 4 \sin (\omega t - \frac{\pi}{4})$ then each may be represented as

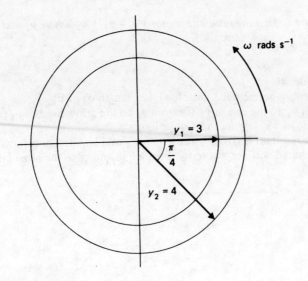

Figure 5

rotating vectors (or phasors) of maximum values 3 and 4 respectively, with y_2 lagging y_1 by $\frac{\pi}{4}$ radians or 45° as shown in Fig. 5, their positions being taken when the time is zero.

When the sum or difference of two periodic functions of the same frequency is required it is usual to represent the phasors as shown in Fig. 6.

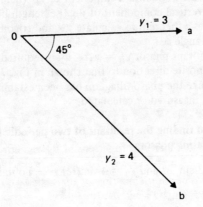

Figure 6

Procedure to find the resultant phasor $y_R = y_1 + y_2$ *where* $y_1 = 3 \sin \omega t$
and $y_2 = 4 \sin \left(\omega t - \dfrac{\pi}{4}\right)$

(i) **By drawing**
1. Draw y_1 horizontal 3 units long, i.e., length oa of Fig. 7.
2. Join y_2 to the end of y_1 (i.e. join y_2 to the arrow head of y_1) at an angle of 45° lagging and 4 units long.
3. The resultant is given by the length y_R and its phase angle ϕ may be measured with respect to y_1. Figure 7 is known as the phasor diagram.

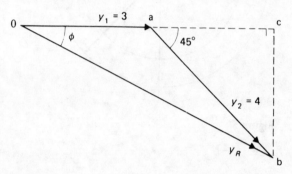

Figure 7

(ii) **By calculation**
Sketch a phasor diagram as in Fig. 7, then,
Either 1. Use the cosine rule to calculate y_R and then the sine rule to calculate angle ϕ.
Or 2. Calculate the horizontal component of y_R (i.e. length oc of Fig. 7), then the vertical component of y_R (i.e. length bc) and then use Pythagoras's theorem to calculate y_R and trigonometric ratios to calculate angle ϕ.
If the resultant phasor $y_R = y_1 - y_2$ is required then y_2 is drawn in the opposite direction to that shown in Fig. 7. This is shown in Fig. 8. Once the phasor diagram has been established y_R and angle ϕ may be measured or calculated.

Worked problems on finding the resultant of two periodic functions of the same frequency by using phasors

Problem 1. If $y_1 = 3 \sin \omega t$ and $y_2 = 4 \sin \left(\omega t - \dfrac{\pi}{4}\right)$ obtain an expression for the resultant $y_R = y_1 + y_2$:
  (a) by drawing
  (b) by calculation

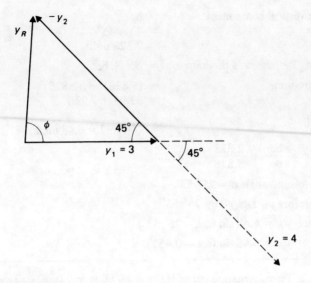

Figure 8

(a) **By drawing**
From the phasor diagram shown in Fig. 7, y_R is measured as 6.5 units and angle ϕ as $26°$.
Hence, by drawing, $y_R = 6.5 \sin(\omega t - 26°)$
or $y_R = 6.5 \sin(\omega t - 0.454)$.

(b) **By calculation**
Method 1.
Using the cosine rule, $y_R{}^2 = 3^2 + 4^2 - 2(3)(4)\cos 135°$
$$= 9 + 16 + 24 \cos 45°$$
$$= 9 + 16 + 16.97 = 41.97$$
Therefore $y_R = \sqrt{41.97} = \textbf{6.48 units.}$

Using the sine rule: $\dfrac{4}{\sin\phi} = \dfrac{6.48}{\sin 135°}$

Therefore $\sin\phi = \dfrac{4 \sin 135°}{6.48} = 0.4365$

Therefore angle $\phi = \textbf{25° 53}'.$

Method 2.
Referring to Fig. 7 the horizontal component,
$$oc = oa + ac$$
$$= 3 + 4 \cos 45°$$
$$= 5.828 \text{ units.}$$

The vertical component	= bc
	$= 4 \sin 45°$
	$= 2.828$ units.

Using Pythagoras's theorem, $ob^2 = oc^2 + bc^2$

Therefore,
$$y_R{}^2 = (5.828)^2 + (2.828)^2$$
$$= 33.97 + 7.998$$
$$= 41.97$$
$$y_R = \sqrt{41.97} = 6.48 \text{ units.}$$

$$\tan \phi = \frac{bc}{oc} = \frac{2.828}{5.828} = .4852.$$

Therefore **angle $\phi = 25° 53'$**.

Therefore y_R lags y_1 by $25° 53'$.

Hence **$y_R = 6.48 \sin (\omega t - 25° 53')$**

or **$y_R = 6.48 \sin (\omega t - 0.452)$**.

Problem 2. Two alternating currents are given by $i_1 = 2.0 \sin \omega t$ amperes and $i_2 = 3.0 \cos \omega t$ amperes. Obtain a sinusoidal expression for $i_1 + i_2$.

To obtain the resultant $i_1 + i_2$ both components need to be of the form $A \sin (\omega t \pm \alpha)$. Thus $3.0 \cos \omega t$ needs to be changed to this form.

$3.0 \cos \omega t = 3.0 \sin (\omega t + 90°)$ since a cosine curve leads a sine curve by $90°$ or $\frac{\pi}{2}$ radians.

The relative positions of i_1 and i_2 at $t = 0$ are shown in Fig. 9(a) and the phasor diagram is shown in Fig. 9(b).

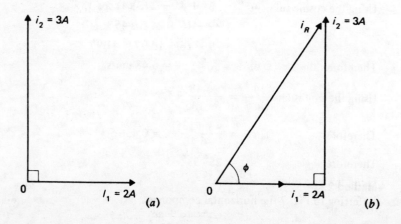

Figure 9

Using Pythagoras's theorem, $i_R = \sqrt{(i_1 + i_2)^2} = \sqrt{(2.0^2 + 3.0^2)}$

$$= \sqrt{13.0} = 3.61 \text{ amperes}$$

$$\tan \phi = \frac{3.0}{2.0}$$

$$\text{angle } \phi = 56° \ 19' \text{ or } 0.983 \text{ radians.}$$

Therefore i_R is leading i_1 by $56° \ 19'$ or 0.983 radians.

Hence $i_R = 2.0 \sin \omega t + 3.0 \cos \omega t = 3.61 \sin (\omega t + 56° \ 19')$

or $\qquad i_R = 3.61 \sin (\omega t + 0.983) \text{ amperes.}$

Problem 3. Two alternating voltages are given by $v_1 = 15.0 \sin \omega t$ volts and $v_2 = 12.0 \sin (\omega t + \frac{\pi}{3})$ volts. Obtain sinusoidal expressions for (a) $v_1 + v_2$ and (b) $v_1 - v_2$.

(a) The relative positions of v_1 and v_2 at $t = 0$ are shown in Fig. 10(a) and the phasor diagram is shown in Fig. 10(b).

The horizontal component of v_R = ob + bc = $15.0 + 12.0 \cos 60°$
$$= 21.0 \text{ volts.}$$

The vertical component of v_R = ac = $12.0 \sin 60° = 10.39$ volts.

$$v_R \ (= oc) = \sqrt{[(21.0)^2 + (10.39)^2]}$$
$$= \sqrt{548.95} = 23.43 \text{ volts}$$

$$\tan \phi = \frac{ac}{oc} = \frac{10.39}{21.0} = 0.494 \ 8.$$

$$\phi = 26° \ 19'.$$

Therefore v_R leads v_1 by $26° \ 19'$ or 0.459 radians.

Hence $v_R = 15.0 \sin \omega t + 12.0 \sin (\omega t + \frac{\pi}{3}) = 23.43 \sin (\omega t + 26° \ 19')$
$$= 23.43 \sin (\omega t + 0.459)$$

(b) To find the resultant $v_R = v_1 - v_2$, the phasor v_2 is reversed in direction. The phasor diagram is shown in Fig. 11.

Using the cosine rule: $v_R^2 = v_1^2 + v_2^2 - 2 v_1 v_2 \cos 60°$
$$= 15.0^2 + 12.0^2 - 2 (15.0)(12.0)(½)$$
$$= 189.0$$
$$v_R = \sqrt{189.0} = 13.75 \text{ volts}$$

Using the sine rule: $\dfrac{12.0}{\sin \phi} = \dfrac{13.75}{\sin 60°}$

$$\sin \phi = \frac{12.0 \sin 60°}{13.75} = 0.755 \ 8$$

$$\therefore \text{ angle } \phi = 49° \ 6'.$$

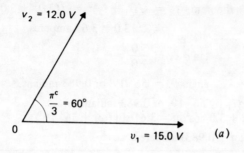

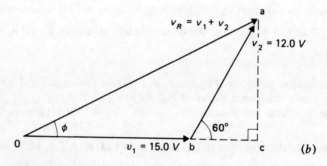

Figure 10

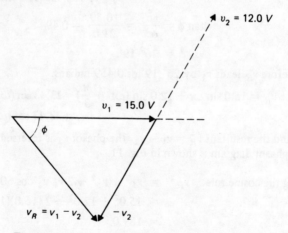

Figure 11

Therefore v_R lags v_1 by $49° \, 6'$ or 0.857 radians.

Hence $v_R = 15.0 \sin \omega t - 12.0 \sin (\omega t + \frac{\pi}{3}) = $ **13.75 sin $(\omega t - 49° \, 6')$**

$\qquad\qquad\qquad\qquad\qquad\qquad\qquad\qquad = $ **13.75 sin $(\omega t - 0.857)$.**

2 Further problems

1. Sketch the curve $y = 3.0 \sin A$ from $A = 0°$ to $A = 360°$. On the same axes sketch $y = \cos A$. By adding ordinates sketch $y = 3.0 \sin A + \cos A$ and obtain a sinusoidal expression for this waveform.

$$[3.16 \sin (A + 18° \, 26') \text{ or } 3.16 \sin (A + 0.322)]$$

2. The instantaneous values of two alternating voltages are given by

$v_1 = 5.0 \sin \omega t$ and $v_2 = 9.0 \sin (\omega t - \frac{\pi}{6})$. By sketching v_1 and v_2 on the same axes, using the same scale, over one cycle, obtain an expression for (a) $v_1 + v_2$, and (b) $v_1 - v_2$.

$$\text{(a) } [13.6 \sin (\omega t - 0.338) \quad \text{(b) } [5.30 \sin (\omega t + 2.126)]$$

3. By drawing up a table of values plot the waveform

$y = 4.0 \sin (\omega t + \frac{\pi}{3}) + 3.0 \cos (\omega t - \frac{\pi}{4})$. Express y in the general form

$y = A \sin (\omega t \pm \alpha)$. $\qquad [6.94 \sin (\omega t + 0.935)]$

4. By calculation obtain an expression for

$y_1 = 4.0 \sin \omega t$ and $y_2 = 6.0 \sin (\omega t - \frac{\pi}{3})$. $\quad [8.72 \sin (\omega t - 0.638)]$

Either by drawing or by calculation express the combination of periodic functions in Problems 5 and 6 in the form $A \sin (\omega t \pm \alpha)$.

5. $5.0 \sin \omega t + 2.0 \sin (\omega t - \frac{\pi}{6})$. $\qquad [6.81 \sin (\omega t - 0.147)]$

6. $16 \sin \omega t - 10 \sin (\omega t + \frac{\pi}{8})$. $\qquad [7.77 \sin (\omega t - 0.515)]$

7. Two alternating currents are given by $i_1 = \sin (\omega t + \frac{\pi}{5})$ and

$i_2 = 2.0 \sin (\omega t - \frac{\pi}{6})$. Obtain an expression for $i_1 - i_2$ in the form

$A \sin (\omega t \pm \alpha)$. $\quad [1.84 \sin (\omega t + 2.097)]$

8. Two voltages, $4 \cos \omega t$ and $-3 \sin \omega t$, are inputs to an analogue circuit. Find an expression for the output voltage in the form $A \sin (\omega t \pm \alpha)$ if this is given by the addition of the two inputs.

$$[5 \sin (\omega t + 126° \, 52') \text{ or } 5 \sin (\omega t + 2.214)]$$

9. Two alternating voltages are given by $v_1 = 25.0 \sin \omega t$ and

$v_2 = 16.0 \sin (\omega t - \frac{\pi}{4})$. Obtain sinusoidal expressions for (a) $v_1 + v_2$

and (b) $v_1 - v_2$.

$$\text{(a) } [38.04 \sin (\omega t - 0.302)] \quad \text{(b) } [17.76 \sin (\omega t + 0.691)]$$

10. In the theory of transmission of polarised light, wave forms have the equations:

$x_1 = \cos \omega t$ $\qquad\qquad y_1 = k \sin \omega t$
$x_2 = k^2 \cos (\omega t + \alpha)$ $\qquad y_2 = -k \sin (\omega t + \alpha)$

Determine the resultant of $x_1 + x_2$ and $y_1 + y_2$.

$$\left[\begin{array}{l} x_1 + x_2 = \sqrt{(1 + k^4 + 2\,k^2\cos\alpha)}\,\cos(\omega t + \beta) \\[2mm] \text{where } \beta = \arcsin\left\{\dfrac{k^2\sin\alpha}{\sqrt{(1 + k^4 + 2k^2\cos\alpha)}}\right\} \\[3mm] y_1 + y_2 = k\sqrt{[2\,(1 - \cos\alpha)]}\,\sin(\omega t - \beta) \\[2mm] \text{where } \beta = \arcsin\left\{\dfrac{\sin\alpha}{\sqrt{[2\,(1 - \cos\alpha)]}}\right\} \end{array}\right]$$

Chapter 7

Curve sketching and the determination of laws

1. Introduction

When a mathematical equation is known, co-ordinates may be calculated for a limited range of values, and the equation may be represented pictorially as a graph, within this range of calculated values. Sometimes, it is useful to show all the characteristic features of an equation, and in this case a sketch depicting the equation can be drawn, in which all the important features are shown, but the accurate plotting of points is less important. This technique is called 'curve sketching' and involves the use of differential calculus, hence is better left until a knowledge of differentiation and its applications has been covered. However, at this stage, certain basic curves such as the circle, parabola, ellipse and hyperbola can be readily drawn and are dealt with in this chapter. The quadratic graph is introduced in Section 2, and in Section 3 simple equations of the circle, parabola, ellipse and hyperbola, together with the characteristic curves associated with these equations are considered.

2. The quadratic graph

A general quadratic equation is given by $y = ax^2 + bx + c$, where a, b and c are constants, and $a \neq 0$.

(i) $y = ax^2$

The simplest quadratic equation is $y = x^2$. In order to plot a graph of $y = x^2$ a table of values is drawn up.

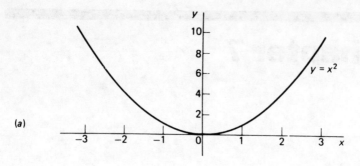

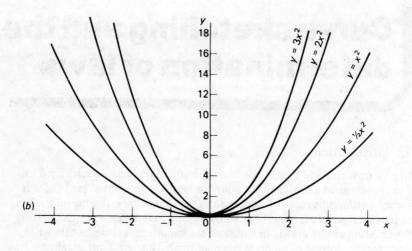

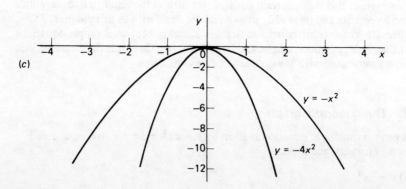

Figure 1

x	-3	-2	-1	0	1	2	3
$y = x^2$	9	4	1	0	1	4	9

Figure 1(a) shows a graph of $y = x^2$ which is symmetrical about the y-axis. (Note that the co-ordinates on the graph are joined by a smooth curve and not from point to point.) A curve of this shape is called a **parabola**. At the origin i.e., at $(0, 0)$, the lowest point on the curve is reached. This is called a **turning-point**. The values of y on either side of this point are greater than at the turning-point. Such a point is called a **minimum value**, and can be thought of as being the 'bottom of a valley'.

The curve depicting $y = ax^2$ could have been sketched by considering the following, easily ascertained values:

(a) when x is 0, y is 0,

(b) when x is large and positive, y is large and positive,

and (c) when x is large and negative, y is large and positive.

It can be seen that the curve shown in Fig. 1(a) meets these three criteria.

Figure 1(b) shows the effect of the constant a where $a = 1, 2, 3$ and ½, i.e. it shows graphs of $y = x^2$, $y = 2x^2$, $y = 3x^2$ and $y = \frac{1}{2}x^2$. As the value of a increases, the curves become more steep; as a decreases the curves become less steep. All the curves of the form $y = ax^2$ are symmetrical about the y-axis, and the y-axis is called the axis of symmetry.

In addition to points (a) to (c) given above, the inclusion of one other pair of points will give the steepness of the curve, e.g. if $y = x^2$ and $x = \pm 2$, then $y = 4$.

(ii) $y = -ax^2$

Figure 1(c) shows graphs of $y = -x^2$ and $y = -4x^2$. This shows the effect of a being negative. The numerical values of y will be the same as previously obtained but will all be negative, giving the inverted parabolas shown. At the origin $(0, 0)$ a turning-point again exists. This time the values of y on either side of this point are less than at the turning-point. Such a point is called a **maximum value** and can be thought of as being the 'crest of a wave'.

(iii) $y = ax^2 + c$

A table of values for $y = x^2$ is shown above. If a table of values is drawn up for say, $y = x^2 + 3$, then all the values of y in the above table will be increased by 3. Similarly, if $y = x^2 - 2$ then all the values of y will be decreased by 2.

Thus when the constant c is a positive value the parabola is raised by c units; when c is a negative value then the parabola is lowered by c units. Figure 2(a) shows graphs of $y = x^2$, $y = 2x^2 + 3$ and $y = 3x^2 - 6$ and Fig 2 (b) shows graphs of $y = -x^2 + 5$ and $y = -3x^2 - 5$.

(iv) $y = ax^2 + bx + c$

A graph of $y = p(x + q)^2 + r$ where p, q and r are constants, is the same general shape as $y = ax^2$, i.e., a parabola.

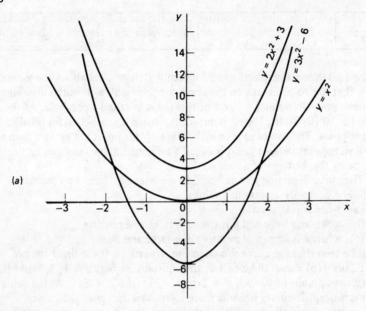

(a)

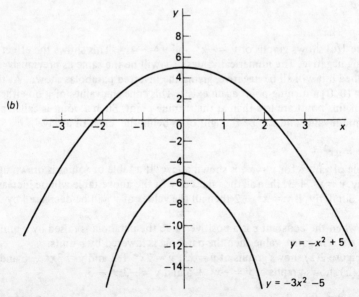

(b)

Figure 2

When the constant r is a positive value the parabola is raised by r units from the zero position; when r is a negative value the parabola is lowered by r units (as in case (iii) above). When the constant q is a positive value the parabola is moved q units to the left from its zero position; when q is a negative value it is moved q units to the right.

For example, the graph of $y = 2(x + 3)^2 + 4$ is shown in Fig. 3. This is a parabola whose turning-point (a minimum value) is situated at $(-3, 4)$. Similarly, the graph of $y = -3 (x - 2)^2 - 4$ is shown in Fig. 3. This is also a parabola, whose turning-point (a maximum value) is situated at $(2, -4)$.

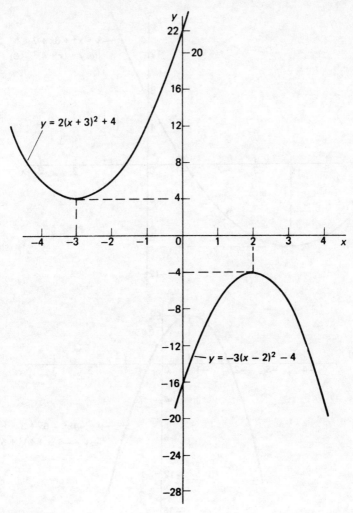

Figure 3

Of course, a quadratic expression is not normally expressed in the form $y = p(x + q)^2 + r$. If, however, the general expression $y = ax^2 + bx + c$ can be changed into the form $y = p(x + q)^2 + r$ then the curve can be readily sketched.

For example, let $y = x^2 + 8x + 7$.

To obtain the q term in $(x + q)^2$, half the coefficient of the x term is taken, since when expanding $(x + q)^2$, the coefficient of x is $2q$.

In this case $q = \dfrac{8}{2}$ or 4.

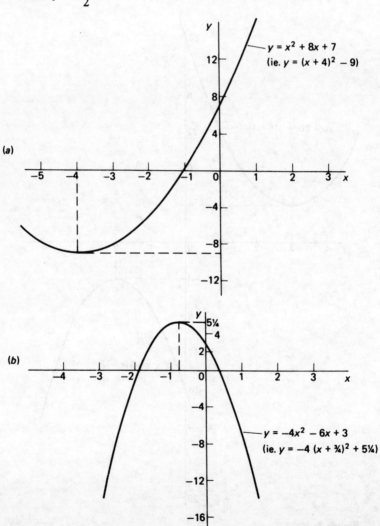

(a)

$y = x^2 + 8x + 7$
(ie. $y = (x + 4)^2 - 9$)

(b)

$y = -4x^2 - 6x + 3$
(ie. $y = -4(x + \frac{3}{4})^2 + 5\frac{1}{4}$)

Figure 4

However, $(x + 4)^2 = x^2 + 8x + 16$, which is 16 more than is needed. The 16 is therefore subtracted.

Hence $y = x^2 + 8x + 7$
$$= [(x + 4)^2 - 16] + 7$$
$$y = (x + 4)^2 - 9, \text{ which is a parabola which a minimum value at}$$
$(-4, -9)$ as shown in Fig. 4(a).

Similarly, if $y = -4x^2 - 6x + 3$

then $y = -4 \left(x^2 + \dfrac{6}{4}x \right) + 3$

$$= -4 \left\{ \left[x + \dfrac{3}{4} \right]^2 - \dfrac{9}{16} \right\} + 3$$

$$= -4 \left[x + \dfrac{3}{4} \right]^2 + 2\dfrac{1}{4} + 3$$

i.e. $y = -4 \left[x + \dfrac{3}{4} \right]^2 + 5\dfrac{1}{4}$

Comparing this with $y = p(x + q)^2 + r$ shows the parabola to be inverted (since p is negative), moved horizontally ¾ units to the left from the zero position (since q is $+ ¾$) and raised by 5¼ units from the zero position (since r is $+ 5¼$). The turning-point on the curve (a maximum value) thus occurs at $(-¾, 5¼)$ as shown in Fig. 4(b).

Worked problems on sketching and plotting quadratic graphs

Problem 1. Sketch on the same axes the following curves:

(a) $y = 2x^2$; (b) $\dfrac{y}{4} = x^2$; (c) $2\sqrt{y} = x$; (d) $-y = 3x^2$.

(a) $y = 2x^2$ is a parabola with its turning-point (a minimum value) at $(0, 0)$.
When $x = \pm 2, y = 2 (\pm 2)^2 = 8$.

(b) $\dfrac{y}{4} = x^2$ or $y = 4x^2$ is a parabola with its turning point (a minimum value) at $(0, 0)$. This curve is steeper than $y = 2x^2$ by a factor of 2. When $x = \pm 2, y = 4 (\pm 2)^2 = 16$.

(c) $2\sqrt{y} = x$ or $y = \dfrac{x^2}{4}$ is a parabola with its turning-point (a minimum value) at $(0, 0)$. This curve is less steep than $y = 2x^2$ by a factor of ⅛. When $x = \pm 2, y = \dfrac{(\pm 2)^2}{4} = 1$.

(d) $-y = 3x^2$ or $y = -3x^2$ is an inverted parabola with its turning-point (a maximum value) at $(0, 0)$.
When $x = \pm 2, y = -3 (\pm 2)^2 = -12$.

Figure 5 shows the four curves.

Problem 2. Sketch the following curves and determine the co-ordinates of their turning-points: (a) $y = 4x^2 + 5$; (b) $y = 4x^2 + 24x + 37$;
(c) $y = -3x^2 - 2$; (d) $y = -2x^2 + 16x - 29$.

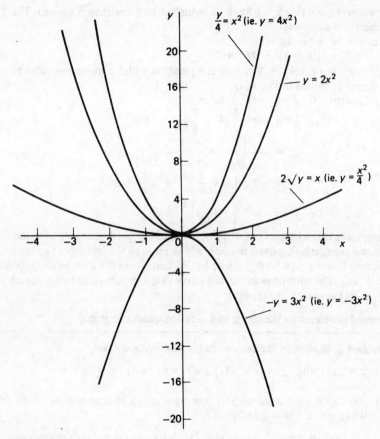

The graph shows:
- $\dfrac{y}{4} = x^2$ (ie. $y = 4x^2$)
- $y = 2x^2$
- $2\sqrt{y} = x$ (ie. $y = \dfrac{x^2}{4}$)
- $-y = 3x^2$ (ie. $y = -3x^2$)

Figure 5

(a) $y = 4x^2 + 5$ is a parabola with its turning-point (a minimum value) at $(0, 5)$. When $x = \pm 1, y = 4\,(\pm 1)^2 + 5 = 9$.

(b) $y = 4x^2 + 24x + 37$
$= 4\,(x^2 + 6x) + 37$
$= 4\,[(x + 3)^2 - 9] + 37$
$= 4\,(x + 3)^2 - 36 + 37$
i.e., $y = 4(x + 3)^2 + 1$
Hence $y = 4x^2 + 24x + 37$ is a parabola with its turning-point (a minimum value) at $(-3, 1)$. When $x = -2, y = 5$. When $x = -4, y = 5$.

(c) $y = -3x^2 - 2$ is an inverted parabola with its turning-point (a maximum value) at $(0, -2)$. When $x = \pm 2, y = -14$.

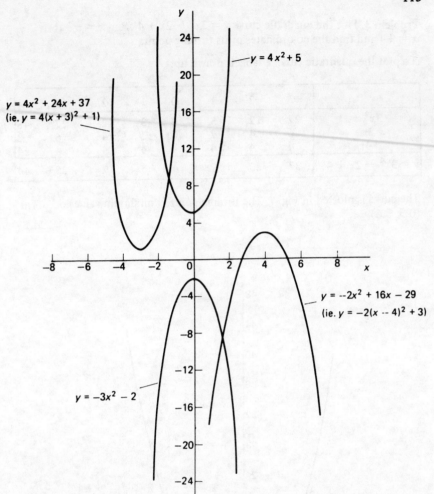

Figure 6

(d) $y = -2x^2 + 16x - 29$
$\quad = -2(x^2 - 8x) - 29$
$\quad = -2[(x-4)^2 - 16] - 29$
$\quad = -2(x-4)^2 + 32 - 29$
i.e., $y = -2(x-4)^2 + 3$

Hence $y = -2x^2 + 16x - 29$ is an inverted parabola with its turning-point (a maximum value) at **(4, 3)**. When $x = 3$, $y = 1$, when $x = 5$, $y = 1$.

Each of the curves is shown in Fig. 6.

Problem 3. Plot the quadratic curve $y = 3x^2 - 2x + 4$ from $x = -3$ to $x = +4$ and find the co-ordinates of its turning-point.

To plot the quadratic curve a table is drawn up.

x	-3	-2	-1	0	1	2	3	4
$3x^2$	27	12	3	0	3	12	27	48
$-2x$	6	4	2	0	-2	-4	-6	-8
$+4$	4	4	4	4	4	4	4	4
$y = 3x^2 - 2x + 4$	37	20	9	4	5	12	25	44

The curve is plotted in Fig. 7. The turning-point (a minimum value) occurs at (0.3, 3.6).

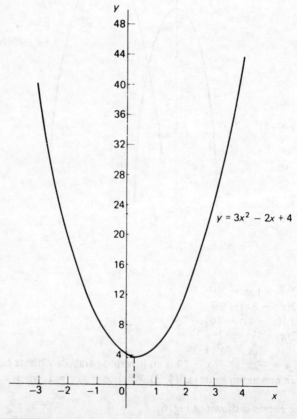

Figure 7

The co-ordinates of the turning-point may be checked as follows:

Since $y = 3x^2 - 2x + 4$

then $y = 3\left(x^2 - \dfrac{2}{3}x\right) + 4$

$= 3\left[\left(x - \dfrac{1}{3}\right)^2 - \dfrac{1}{9}\right] + 4$

$= 3\left(x - \dfrac{1}{3}\right)^2 - \dfrac{1}{3} + 4$

i.e., $y = 3\left(x - \dfrac{1}{3}\right)^2 + 3\dfrac{2}{3}$

Hence the turning-point is at $\left(\dfrac{1}{3}, 3\dfrac{2}{3}\right)$

Further problems on the quadratic graph may be found in Section 5 (Problems 1–23), p. 137.

3. Simple curves of the circle, parabola, ellipse and hyperbola

(i) The circle

The simplest form of the equation of a circle is that of a circle of radius a, having its centre at the origin of a rectangular co-ordinate system $(0, 0)$. The equation is:

$$x^2 + y^2 = a^2 \text{ or } y = \sqrt{(a^2 - x^2)}$$

The co-ordinates of the equation $x^2 + y^2 = 9$ may be determined as shown below.

x	−3.0	−2.5	−2.0	−1.5	−1.0	−0.5
x^2	9.0	6.25	4.0	2.25	1.0	0.25
$9 - x^2$	0	2.75	5.0	6.75	8.0	8.75
$y = \sqrt{(9 - x^2)}$	0	±1.66	±2.24	±2.60	±2.83	±2.96

x	0	0.5	1.0	1.5	2.0	2.5	3.0
x^2	0	0.25	1.0	2.25	4.0	6.25	9.0
$9 - x^2$	9.0	8.75	8.0	6.75	5.0	2.75	0
$y = \sqrt{(9 - x^2)}$	±3	±2.96	±2.83	±2.60	±2.24	±1.66	0

A graph of these values is as shown in Fig. 8. The graph produced confirms that $x^2 + y^2 = 9$ is a circle, centre at the origin and of radius 3 units.

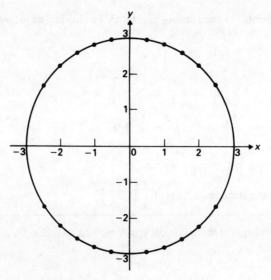

Figure 8 Circle, $x^2 + y^2 = 9$

(ii) The parabola
Parabolas having an equation of the form $y = ax^2 + bx + c$ are introduced in Section 2, these parabolas having their axes of symmetry parallel to or coinciding with the y-axis. The simplest form of the equation of a parabola is:

$$y = a\sqrt{x} \text{ or } y = ax^{\frac{1}{2}}$$

Parabolas having equations of this form have their axes of symmetry coincident with the x-axis, and their vertices at the origin $(0, 0)$. The co-ordinates of the equation $y = 2\sqrt{x}$, for example, may be determined as shown below for positive values of x, (negative values of x give a complex result).

x	0	0.5	1.0	1.5	2.0	2.5	3.0
$\sqrt{x}$	0	±0.71	±1.0	±1.22	±1.41	±1.58	±1.73
$y = 2\sqrt{x}$	0	±1.42	±2.00	±2.44	±2.82	±3.16	±3.46

A graph of these values is shown in Fig. 9, the resulting curve being a parabola with its axis of symmetry coinciding with the x-axis and its vertex at the origin $(0, 0)$.

(iii) The ellipse
An ellipse has two axes at right angles to one another, corresponding to the maximum and minimum lengths which can be obtained within the ellipse.

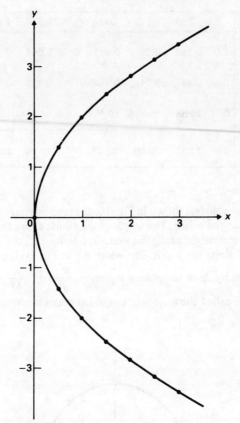

Figure 9 Parabola, $y = 2x^{1/2}$

These axes are called the major axis for the greatest length and the minor axis for the least length.

The equation of an ellipse having its centre at origin of a rectangular co-ordinate system and its axes, coinciding with the axes of the co-ordinate system is:

$$\frac{x^2}{a^2} + \frac{y^2}{b^2} = 1 \text{ or } y = b\sqrt{\left(1 - \frac{x^2}{a^2}\right)}$$

When $a = b$, this equation becomes $x^2 + y^2 = a^2$, i.e., a circle, centre at the origin of the co-ordinate system and of radius a, (see (i) above).

The co-ordinates of the equation $\dfrac{x^2}{4} + \dfrac{y^2}{9} = 1$, i.e., $y = 3\sqrt{\left(1 - \dfrac{x^2}{4}\right)}$ may be determined as shown below.

x		-2.0	-1.5	-1.0	-0.5	0	0.5	1.0	1.5	2.0
$\dfrac{x^2}{4}$		1.0	0.563	0.25	0.063	0	0.063	0.25	0.563	1.0
$1 - \dfrac{x^2}{4}$		0	0.437	0.75	0.937	1.0	0.937	0.75	0.437	0
$\sqrt{\left(1 - \dfrac{x^2}{4}\right)}$		0	±0.661	±0.866	±0.968	±1.0	±0.968	±0.866	±0.661	0
$y = 3\sqrt{\left(1 - \dfrac{x^2}{4}\right)}$		0	±1.98	±2.60	±2.90	±3	±2.90	±2.60	±1.98	0

A graph of these values is shown in Fig. 10, the resulting curve being an ellipse with its centre at the origin. The width of the ellipse along the x-axis is 4 units and the total height along the y-axis is 6 units, i.e., the major axis is from $+3$ to -3 along the y-axis. The width AB in Fig. 10 is called the **minor axis** and is given by $2a$ in the general equation $\dfrac{x^2}{a^2} + \dfrac{y^2}{b^2} = 1$. The height CD in Fig. 10 is called the **major** (or longer) **axis** and is given by $2b$ in the equation $\dfrac{x^2}{a^2} + \dfrac{y^2}{b^2} = 1$.

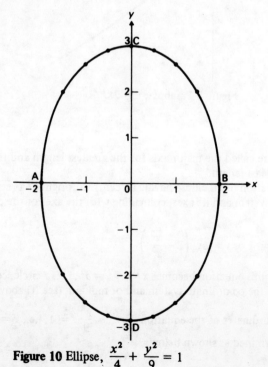

Figure 10 Ellipse, $\dfrac{x^2}{4} + \dfrac{y^2}{9} = 1$

(iv) The Hyperbola

The equation of a hyperbola is of the form

$$\frac{x^2}{a^2} - \frac{y^2}{b^2} = 1 \text{ or } y = b\sqrt{\left(\frac{x^2}{a^2} - 1\right)}$$

The co-ordinates of the equation $\frac{x^2}{4} - \frac{y^2}{9} = 1$, i.e., $y = 3\sqrt{\left(\frac{x^2}{4} - 1\right)}$ may be determined as shown below.

x	−10	−8	−6	−4	−2
$\frac{x^2}{4}$	25	16	9	4	1
$\frac{x^2}{4} - 1$	24	15	8	3	0
$\sqrt{\left(\frac{x^2}{4} - 1\right)}$	±4.90	±3.87	±2.83	±1.73	0
$y=3\sqrt{\left(\frac{x^2}{4} - 1\right)}$	±14.70	±11.61	±8.49	±5.19	0

x	0	2	4	6	8	10
$\frac{x^2}{4}$	0	1	4	9	16	25
$\frac{x^2}{4} - 1$	−1	0	3	8	15	24
$\sqrt{\left(\frac{x^2}{4} - 1\right)}$	Complex	0	±1.73	±2.83	±3.87	±4.90
$y=3\sqrt{\left(\frac{x^2}{4} - 1\right)}$	Complex	0	±5.19	±8.49	±11.61	±14.70

[For complex numbers and their representation, see Chapter 10.]
The graph of these values is shown in Fig. 11, the resulting curve being a hyperbola which is symmetrical about both the x and the y-axes. The distance AB in Fig. 11 is given by $2a$ in the general equation

$$\frac{x^2}{a^2} - \frac{y^2}{b^2} = 1.$$

The distance OB is the value of x when y is equal to zero, i.e., when $\frac{x^2}{a^2} = 1$ or when $x = a$. Thus, due to symmetry, distance AB is $2a$ as stated.

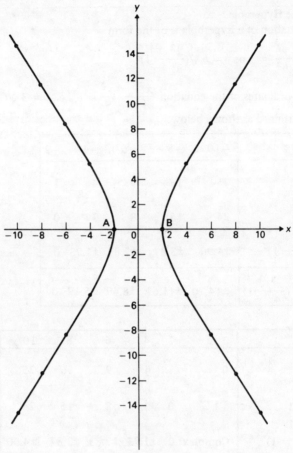

Figure 11 Hyperbola, $\dfrac{x^2}{4} - \dfrac{y^2}{9} = 1$

The simplest equation of a hyperbola is of the form $y = \dfrac{a}{x}$, this being the equation of a rectangular hyperbola which is symmetrical about both the x and y-axes and lies entirely in the first and third quadrants. The co-ordinates of the equation $y = \dfrac{5}{x}$ may be determined as shown below:

x	-7	-6	-5	-4	-3	-2	-1
$\dfrac{1}{x}$	-0.14	-0.17	-0.20	-0.25	-0.33	-0.50	-1
$y = \dfrac{5}{x}$	-0.70	-0.85	-1	-1.25	-1.65	-2.5	-5

x	0	1	2	3	4	5	6	7
$\dfrac{1}{x}$	∞	1	0.50	0.33	0.25	0.20	0.17	0.14
$y = \dfrac{5}{x}$	∞	5	2.5	1.65	1.25	1	0.85	0.70

A graph of these values is shown in Fig. 12, the resulting curve being a rectangular hyperbola lying in the first and third quadrants and being symmetrical about both the x and the y-axes.

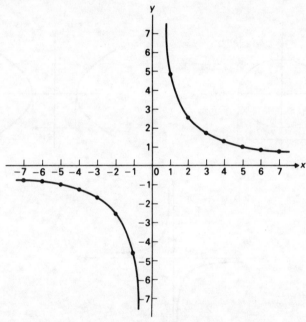

Figure 12 Rectangular hyperbola, $y = \dfrac{5}{x}$

Worked problems on simple curves of the circle, parabola, ellipse and hyperbola

Problem 1. Sketch curves depicting the following equations, showing the significant values where possible.
(a) $x = \sqrt{(5 - y^2)}$; (b) $y^2 = 9x$; (c) $5x^2 = 35 - 7y^2$; (d) $3y^2 = 5x^2 - 15$; and (e) $xy = 7$

(a) Squaring both sides of the equation and transposing gives $x^2 + y^2 = 5$. Comparing this with the standard equation of a circle, centre origin, radius a, i.e., $x^2 + y^2 = a^2$, shows that $x^2 + y^2 = 5$ represents a circle,

122

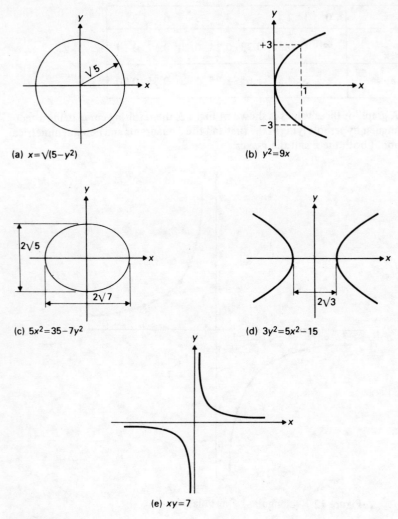

(a) $x = \sqrt{(5 - y^2)}$

(b) $y^2 = 9x$

(c) $5x^2 = 35 - 7y^2$

(d) $3y^2 = 5x^2 - 15$

(e) $xy = 7$

Figure 13

centre origin, radius $\sqrt{5}$. A sketch of this circle is shown in Fig. 13(a).

(b) One form of the equation of a parabola is $y = a\sqrt{x}$. Squaring both sides of this equation gives $y^2 = a^2 x$. The equation $y^2 = 9x$ is of this form and thus represents a parabola which is symmetrical about the x-axis and having its vertex at the origin, (0, 0). Also, when $x = 1$, $y = \pm 3$. A sketch of this parabola is shown in Fig. 13(b).

(c) By dividing throughout by 35 and transposing, the equation

$5x^2 = 35 - 7y^2$ can be written as $\dfrac{x^2}{7} + \dfrac{y^2}{5} = 1$. The equation of an ellipse is of the form $\dfrac{x^2}{a^2} + \dfrac{y^2}{b^2} = 1$, where $2a$ and $2b$ represent the length of the axes of the ellipse. Thus $\dfrac{x^2}{(\sqrt{7})^2} + \dfrac{y^2}{(\sqrt{5})^2} = 1$ represents an ellipse, having its axes coinciding with the x and y-axes of a rectangular co-ordinate system, the major axis being $2\sqrt{7}$ units long and the minor axis $2\sqrt{5}$ units long, as shown in Fig. 13(c).

(d) Dividing $3y^2 = 5x^2 - 15$ throughout by 15 and transposing gives: $\dfrac{x^2}{3} - \dfrac{y^2}{5} = 1$. The equation $\dfrac{x^2}{a^2} - \dfrac{y^2}{b^2} = 1$ represents a hyperbola which is symmetrical about both the x and y-axes, the distance between the vertices being given by $2a$. Thus a sketch of $\dfrac{x^2}{3} - \dfrac{y^2}{5} = 1$ is as shown in Fig. 13(d), having a distance of $2\sqrt{3}$ between its vertices.

(e) The equation $y = \dfrac{a}{x}$ represents a rectangular hyperbola lying entirely within the first and third quadrants. Transposing $xy = 7$ gives $y = \dfrac{7}{x}$, and therefore represents the rectangular hyperbola shown in Fig. 13(e).

Problem 2. Describe the shape of the curves represented by the following equations:

(a) $x = 3\sqrt{\left[1 - \left(\dfrac{y}{3}\right)^2\right]}$

(b) $\dfrac{y^2}{5} = 2x$

(c) $y = 6\left(1 - \dfrac{x^2}{16}\right)^{1/2}$

(d) $x = 5\sqrt{\left[1 + \left(\dfrac{y}{2}\right)^2\right]}$

(e) $\dfrac{y}{4} = \dfrac{13}{3x}$

(a) Squaring the equation gives $x^2 = 9\left[(1 - \left(\dfrac{y}{3}\right)^2\right]$ and transposing gives $x^2 + y^2 = 9$. Comparing this equation with $x^2 + y^2 = a^2$ shows that $x^2 + y^2 = 9$ is the equation of a circle having centre at the origin $(0, 0)$, and of radius 3 units.

(b) Transposing $\dfrac{y^2}{5} = 2x$ gives $y = \sqrt{(10)}\sqrt{x}$. Thus $\dfrac{y^2}{5} = 2x$ is the equation of a parabola having its axis of symmetry coinciding with the x-axis and its vertex at the origin of a rectangular co-ordinate system.

(c) $y = 6 (1 - \frac{x^2}{16})^{1/2}$ can be transposed to $\frac{y}{6} = (1 - \frac{x}{16})^{1/2}$ and squaring both sides gives $\frac{y^2}{36} = 1 - \frac{x^2}{16}$, i.e., $\frac{x^2}{16} + \frac{y^2}{36} = 1$.

This is the equation of an ellipse, centre at the origin of a rectangular co-ordinate system, the major axis coinciding with the y-axis and being $2\sqrt{36}$, i.e., 12 units long. The minor axis coincides with the x-axis and is $2\sqrt{16}$, i.e., 8 units long.

(d) Since $x = 5\sqrt{[1 + (\frac{y}{2})^2]}$

$$x^2 = 25 \; [1 + (\frac{y}{2})^2]$$

i.e. $\frac{x^2}{25} - \frac{y^2}{4} = 1$

This is a hyperbola which is symmetrical about both the x and y-axes, the vertices being $2\sqrt{25}$, i.e., 10 units apart. (With reference to section 1(iv), a is equal to ± 5)

(e) The equation $\frac{y}{4} = \frac{13}{3x}$ is of the form $y = \frac{a}{x}$ where $a = \frac{52}{3} = 17.3$.

This represents a rectangular hyperbola, symmetrical about both the x and y-axes and lying entirely in the first and third quadrants, similar in shape to the curves shown in Fig. 13(e).

Further problems on simple curves of the circle, parabola, ellipse and hyperbola may be found in Section 5 (Problems 24–39), p. 138.

4 Reduction of non-linear laws to a linear form (i.e. determination of laws)

In experimental work, when two variables are believed to be connected, a set of corresponding measurements can be made. Such results can then be used to discover if there is a mathematical law relating the two variables. If such a law is found it can be used to predict further values. Usually the results obtained from experiments are plotted as a graph and an attempt is made to deduce the law from the graph. Now the relationship between two variables believed to be of the linear form $y = mx + c$ can be proved by plotting the measured values x and y and seeing if a straight-line graph results. If a straight line does fit the plotted points then the slope m and y-axis intercept c can be found, which establishes the law relating x and y for all values **in the given range**. However, frequently the relationship between variables x and y is not a linear one, i.e., when x is plotted against y a curve results. In such cases the non-linear equation is modified to the linear form $y = mx + c$ so that the constants can be found and the law relating the variables determined. This process is called the determination of laws. Some common forms of non-linear equations are given below. These are rearranged into a linear form by making a direct comparison with the straight-line form $y = mx + c$, that is, arranging in the form a variable = (a constant $\times$ a variable) + a constant.

In the conversion of non-linear laws to a linear form it is useful to isolate the constant term first.

(i) $y = ax^2 + b$

$$\boxed{y} = a \boxed{x^2} + b$$

compares with $\boxed{y} = m \boxed{x} + c$

Hence plot y against x^2 to produce a straight-line graph of slope a and y-axis intercept b (see worked Problem 1).

(ii) $y = \dfrac{a}{x} + b$

$$\boxed{y} = a \boxed{\dfrac{1}{x}} + b$$

compares with $\boxed{y} = m \boxed{x} + c$

Hence plot y against $\dfrac{1}{x}$ to produce a straight-line graph of slope a and y-axis intercept b (see worked Problem 2).

(iii) $y = \dfrac{a}{x^2} + b$

$$\boxed{y} = a \boxed{\dfrac{1}{x^2}} + b$$

compares with $\boxed{y} = m \boxed{x} + c$

Hence plot y against $\dfrac{1}{x^2}$ to produce a straight-line graph of slope a and y-axis intercept b.

(iv) $y = ax^2 + bx$

In this case there is no constant term as it stands, but by dividing throughout by x a constant term b is produced. Dividing both sides of the equation by x gives:

$$\boxed{\dfrac{y}{x}} = a \boxed{x} + b$$

compares with $\boxed{y} = m \boxed{x} + c$

Hence plot $\dfrac{y}{x}$ against x to produce a straight-line graph of slope a and $\dfrac{y}{x}$ -axis intercept b (see worked Problem 3).

(v) $xy = ax + by$

Dividing both sides of the equation by y gives:

$$\boxed{x} = a \boxed{\dfrac{x}{y}} + b$$

compares with $\boxed{y} = m \boxed{x} + c$

Hence plot x against $\dfrac{x}{y}$ to produce a straight-line graph of slope a and x-axis intercept b.

(vi) $y = ax^n$

Taking logarithms (usually to a base 10) of each side of the equation gives:

$\lg y = \lg (ax^n)$
$\lg y = \lg a + \lg x^n$
$\lg y = \lg a + n \lg x$

$$\text{or } \boxed{\lg y} = n \boxed{\lg x} + \lg a$$

compares with $\boxed{y} = m \boxed{x} + c$

Hence plot $\lg y$ against $\lg x$ to produce a straight-line graph of slope n and $\lg y$-axis intercept $\lg a$ (a is obtained by taking antilogarithms of $\lg a$) (see worked Problems 4 and 5).

(vii) $y = ab^x$

Taking logarithms of each side of the equation gives:

$\lg y = \lg ab^x$
$\lg y = \lg a + \lg b^x$
$\lg y = \lg a + x \lg b$

$$\text{i.e. } \boxed{\lg y} = (\lg b) \boxed{x} + \lg a$$

compares with $\boxed{y} = m \boxed{x} + c$

Hence plot $\lg y$ against x to produce a straight-line graph of slope $\lg b$ and $\lg y$-axis intercept $\lg a$ (a and b are obtained by taking antilogarithms of $\lg a$ and $\lg b$ respectively) (see worked Problem 6).

Worked problems on determination of laws

Problem 1. The following experimental values of x and y are believed to be related by the law $y = ax^2 + b$. By plotting a suitable graph test if this is so and find the approximate values of a and b.

x	0	1	2	3	4	5	6
y	3.0	4.8	12.0	23.3	38.1	59.5	83.5

If y is plotted against x the non-linear curve shown in Fig. 14 is produced.

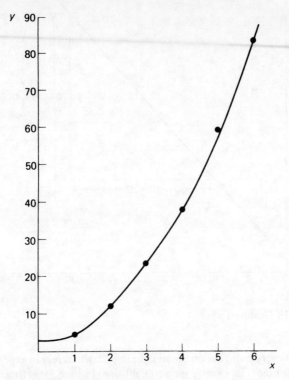

Figure 14 Graph of y/x

It is not possible to determine the values of a and b from such a curve.
Comparing $\boxed{y} = a \boxed{x^2} + b$ with the straight-line form

$$\boxed{y} = m \boxed{x} + c$$

shows that y is to be plotted vertically against x^2 horizontally to produce a straight line of slope a and y-axis intercept b. Thus an extension to the above table of values needs to be produced. This is shown below.

y	3.0	4.8	12.0	23.3	38.1	59.5	83.5
x	0	1.0	2.0	3.0	4.0	5.0	6.0
x^2	0	1.0	4.0	9.0	16.0	25.0	36.0

The best straight-line that fits the points is shown in the graph of Fig. 15.

128

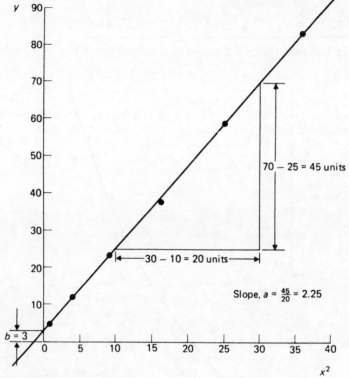

Figure 15 Graph of y/x^2

Note that not every point lies on the straight line drawn; rarely in experimental results will all points lie exactly on a straight line. In such cases there is likely to be a difference of opinion as to the exact position of the line. Hence any results are only approximate.

From the graph the slope a is found to be **2.25** and the y-axis intercept b is found to be **3**.

Hence the law relating the variables x and y is $y = 2.25\,x^2 + 3$.

Problem 2. In an experiment the following values of resistance R and voltage V were taken:

R ohms	45.3	49.8	52.4	57.6	62.3
V millivolts	113	102	96	86	79

It is thought that R and V are connected by a law of the form $R = \dfrac{d}{V} + e$ where d and e are constants. Verify the law and find approximate values of d and e.

$$R = \frac{d}{V} + e \qquad \text{i.e.} \qquad \boxed{R} = d \ \boxed{\dfrac{1}{V}} + e.$$

$$\text{Comparing with} \qquad \boxed{y} = m \ \boxed{x} + c$$

shows that R is to be plotted vertically against $\dfrac{1}{V}$ horizontally to produce a

straight line of slope d and R-axis intercept e. Another table of values is drawn up with V in this case changed from millivolts to volts so that when taking reciprocals of V, more manageable numbers result.

R	45.3	49.8	52.4	57.6	62.3
V	0.113	0.102	0.096	0.086	0.079
$\dfrac{1}{V}$	8.85	9.80	10.42	11.63	12.66

A graph of R against $\dfrac{1}{V}$ is shown plotted in Fig. 16.

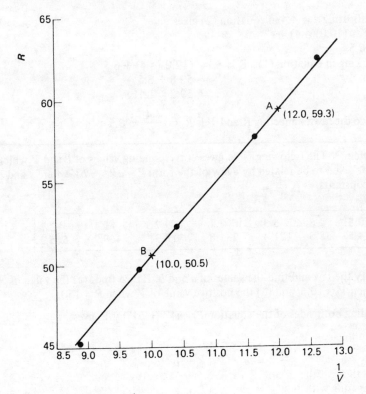

Figure 16 Graph of $R/\dfrac{1}{V}$

A straight line fits the points which verifies that the law $R = \dfrac{d}{V} + e$ is obeyed.

It is not practical in this case to commence the scaling of each axis at zero. Thus it is not possible to find the R-axis intercept (i.e. at $\dfrac{1}{V} = 0$) from the graph. A simultaneous equation approach is therefore necessary. Any two points such as A and B may be used.

At A, $R = 59.3$ and $\dfrac{1}{V} = 12.0$

At B, $R = 50.5$ and $\dfrac{1}{V} = 10.0$

Hence, since $R = \dfrac{1}{V} d + e$:

$$59.3 = 12.0\,d + e \tag{1}$$
$$\text{and} \quad 50.5 = 10.0\,d + e \tag{2}$$

Subtracting equation (2) from equation (1) gives:

$8.8 = 2.0d$

$d = 4.4$

Substituting $d = 4.4$ in equation (2) gives:

$50.5 = (10.0)(4.4) + e$

$e = 6.5$

Checking in equation (1):   R.H.S. $= (12.0)(4.4) + 6.5$
$$= 52.8 + 6.5$$
$$= 59.3 = \text{L.H.S.}$$

Hence the law connecting R and V is $R = \dfrac{4.4}{V} + 6.5$

Problem 3. The following table gives corresponding values of P and V which are believed to be related by a law of the form $P = aV^2 + bV$ where a and b are constants.

V	0.5	2.6	5.3	7.7	9.2	11.4	12.7
P	4.5	38.5	121.4	231.8	318.3	469.7	565.2

Verify the law and find the values of a and b. Hence find: (a) the value of P when V is 10.6, and (b) the positive value of V when $P = 150$.

Dividing both sides of the equation $P = aV^2 + bV$ by V gives:

$$\boxed{\dfrac{P}{V}} = a\,\boxed{V} + b$$

Comparing with $\boxed{y} = m\,\boxed{x} + c$

shows that $\frac{P}{V}$ is to be plotted vertically against V horizontally to produce a straight line of slope a and $\frac{P}{V}$ -axis intercept b.

Another table of values is drawn up.

V	0.5	2.6	5.3	7.7	9.2	11.4	12.7
P	4.5	38.5	121.4	231.8	318.3	469.7	565.2
$\frac{P}{V}$	9.0	14.8	22.9	30.1	34.6	41.2	44.5

A graph of $\frac{P}{V}$ against V is shown in Fig. 17 where a straight line fits the points. Thus the law is verified.

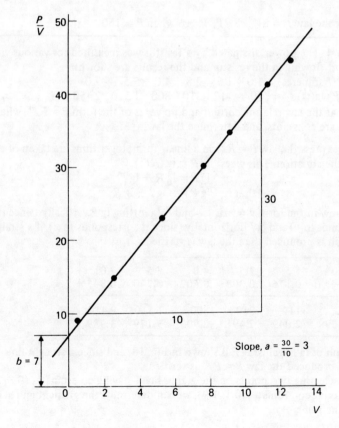

Figure 17 Graph of $\frac{p}{V}/V$

The $\dfrac{P}{V}$ -axis intercept, $b = 7$

The slope, or gradient, $a = 3$

Hence the law relating P and V is: $\mathbf{P = 3V^2 + 7V}$

(a) When $V = 10.6, P = 3(10.6)^2 + 7(10.6)$
$$= 337.1 + 74.2 = \mathbf{411.3}$$

(b) When $P = 150, 150 = 3V^2 + 7V$

i.e., $3V^2 + 7V - 150 = 0$

Thus: $V = \dfrac{-7 \pm \sqrt{[(7)^2 - 4(3)(-150)]}}{2(3)}$

$$= \dfrac{-7 \pm \sqrt{[49 + 1\,800]}}{6} = \dfrac{-7 \pm 43}{6}$$

$$= 6 \text{ or } -8\,\dfrac{1}{3}$$

Thus for the law $P = 3V^2 + 7V$, $V = \mathbf{6}$ when $P = 150$.

Problem 4. The power dissipated by a resistor was measured for various values of current flowing in the resistor and the results are shown:

Current (I amperes) 1.0 1.5 2.5 4.0 5.5 7.0
Power (P watts) 50 112 310 800 1 510 2 450

Prove that the law relating current and power is of the form $P = RI^n$, where R and n are constants, and determine the law.

To express the law $P = RI^n$ in a linear form, logarithms are taken of each side of the equation. This gives: $\lg P = \lg (RI^n)$

or $\lg P = \lg R + \lg I^n$

that is, $\lg P = n \lg I + \lg R$

This is now in the form $y = mx + c$ and by plotting $\lg P$ vertically (since it corresponds to y) and $\lg I$ horizontally (since it corresponds to x), if a straight-line graph is produced then the law is verified.

I	1.0	1.5	2.5	4.0	5.5	7.0
$\lg I$	0	0.176	0.398	0.602	0.740	0.845
P	50	112	310	800	1 510	2 450
$\lg P$	1.699	2.049	2.491	2.903	3.179	3.389

The graph of $\lg I$ against $\lg P$ is shown in Fig. 18, and since a straight-line graph is produced the law $P = RI^n$ is verified.

By selecting two points on the graph, say T having co-ordinates $(0.8, 3.3)$ and Q having co-ordinates $(0.1, 1.9)$, we can determine the gradient and hence obtain the value of n.

Hence $n = \dfrac{3.3 - 1.9}{0.8 - 0.1} = \dfrac{1.4}{0.7} = 2$

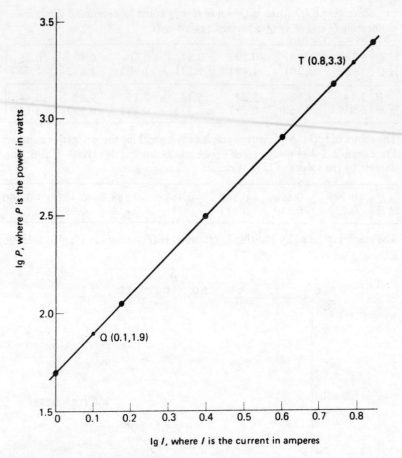

Figure 18 Variation of lg I/lg P

The vertical-axis intercept value when lg I is equal to zero is 1.7, this being the value of lg R. By finding the antilogarithm of 1.7, i.e., 50.1, the value of R is ascertained.

Thus the required law is $P = 50.1\ I^2$.

Problem 5. Two quantities Q and H are believed to be related by the equation $Q = k\ H^n$. The experimental values obtained for Q and H are as shown:

Q	0.16	0.20	0.27	0.34	0.40	0.47	0.55
H	1.14	1.78	3.24	5.14	7.11	9.82	13.44

Determine the law connecting Q and H, and the value of Q when H is 6.00.

Since $Q = k\,H^n$, then $\lg Q = n\lg H + \lg k$ and to determine the law connecting Q and H, $\lg Q$ is plotted against $\lg H$.

Q	0.16	0.20	0.27	0.34	0.40	0.47	0.55
$\lg Q$	$\overline{1}.204$	$\overline{1}.301$	$\overline{1}.431$	$\overline{1}.531$	$\overline{1}.602$	$\overline{1}.672$	$\overline{1}.740$
H	1.14	1.78	3.24	5.14	7.11	9.82	13.44
$\lg H$	0.057	0.250	0.511	0.711	0.852	0.992	1.128

The values of $\lg Q$ can be plotted graphically by making them negative numbers. For example, $\overline{1}.204$ means $-1 + 0.204$ and evaluating this gives -0.796. Thus, expressing the values of $\lg Q$ as negative numbers gives:

$\lg Q$	-0.796	-0.699	-0.569	-0.469	-0.398	-0.328	-0.260
$\lg H$	0.057	0.250	0.511	0.711	0.852	0.992	1.128

The graph produced by plotting $\lg Q$ against $\lg H$ is shown in Fig. 19. Selecting

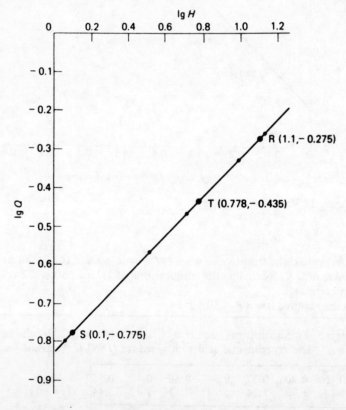

Figure 19 Variation of $\lg Q/\lg H$

two points which lie on the graph, say R, (1.1, −0.275), and S, (0.1, −0.775), give a gradient of

$$\frac{-0.775 - (-0.275)}{0.1 - 1.1} \quad \text{or} \quad \frac{-0.5}{-1} \text{ i.e. } \frac{1}{2}$$

The vertical-axis intercept value, $\lg k = -0.825$ or $\bar{1}.175$ and by finding the antilogarithm, $k \simeq 0.150$. Hence the law connecting Q and H is

$$Q = 0.150 \, H^{\frac{1}{2}} \text{ or } Q = 0.150 \, \sqrt{H}.$$

When H is 6.00, $\lg H$ is 0.778. From the graph, the corresponding value of $\lg Q$ is −0.435, shown as point T. This value must be turned into a negative characteristic and positive mantissa before the value of the antilogarithm can be found. Now $-0.435 = -1 + 0.565$ or $\bar{1}.565$, and finding the antilogarithm gives $Q = \mathbf{0.367}$ when $H = \mathbf{6.00}$.

Problem 6. Values of x and y are believed to be related by a law of the form $y = ab^x$ where a and b are constants. The values of y and corresponding values of x are shown:

y	4.5	7.4	11.2	15.8	39.0	68.0	271.5
x	0.6	1.3	1.9	2.4	3.7	4.5	6.5

Verify that the law relating y and x is as stated and determine the approximate values of a and b.

Hence determine: (a) the value of y when x is 3.2, and (b) the value of x when y is 126.7.

$y = ab^x$.
Taking logarithms to base 10 of both sides of the equation gives:
$\lg y = \lg (ab^x) = \lg a + \lg b^x = \lg a + x \lg b$

$$\text{i.e.} \quad \lg y = (\lg b) \, x + \lg a$$
$$\text{Comparing with} \quad y = m \quad x + c$$

shows that $\lg y$ is plotted vertically against x horizontally to produce a straight-line graph of slope $\lg b$ and $\lg y$-axis intercept $\lg a$. Another table of values is drawn up.

y	4.5	7.4	11.2	15.8	39.0	68.0	271.5
$\lg y$	0.65	0.87	1.05	1.20	1.5	1.83	2.43
x	0.6	1.3	1.9	2.4	3.7	4.5	6.5

A graph of $\lg y/x$ is shown in Fig. 20. A straight line fits the points, which verifies the law.

The intercept on the $\lg y$-axis is 0.47, i.e. $\lg a = 0.47$.
Taking antilogarithms, $a = 2.951 = 3.0$, correct to 2 significant figures.

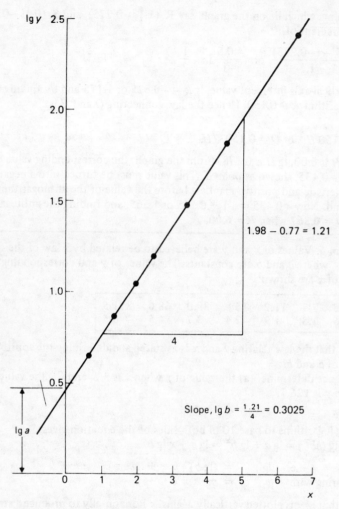

Figure 20 Graph of lg y/x

Slope, or gradient, lg $b = \dfrac{1.21}{4} = 0.302\,5$

Taking antilogarithms, $b = 2.007 = 2.0$ correct to 2 significant figures.

Hence the law relating x and y is $y = (3.0)(2.0)^x$

From the graph, when $x = 3.2$, lg $y \simeq 1.44$, giving $y \simeq 27.5$

and when $y = 126.7$, lg $y = 2.10$ giving $x \simeq 5.4$.

Alternatively: (a) When $x = 3.2$, $\quad y = (3.0)(2.0)^{3.2} = \mathbf{27.6}$

(b) When $y = 126.7$, $126.7 = (3.0)(2.0)^x$

i.e., $\dfrac{126.7}{3.0} = (2.0)^x$

$42.23 = (2.0)^x$

Taking logarithms: $\lg 42.23 = x \lg 2.0$

$x = \dfrac{\lg 42.23}{\lg 2.0} = \dfrac{1.625\,6}{0.301\,0} = \mathbf{5.40}$

Further problems on reduction of non-linear laws to a linear form (i.e. determination of laws) may be found in the following section (5) (Problems 40–73), p. 139.

5. Further problems

The quadratic graph

In problems 1 to 10, sketch the quadratic graphs and determine the co-ordinates of the turning points.

1. $y = 5x^2$ $[(0, 0)]$
2. $\dfrac{y}{3} = x^2$ $[(0, 0)]$
3. $y = 2x^2 + 4$ $[(0, 4)]$
4. $y = 4x^2 - 1$ $[(0, -1)]$
5. $y + 2x^2 = 6$ $[(0, 6)]$
6. $y = -(5x^2 + 7)$ $[(0, -7)]$
7. $y = 2x^2 + 5x + 2$ $[(-1\frac{1}{4}, -1\frac{1}{8})]$
8. $y - 19 = 3x^2 - 12x$ $[(2, 7)]$
9. $y + 5 = 2x(2 - x)$ $[(1, -3)]$
10. $y + 3x^2 = 1 - 6x$ $[(-1, 4)]$

In problems 11 to 19, plot the graphs and determine the co-ordinates of the turning points, stating whether they are maximum or minimum values.

11. $y = 3x^2 + 4x + 8$ $[(-\frac{2}{3}, 6\frac{2}{3}); \text{Minimum}]$
12. $y = x^2 - 3x + 6$ $[(1\frac{1}{2}, 3\frac{3}{4}); \text{Minimum}]$
13. $y + \dfrac{97}{24} = 7x - 6x^2$ $[(\frac{7}{12}, -2); \text{Maximum}]$
14. $3x^2 + 4x + y = 5$ $[(-\frac{2}{3}, 6\frac{1}{3}); \text{Maximum}]$
15. $y + \dfrac{2}{3} = x(3x + 16)$ $[(-2\frac{2}{3}, -22); \text{Minimum}]$
16. $\dfrac{3}{16} + y = x(3 - 4x)$ $[(\frac{3}{8}, \frac{3}{8}); \text{Maximum}]$
17. $y + 7x = x^2 + 2\frac{1}{4}$ $[(3\frac{1}{2}, -10); \text{Minimum}]$

18. $15x + y = 18x^2 + 7\frac{1}{8}$ $[(\frac{5}{12}, 4); \text{Minimum}]$

19. $20x^2 + 1 = 4x - y$ $[(\frac{1}{10}, -\frac{4}{5}); \text{Maximum}]$

20. Find the point of intersection of the two curves $y = 3x^2$ and $y + 15x = 3x^2 + 5$ by plotting the two curves. $[(\frac{1}{3}, \frac{1}{3})]$

21. Determine the co-ordinates of the points of intersection of the two curves $y + 2 = 5x^2$ and $y = 2x^2 - 6x + 7$ by plotting the two curves.
$$[(1, 3); (-3, 43)]$$

22. Plot the graph of $y = 5x^2 - 3x + 4$. From the graph find: (a) the value of y when $x = 2.4$; and (b) the values of x when $y = 11.6$.
(a) [25.6] (b) [1.57 and −0.97]

23. Draw up a table of values and plot the graph $y = -3x^2 + 4x - 6$ and from the graph find: (a) the value of y when $x = 1.7$; and (b) the values of x when $y = -8.8$.   (a) [−7.87] (b) [1.84 and −0.51]

Simple curves of the circle, parabola, ellipse and hyperbola

In problems 24 to 31, sketch the curves depicting the equations given, showing significant values where possible.

24. $x = 7\sqrt{[1 - (\frac{y}{7})^2]}$ [Circle, centre (0, 0), radians 7 units]

25. $\frac{y^2}{3x} = 4$ [Parabola, symmetrical about x-axis, vertex at (0, 0)]

26. $\sqrt{x} = \frac{y}{5}$ [Parabola, symmetrical about x-axis, vertex at (0, 0)]

27. $y^2 = \frac{x^2 - 12}{4}$ [Hyperbola, symmetrical about x and y-axes, distance between vertices $4\sqrt{3}$ units along x-axis]

28. $\frac{y^2}{5} = 5 - x^2$ [Ellipse, centre (0, 0), major axis 10 units along y-axis, minor axis $2\sqrt{5}$ units along x-axis]

29. $x = \frac{1}{3}\sqrt{[(99 - 11y^2]}$ [Ellipse, centre (0, 0), major axis $2\sqrt{11}$ units along x-axis, minor axis 6 units along y-axis]

30. $x = 2\sqrt{(1 + y^2)}$ [Hyperbola, symmetrical about x and y-axes, distance between vertices 4 units along x-axis]

31. $x^2 y^2 = 5$ [Rectangular hyperbola, lying in first and third quadrants only]

In problems 32 to 39, describe the shape of the curves represented by the equations given.

32. $y = \sqrt{[2(1 - x^2)]}$ [Ellipse, centre (0, 0), major axis $2\sqrt{2}$ units along y-axis, minor axis 2 units along x-axis]

33. $y = \sqrt{[2(1 + x^2)]}$ [Hyperbola, symmetrical about x and y-axes, vertices 2 units apart along x-axis]

34. $y = \sqrt{(2 - x^2)}$ [Circle, centre (0, 0), radius $\sqrt{2}$ units]

35. $y = 2x^{-1}$ [Rectangular hyperbola, lying in first and third quadrants, symmetrical about x and y-axes]

36. $y = (2x)^{\frac{1}{2}}$ [Parabola, vertex at $(0, 0)$, symmetrical about the x-axis]

37. $2y^2 - 6 = -3x^2$ [Ellipse, centre $(0, 0)$, major axis $2\sqrt{3}$ units along the y-axis, minor axis $2\sqrt{2}$ units along the x-axis]

38. $y^2 = 13 - x^2$ [Circle, centre $(0, 0)$ radius $\sqrt{13}$]

39. $4x^2 - 3y^2 = 12$ [Hyperbola, symmetrical about x and y-axes, vertices on x-axis distance $2\sqrt{3}$ apart]

Determination of laws

In problems 40 to 51, x and y are variables and all other letters denote constants. For the stated laws to be verified it is necessary to modify them into a straight-line form. In order to plot a straight-line graph state: (a) what should be plotted on the vertical axis; (b) what should be plotted on the horizontal axis; (c) the slope or gradient; and (d) the vertical-axis intercept.

40. $y = ax + b$ (a) $[y]$ (b) $[x]$ (c) $[a]$ (d) $[b]$

41. $y = cx^2 + d$ (a) $[y]$ (b) $[x^2]$ (c) $[c]$ (d) $[d]$

42. $y - f = e\sqrt{x}$ (a) $[y]$ (b) $[\sqrt{x}]$ (c) $[e]$ (d) $[f]$

43. $y = \dfrac{g}{x} + h$ (a) $[y]$ (b) $[\dfrac{1}{x}]$ (c) $[g]$ (d) $[h]$

44. $y = \sqrt{(\dfrac{j}{x})} + k$ (a) $[y]$ (b) $[\dfrac{1}{\sqrt{x}}]$ (c) $[\sqrt{j}]$ (d) $[k]$

45. $y = lx^2 + mx$ (a) $[\dfrac{y}{x}]$ (b) $[x]$ (c) $[l]$ (d) $[m]$

46. $y - p = \dfrac{n}{x^2}$ (a) $[y]$ (b) $[\dfrac{1}{x^2}]$ (c) $[n]$ (d) $[p]$

47. $y = \dfrac{q}{x} + rx$ (a) $[\dfrac{y}{x}]$ (b) $[\dfrac{1}{x^2}]$ (c) $[q]$ (d) $[r]$

48. $y = sx^t$ (a) $[\lg y]$ (b) $[\lg x]$ (c) $[t]$ (d) $[\lg s]$

49. $y = uv^x$ (a) $[\lg y]$ (b) $[x]$ (c) $[\lg v]$ (d) $[\ln u]$

50. $y = \dfrac{a}{x - b}$ (a) $[\dfrac{1}{y}]$ (b) $[x]$ (c) $[\dfrac{1}{a}]$ (d) $[-\dfrac{b}{a}]$

51. $y = \dfrac{1}{wx + z}$ (a) $[\dfrac{1}{y}]$ (b) $[x]$ (c) $[w]$ (d) $[z]$

52. The following experimental values of x and y are believed to be related by the law $y = mx^2 + c$ where m and c are constants. By plotting a suitable graph verify this law and find the approximate values of m and c.

x	2.3	4.1	6.0	8.4	9.9	11.3	
y	13.9	31.2	60.2	111.8	153.0	197.5	$[m = 1.5, c = 6.0]$

53. Show that the following values of p and q obey a law of the form $p = m\sqrt{q} + n$, where m and n are constants.

p	5.6	8.0	10.0	12.8	14.9	16.7	18.8
q	0.64	3.61	9.0	18.5	30.3	39.7	54.8

Determine approximate values of m and n. $[m = 2.0, n = 4.1]$

54. Experimental values of load W newtons and distance l metres are shown in the following table:

W	33.2	30.4	27.4	23.2	18.6	14.0	9.4	5.5
l	0.741	0.364	0.233	0.163	0.116	0.093	0.076	0.067

Verify that W and l are related by a law of the form $W = \dfrac{a}{l} + b$ and find the approximate values of a and b. $[a = -2.05, b = 36]$

55. The solubility S of potassium chlorate is shown by the following table:

$t(°C)$	10	20	30	40	50	60	80	100
S	4.5	7	10	14	19	25	39	57

The relation between S and t is thought to be of the form $S = 3 + at + bt^2$. Plot a graph in order to test the supposition, and, if correct, use your graph to find probable values of a and b, explaining your methods. $[a = 0.12, b = 0.004]$

56. The pressure p and volume v of a gas at constant temperature are related by the law $pv = c$, where c is a constant. Show that the given values of p and v follow this law and determine the value of c.

Pressure, p (bar)	10.6	8.0	6.4	5.3	4.6	4.0	
Volume, v (m^3)	1.5	2.0	2.5	3.0	3.5	4.0	$[c = 15.85]$

57. Measurements of the resistance (R ohms) of varying diameters (d mm) of wire were made in an experiment with the following results:

R	1.44	1.13	0.88	0.73	0.66
d	1.13	1.38	1.78	2.26	2.76

It is suspected that R is related to d by the law $R = \dfrac{c}{d^2} + a$. Verify this and find approximate values for c and a. Estimate also the cross-sectional area of wire needed for a resistance reading of 0.52 ohms.
$$[c = 1.2, a = 0.5, 47.1 \text{ mm}^2]$$

58. Show that the following values of s and t follow a law of the type $s = at^3 + b$ (where a and b are constants) and find approximate values for a and b.

s	49.7	47.4	41.4	29.5	10.0	
t	1.0	2.0	3.0	4.0	5.0	$[a = -0.32, b = 50]$

59. The periodic time, T, of oscillation of a pendulum is believed to be related to its length, l, by a law of the form $T = kl^n$ where k and n are constants. Values of T were measured for various lengths of the pendulum and the results are as shown:

Periodic time, T (s)	1.0	1.2	1.4	1.6	1.8	2.0	2.4
Length, l (m)		2.4	3.5	4.8	6.3	7.9	9.8	14.1

Prove the law is true. Determine the values of k and n and hence state the law. $[T = 0.64\sqrt{l}]$

60. Current I and resistance R were measured experimentally and the results relating these quantities were:

I	3.7	5.9	7.4	9.1	11.6	13.8
R	6.2	3.9	3.1	2.5	2.0	1.7

Show that I and R are related by a law of the form $R = aI^n$ and determine the approximate values of a and n. $[23, -1]$

61. The pH of a one-twentieth molar solution of potassium hydrogen phthalate

varies with temperature (t) as shown:

ph	4.011	4.001	4.001	4.011	4.031	4.061
$t\,^\circ C$	0	10	20	30	40	50

Show that these results obey an equation of the form $pH = a + (t - 15)^2/b$ and determine the constants a and b. $[a = 4.0, b = 20\,000]$

62. The luminosity, I, of a lamp varies with the applied voltage, V, and it is anticipated that the relationship between these two quantities is of the form $I = k\,V^n$. Experimental values of I and V are:

I candela	2.5	4.9	8.1	12.1	16.9	22.5
V volts	50	70	90	110	130	150

Verify the law and state it. Find the luminosity when 100 volts is applied to the lamp. $[I = 0.001\,V^2 ; 10$ candela$]$

63. A physical quantity L, and another, C, were found to vary as shown when measured experimentally:

L	300	350	400	450	500	550
C	3 464	3 742	4 000	4 243	4 472	4 690

Show that the law relating L and C is of the form $C = fL^n$ where f and n are constants and determine the values of f and n. $[200, \dfrac{1}{2}]$

64. The following table gives corresponding values of two quantities x and y which are believed to be related by a law of the form $y = ax^2 + bx$ where a and b are constants.

y	28.6	49.0	63.5	81.4	115.7	136.3
x	2.8	4.6	5.8	7.2	9.7	11.1

Verify the law and estimate the values of a and b. Hence find: (i) the value of y when x is 6.6; and (ii) the value of x when y is 102.5.
$$[a = 0.25, b = 9.5; (i)\ 73.3\ (ii)\ 8.8]$$

65. Quantities p and q are believed to be related by a law of the form $q = ab^p$. The value of p and corresponding values of q are as shown:

p	0	0.5	1.0	1.5	2.0	2.5	3.0
q	1.0	3.2	10.0	31.6	100.0	316.2	1 000.0

Verify the law and find approximate values of a and b. $[a = 1, b = 10]$

66. Variation of the admittance Y of an electrical circuit with the applied voltage V is as shown:

Voltage, V volts	0.37	0.51	0.74	0.98	1.13	1.34
Admittance, Y siemens	2.24	1.62	1.12	0.85	0.73	0.62

Show that the law connecting V and Y is of the form $V = RY^n$ where R and n are constants and determine the approximate values of R and n. From the graph, determine the value of admittance when the voltage is 0.86 volts. $[0.83, -1, 0.965$ siemen$]$

67. Two variables x and y are believed to be related by the law $xy = ax + by$ where a and b are constants. Results obtained by experiment are as follows:

x	1.5	3.0	4.5	6.0	7.5	9.0
y	20.0	6.7	5.5	5.0	4.8	4.6

Verify the law and find approximate values of a and b. Hence find

(i) the value of y when x is 5.2; and (ii) the value of x when y is 7.0.
$[a = 4, b = 1.2, \text{(i) } 5.2 \text{ (ii) } 2.8]$

68. In an experiment on moments, a bar was loaded with a mass, W, at a distance x from the fulcrum. The results of the experiment were:

x cm	28	30	32	34	36	38
W kg	22.1	20.7	19.4	18.2	17.2	16.3

Verify that a law of the form $W = ax^n$ is obeyed where a and n are constants and determine the law. $\left[W = \dfrac{620}{x} \text{ or } W = 620x^{-1}\right]$

69. Experimental values of the variation of current I amperes and the radii of copper strands r millimetres were measured and are as shown.

r (mm)	0.1	0.3	0.5	0.7	0.9	1.1	1.3
I (A)	0.000 17	0.001 5	0.004 3	0.008 3	0.014	0.021	0.029

Prove that the law relating I and r is of the form $I = mr^n$ where m and n are constants and determine the law. What will be the radius of the strands when I is $0.006\,0$ A? $[I = 0.017r^2 ; r = 0.594 \text{ mm}]$

70. The values of m and corresponding values of n are as follows:

m	0.2	0.7	1.3	1.9	2.4	3.6
n	6.0	14.2	39.4	109.7	257.2	1 990

The law relating these quantities is of the form $n = ab^m$. Determine the approximate values of a and b. $[a = 4.3, b = 5.5]$

71. The power dissipated by a resistor was measured for various values of current flowing in the resistor and the results are as shown below:

Current, I amperes	1.3	2.4	3.7	4.9	5.8
Power, P watts	37	127	301	528	740

Prove that the law relating current and power is of the form $P = RI^n$, where R and n are constants, and determine the law. $[P = 22I^2]$

72. The vapour pressure (p) of triethylamine at various temperatures (T) are given below.

p (Pa)	0.439	10.120	93.330
T (K)	100	120	140

Show that these results are related by an equation of the form $\lg p = A - \dfrac{B}{T - 3.12}$. Find A and B. $[A = 7.6, B = 770]$

73. The values of resistance R and voltage V were measured in an experiment and the results are shown below

R ohms	59.5	74.2	84.1	94.8	152.2
V millivolts	135	107	94	83	51

Resistance and voltage are thought to be connected by a law of the form $R = \dfrac{a}{V} + b$, where a and b are constants. Verify the law and find the approximate values of a and b. Determine the voltage when the resistance is 90.0 ohms. $[a = 7.6, b = 3.2; 87.6 \text{ millivolts}]$

Chapter 8

The notation of second order matrices and determinants

1 Introduction

Matrices are used in engineering and science for solving linear simultaneous equations.

Terms used in connection with matrices

Consider the linear simultaneous equations:

$$2x + 3y = 4 \tag{1}$$
$$\text{and } 5x - 6y = 7 \tag{2}$$

In **matrix** notation, the coefficients of x and y are written as $\begin{pmatrix} 2 & 3 \\ 5 & -6 \end{pmatrix}$,

that is, occupying the same relative positions as in equations (1) and (2) above. The grouping of the coefficients of x and y in this way is called an **array** and the coefficients forming the array are called the **elements** of the matrix.

If there are m rows across an array and n columns down an array, then the matrix is said to be of order $m \times n$, called 'm by n'. Thus for the equations

$$2x + 3y - 4z = 5 \tag{3}$$
$$6x - 7y + 8z = 9 \tag{4}$$

the matrix of the coefficients of x, y and z is $\begin{pmatrix} 2 & 3 & -4 \\ 6 & -7 & 8 \end{pmatrix}$ and is a

'2 by 3' matrix. A matrix having a single row is called a **row** matrix and one having a single column is called a **column** matrix. For example, in equation (3) above, the coefficients of x, y and z form a row matrix of $(2 \quad 3 \quad -4)$ and the coefficients of x in equations (3) and (4) form a column matrix of $\begin{pmatrix} 2 \\ 6 \end{pmatrix}$.

A matrix having the same number of rows as columns is called a **square** matrix. Thus the matrix for the coefficients of x and y in equations (1) and (2) above, i.e. $\begin{pmatrix} 2 & 3 \\ 5 & -6 \end{pmatrix}$, is a square matrix, and is called a second order matrix. Matrices are generally denoted by capital letters and if the matrix representing the coefficients of x and y in equations (1) and (2) above is A, then $A = \begin{pmatrix} 2 & 3 \\ 5 & -6 \end{pmatrix}$.

2 Addition, subtraction and multiplication of second order matrices

In arithmetic, once the basic procedures associated with addition, subtraction, multiplication and division have been mastered, simple problems may be solved. With matrices, the various rules governing them have to be understood before they can be used to solve practical problems. In this section the basic laws of addition, subtraction and multiplication are introduced.

A matrix does not have a single numerical value and cannot be simplified to a particular answer. The main advantage of using matrices is that by applying the laws of matrices, given in this section, they can be simplified, and by comparing one matrix with another similar matrix, values of unknown elements can be determined. It will be seen in Chapter 9 that matrices can be used in this way for solving simultaneous equations. Matrices can be added, subtracted and multiplied and suitable definitions for these operations are formulated, so that they obey most of the laws which govern the algebra of numbers.

Addition

Only matrices of the same order may be added. Thus a 2 by 2 matrix can be added to a 2 by 2 matrix by adding corresponding elements, but a 3 by 2 matrix cannot be added to a 2 by 2 matrix, since some elements in one matrix do not have corresponding elements in the other. The sum of two matrices is the matrix obtained by adding the elements occupying corresponding positions in the matrix, and results in two matrices being simplified to a single matrix.

For example, the matrices $\begin{pmatrix} 1 & 3 \\ 2 & -4 \end{pmatrix}$ and $\begin{pmatrix} 2 & 5 \\ 6 & -7 \end{pmatrix}$

are added as follows:

$$\begin{pmatrix} 1 & 3 \\ 2 & -4 \end{pmatrix} + \begin{pmatrix} 2 & 5 \\ 6 & -7 \end{pmatrix} = \begin{pmatrix} 1+2 & 3+5 \\ 2+6 & (-4)+(-7) \end{pmatrix}$$

$$= \begin{pmatrix} 3 & 8 \\ 8 & -11 \end{pmatrix}$$

Subtraction

Only matrices of the same order can be subtracted and the difference between two matrices, say $A - B$, is the matrix obtained by subtracting the elements of matrix B from those occupying the corresponding positions in matrix A.

For example:

$$\begin{pmatrix} 1 & 3 \\ 2 & -4 \end{pmatrix} - \begin{pmatrix} 2 & 5 \\ 6 & -7 \end{pmatrix} = \begin{pmatrix} 1-2 & 3-5 \\ 2-6 & (-4)-(-7) \end{pmatrix}$$

$$= \begin{pmatrix} -1 & -2 \\ -4 & 3 \end{pmatrix}$$

By adding the single matrix obtained by adding A and B to, say, matrix C, the single matrix representing $A + B + C$ is obtained. By taking, say, matrix D from this single matrix, $A + B + C - D$ is obtained. Thus the laws of addition and subtraction can be applied to more than two matrices, providing that they are all of the same order.

Multiplication

(a) Scalar multiplication

When a matrix is multiplied by a number, the resultant matrix is one of the same order having each element multiplied by the number.

Thus, if matrix $A = \begin{pmatrix} 1 & 3 \\ 2 & -4 \end{pmatrix}$, then $2A = 2 \begin{pmatrix} 1 & 3 \\ 2 & -4 \end{pmatrix}$

$$= \begin{pmatrix} 2 \times 1 & 2 \times 3 \\ 2 \times 2 & 2 \times (-4) \end{pmatrix}$$

$$= \begin{pmatrix} 2 & 6 \\ 4 & -8 \end{pmatrix}$$

(b) Multiplication of matrices

Two matrices can only be multiplied together when the number of columns in the first one is equal to the number of rows in the second one. This is because the process of matrix multiplication depends on finding the sum of the products of the rows in one matrix with the columns in the other. Thus it is possible to multiply a 2 by 2 matrix by a column matrix having two elements or by another 2 by 2 matrix, but it is not possible to multiply it by a row matrix. Thus if:

$$A = \begin{pmatrix} 2 & 3 \\ 5 & 6 \end{pmatrix}, B = \begin{pmatrix} 1 \\ 8 \end{pmatrix} \text{ and } C = (4 \quad 9)$$

it is possible to find $A \times B$, since the number of columns in A is equal to the number of rows in B, but it is not possible to find $A \times C$ since there are two columns in A but only one row in C. If a 2 by 2 matrix A is multiplied by a column matrix, B, having two elements, the resulting matrix is a two element column matrix. The top element is the sum of the products obtained by taking the elements of the top row of A with B. The bottom element is the sum of the products obtained by taking the bottom elements of A with B.

If $A = \begin{pmatrix} a & b \\ c & d \end{pmatrix}$ and $B = \begin{pmatrix} p \\ q \end{pmatrix}$

then $A \times B = \begin{pmatrix} a & b \\ c & d \end{pmatrix} \times \begin{pmatrix} p \\ q \end{pmatrix} = \begin{pmatrix} ap + bq \\ cp + dq \end{pmatrix}$

For example, to multiply the matrices, say, $\begin{pmatrix} 2 & -5 \\ 4 & 3 \end{pmatrix}$ and $\begin{pmatrix} 1 \\ 6 \end{pmatrix}$ gives

$$\begin{pmatrix} 2 & -5 \\ 4 & 3 \end{pmatrix} \times \begin{pmatrix} 1 \\ 6 \end{pmatrix} = \begin{pmatrix} 2 \times 1 + (-5) \times 6 \\ 4 \times 1 + 3 \times 6 \end{pmatrix} = \begin{pmatrix} 2 - 30 \\ 4 + 18 \end{pmatrix}$$

$$= \begin{pmatrix} -28 \\ 22 \end{pmatrix}$$

If a 2 by 2 matrix, say, A, is multiplied by a 2 by 2 matrix, say B, the resulting matrix is a 2 by 2 matrix, say C. The top elements of C are the sum of the products obtained by taking the top row of A with the columns of B. The bottom elements of C are the sum of the products obtained by taking the bottom row of A with the columns of B.

For example:

$$\begin{pmatrix} 1 & 3 \\ -2 & 4 \end{pmatrix} \times \begin{pmatrix} 5 & 0 \\ 7 & -6 \end{pmatrix} = \begin{pmatrix} 1 \times 5 + 3 \times 7 & 1 \times 0 + 3 \times (-6) \\ -2 \times 5 + 4 \times 7 & -2 \times 0 + 4 \times (-6) \end{pmatrix}$$

$$= \begin{pmatrix} 26 & -18 \\ 18 & -24 \end{pmatrix}$$

In general, when a matrix of dimension (m by n) is multiplied by a matrix of dimension (n by q), the resulting matrix is one of dimension (m by q).

Although the laws of matrices are so formulated that they follow most of the laws which govern the algebra of numbers, frequently in the multiplication of matrices

$$A \times B \neq B \times A,$$

It is shown above that

$$A \times B = \begin{pmatrix} 1 & 3 \\ -2 & 4 \end{pmatrix} \times \begin{pmatrix} 5 & 0 \\ 7 & -6 \end{pmatrix} = \begin{pmatrix} 26 & -18 \\ 18 & -24 \end{pmatrix}$$

However, $B \times A = \begin{pmatrix} 5 & 0 \\ 7 & -6 \end{pmatrix} \times \begin{pmatrix} 1 & 3 \\ -2 & 4 \end{pmatrix}$

$$= \cdot \begin{pmatrix} 5 \times 1 + 0 \times (-2) & 5 \times 3 + 0 \times 4 \\ 7 \times 1 + (-6) \times (-2) & 7 \times 3 + (-6) \times 4 \end{pmatrix}$$

i.e. $B \times A = \begin{pmatrix} 5 & 15 \\ 19 & -3 \end{pmatrix}$

That is, $A \times B \neq B \times A$ in this case. The results are said to be *non-commutative* (i.e., they are not in agreement).

Worked problems on the addition, subtraction and multiplication of second order matrices

Problem 1. If $A = \begin{pmatrix} 1 & 4 \\ -3 & 2 \end{pmatrix}$, $B = \begin{pmatrix} 5 & -1 \\ 0 & 1 \end{pmatrix}$ and $C = \begin{pmatrix} 3 & -4 \\ 7 & 2 \end{pmatrix}$

determine the single matrix for (a) $A + C$, (b) $A - C$, and (c) $A + B - C$.

(a) $A + C = \begin{pmatrix} 1 & 4 \\ -3 & 2 \end{pmatrix} + \begin{pmatrix} 3 & -4 \\ 7 & 2 \end{pmatrix} = \begin{pmatrix} 1+3 & 4+(-4) \\ (-3)+7 & 2+2 \end{pmatrix}$

$$= \begin{pmatrix} 4 & 0 \\ 4 & 4 \end{pmatrix}$$

(b) $A - C = \begin{pmatrix} 1 & 4 \\ -3 & 2 \end{pmatrix} - \begin{pmatrix} 3 & -4 \\ 7 & 2 \end{pmatrix} = \begin{pmatrix} 1-3 & 4-(-4) \\ (-3)-7 & 2-2 \end{pmatrix}$

$$= \begin{pmatrix} -2 & 8 \\ -10 & 0 \end{pmatrix}$$

(c) From part (b), $A - C = \begin{pmatrix} -2 & 8 \\ -10 & 0 \end{pmatrix}$

Hence $A + B - C = \begin{pmatrix} -2 & 8 \\ -10 & 0 \end{pmatrix} + \begin{pmatrix} 5 & -1 \\ 0 & 1 \end{pmatrix}$

$$= \begin{pmatrix} -2+5 & 8+(-1) \\ -10+0 & 0+1 \end{pmatrix}$$

$$= \begin{pmatrix} 3 & 7 \\ -10 & 1 \end{pmatrix}$$

Problem 2. Determine the single matrix for (a) $A \cdot C$ and (b) $A \cdot B$, where

$A = \begin{pmatrix} 2 & 4 \\ 1 & -3 \end{pmatrix}$, $B = \begin{pmatrix} 3 & -7 \\ 4 & -5 \end{pmatrix}$ and $C = \begin{pmatrix} 2 \\ -5 \end{pmatrix}$

(a) $A \cdot C = \begin{pmatrix} 2 & 4 \\ 1 & -3 \end{pmatrix} \times \begin{pmatrix} 2 \\ -5 \end{pmatrix} = \begin{pmatrix} 2 \times 2 + 4 \times (-5) \\ 1 \times 2 + (-3) \times (-5) \end{pmatrix}$

$$= \begin{pmatrix} 4 - 20 \\ 2 + 15 \end{pmatrix} = \begin{pmatrix} -16 \\ 17 \end{pmatrix}$$

(b) $A \cdot B = \begin{pmatrix} 2 & 4 \\ 1 & -3 \end{pmatrix} \times \begin{pmatrix} 3 & -7 \\ 4 & -5 \end{pmatrix}$

$\qquad = \begin{pmatrix} [2 \times 3 + 4 \times 4] & [2 \times (-7) + 4 \times (-5)] \\ [1 \times 3 + (-3) \times 4] & [1 \times (-7) + (-3) \times (-5)] \end{pmatrix}$

$\qquad = \begin{pmatrix} 6 + 16 & -14 + (-20) \\ 3 + (-12) & -7 + 15 \end{pmatrix}$

$\qquad = \begin{pmatrix} 22 & -34 \\ -9 & 8 \end{pmatrix}$

Further problems on the addition, subtraction and multiplication of matrices may be found in Section 5 (Problems 1–10), p. 150.

3 The unit matrix

A unit matrix is one in which the values of the elements in the leading diagonal, ($\backslash$), are 1, the remaining elements being 0. Thus, a 2 by 2 unit

matrix is $\begin{pmatrix} 1 & 0 \\ 0 & 1 \end{pmatrix}$, and is usually denoted by the symbol I. If A is a

square matrix and I the unit matrix, then $A \times I = I \times A$, that is, this is one case in matrices where the law $A \times B = B \times A$ of the algebra of numbers is true. The unit matrix is analogous to the number 1 in ordinary algebra.

4 Second order determinants

The solution of the linear simultaneous equations:

$$a_1 x + b_1 y + c_1 = 0 \qquad (1)$$
$$a_2 x + b_2 y + c_2 = 0 \qquad (2)$$

may be found by the elimination method of solving simultaneous equations. To eliminate y:

Equation (1) $\times b_2$: $a_1 b_2 x + b_1 b_2 y + c_1 b_2 = 0$
Equation (2) $\times b_1$: $a_2 b_1 x + b_1 b_2 y + c_2 b_1 = 0$

Subtracting: $(a_1 b_2 - a_2 b_1) x + (c_1 b_2 - c_2 b_1) = 0$

Thus, $x = \dfrac{-(c_1 b_2 - c_2 b_1)}{a_1 b_2 - a_2 b_1}$

i.e. $x = \dfrac{(b_1 c_2 - b_2 c_1)}{a_1 b_2 - a_2 b_1}$ \qquad (3)

Similarly, to eliminate x:

Equation (1) $\times a_2$: $a_1 a_2 x + a_2 b_1 y + a_2 c_1 = 0$

Equation (2) $\times a_1$: $a_1 a_2 x + a_1 b_2 y + a_1 c_2 = 0$

Subtracting: $(a_2 b_1 - a_1 b_2) y + (a_2 c_1 - a_1 c_2) = 0$

Thus, $y = \dfrac{-(a_2 c_1 - a_1 c_2)}{(a_2 b_1 - a_1 b_2)} = \dfrac{(a_1 c_2 - a_2 c_1)}{(a_2 b_1 - a_1 b_2)} = \dfrac{(a_1 c_2 - a_2 c_1)}{-(a_1 b_2 - a_2 b_1)}$

i.e. $-y = \dfrac{(a_1 c_2 - a_2 c_1)}{(a_1 b_2 - a_2 b_1)}$ $\qquad\qquad$ (4)

Equations (3) and (4) can be written in the form:

$$\frac{x}{b_1 c_2 - b_2 c_1} = \frac{-y}{a_1 c_2 - a_2 c_1} = \frac{1}{a_1 b_2 - a_2 b_1} \qquad (5)$$

The denominators of equation (5) are all of the general form:

$pq - rs$.

Although as stated in Section 2 a matrix does not have a single numerical value and cannot be simplified to a particular answer, coefficients written in this form may be expressed as a special matrix, denoted by an array within vertical lines, rather than brackets. In this case:

$$\begin{vmatrix} a & b \\ c & d \end{vmatrix} = ad - bc,$$ and is called a second order **determinant**.

It is shown in Chapter 9 following that determinants can be used to solve linear simultaneous equations such as those given in equations (1) and (2) above.

Worked problem on second order determinants

Problem 1. Evaluate the determinants: (a) $\begin{vmatrix} 3 & -1 \\ 4 & 2 \end{vmatrix}$ and (b) $\begin{vmatrix} a & -2b \\ 2a & -3b \end{vmatrix}$

By the definition of a determinant, $\begin{vmatrix} a & b \\ c & d \end{vmatrix} = ad - bc$, hence,

(a) $\begin{vmatrix} 3 & -1 \\ 4 & 2 \end{vmatrix} = (3 \times 2) - ((-1) \times 4) = 6 + 4 = \mathbf{10}.$

(b) $\begin{vmatrix} a & -2b \\ 2a & -3b \end{vmatrix} = (a \times (-3b)) - ((-2b) \times 2a) = -3ab + 4ab$

$\qquad\qquad\qquad\qquad\qquad\qquad\qquad\qquad\qquad = \mathbf{ab}.$

Further problems on second order determinants may be found in Section 5 following (Problems 11–15) on p. 151.

5 Further problems

Addition, subtraction and multiplication of second order matrices

In Problems 1 to 5, matrices A, B, C and D are given by:

$$A = \begin{pmatrix} 1 & 4 \\ -3 & 2 \end{pmatrix}, B = \begin{pmatrix} 2 & 7 \\ -1 & 0 \end{pmatrix},$$

$$C = \begin{pmatrix} 5 & -1 \\ 0 & 1 \end{pmatrix}, \text{ and } D = \begin{pmatrix} 3 & -4 \\ 7 & 2 \end{pmatrix}$$

Determine the single matrix for the expressions given.

1. (a) $A + B$ $\quad \left[\begin{pmatrix} 3 & 11 \\ -4 & 2 \end{pmatrix} \right]$

   (b) $A + C$ $\quad \left[\begin{pmatrix} 6 & 3 \\ -3 & 3 \end{pmatrix} \right]$

2. (a) $C + D$ $\quad \left[\begin{pmatrix} 8 & -5 \\ 7 & 3 \end{pmatrix} \right]$

   (b) $B + D$ $\quad \left[\begin{pmatrix} 5 & 3 \\ 6 & 2 \end{pmatrix} \right]$

3. (a) $B - A$ $\quad \left[\begin{pmatrix} 1 & 3 \\ 2 & -2 \end{pmatrix} \right]$

   (b) $D - B$ $\quad \left[\begin{pmatrix} 1 & -11 \\ 8 & 2 \end{pmatrix} \right]$

4. (a) $C - A$ $\quad \left[\begin{pmatrix} 4 & -5 \\ 3 & -1 \end{pmatrix} \right]$

   (b) $B - C$ $\quad \left[\begin{pmatrix} -3 & 8 \\ -1 & -1 \end{pmatrix} \right]$

5. (a) $A + B + C$ $\quad \left[\begin{pmatrix} 8 & 10 \\ -4 & 3 \end{pmatrix} \right]$

   (b) $A - B + C - D$ $\quad \left[\begin{pmatrix} 1 & 0 \\ -9 & 1 \end{pmatrix} \right]$

In Problems 6 to 10, matrices A, B, C, D and E are given by:

$$A = \begin{pmatrix} 3 & 1 \\ -2 & 4 \end{pmatrix}, B = \begin{pmatrix} 2 & -5 \\ 0 & 1 \end{pmatrix}, C = \begin{pmatrix} -1 & 6 \\ 3 & 0 \end{pmatrix}$$

$$D = \begin{pmatrix} 2 \\ 3 \end{pmatrix} \text{ and } E = \begin{pmatrix} -1 \\ 4 \end{pmatrix}.$$

Determine the single matrix for the expressions given.

6. (a) $A \cdot D$ $\left[\begin{pmatrix} 9 \\ 8 \end{pmatrix}\right]$

   (b) $B \cdot E$ $\left[\begin{pmatrix} -22 \\ 4 \end{pmatrix}\right]$

7. (a) $C \cdot D$ $\left[\begin{pmatrix} 16 \\ 6 \end{pmatrix}\right]$

   (b) $A \cdot E$ $\left[\begin{pmatrix} 1 \\ 18 \end{pmatrix}\right]$

8. (a) $A \cdot C$ $\left[\begin{pmatrix} 0 & 18 \\ 14 & -12 \end{pmatrix}\right]$

   (b) $C \cdot B$ $\left[\begin{pmatrix} -2 & 12 \\ 6 & -15 \end{pmatrix}\right]$

9. (a) $A \cdot B$ $\left[\begin{pmatrix} 6 & -14 \\ -4 & 14 \end{pmatrix}\right]$

   (b) $B \cdot A$ $\left[\begin{pmatrix} 16 & -18 \\ -2 & 4 \end{pmatrix}\right]$

(Note that $A \cdot B \neq B \cdot A$)

10. (a) $B \cdot C$ $\left[\begin{pmatrix} -17 & 12 \\ 3 & 0 \end{pmatrix}\right]$

   (b) $C \cdot A$ $\left[\begin{pmatrix} -15 & 23 \\ 9 & 3 \end{pmatrix}\right]$

Second order determinants
In Problems 11 to 15, evaluate the determinants given.

11. (a) $\begin{vmatrix} 2 & 3 \\ 4 & 5 \end{vmatrix}$ (b) $\begin{vmatrix} -1 & -1 \\ 7 & 2 \end{vmatrix}$ (a) [−2]   (b) [5]

12. (a) $\begin{vmatrix} 3 & -1 \\ 4 & 7 \end{vmatrix}$ (b) $\begin{vmatrix} 5 & -2 \\ 3 & 1 \end{vmatrix}$ (a) [25]   (b) [11]

13. (a) $\begin{vmatrix} -2 & 4 \\ 3 & 1 \end{vmatrix}$ (b) $\begin{vmatrix} 1 & -4 \\ 5 & 1 \end{vmatrix}$ (a) [−14]   (b) [21]

14. (a) $\begin{vmatrix} x & 2x \\ -3x & 5 \end{vmatrix}$ (b) $\begin{vmatrix} y^2 & 3y \\ 4y^2 & -2y \end{vmatrix}$

(a) $[5x + 6x^2]$ (b) $[-14y^3]$

15. (a) $\begin{vmatrix} c & -2b \\ 4c & -3b \end{vmatrix}$ (b) $\begin{vmatrix} a & c \\ 2a & 4c \end{vmatrix}$

(a) $[5bc]$ (b) $[2ac]$

Chapter 9

The solution of simultaneous equations having two unknowns using matrices and determinants

1 The solution of simultaneous equations having two unknowns using determinants

When introducing determinants in Chapter 8, Section 4, the simultaneous equations

$$a_1x + b_1y + c_1 = 0 \qquad (1)$$
$$a_2x + b_2y + c_2 = 0 \qquad (2)$$

are solved using the elimination method of solving simultaneous equations, and it is shown that

$$\frac{x}{b_1c_2 - b_2c_1} = \frac{-y}{a_1c_2 - a_2c_1} = \frac{1}{a_1b_2 - a_2b_1} \qquad (3)$$

It is also stated that the denominators of equation (3) are all of the general form:

$pq - rs.$

This algebraic expression is denoted by a special matrix having its array within vertical lines and is called a **determinant**. Thus

$$\begin{vmatrix} a & b \\ c & d \end{vmatrix} = ad - bc,$$

and is called a second order determinant.

The denominators of equation (3) can be written in determinant form, giving:

$$\frac{x}{\begin{vmatrix} b_1 & c_1 \\ b_2 & c_2 \end{vmatrix}} = \frac{-y}{\begin{vmatrix} a_1 & c_1 \\ a_2 & c_2 \end{vmatrix}} = \frac{1}{\begin{vmatrix} a_1 & b_1 \\ a_2 & b_2 \end{vmatrix}} \qquad (4)$$

This expression is used to solve simultaneous equations by determinants and can be remembered by the 'cover-up' rule. In this rule:

(i) the equations are written in the form $a_1 x + b_1 y + c_1 = 0$.

(ii) If equation (4) is written in the form:

$$\frac{x}{|D_1|} = \frac{-y}{|D_2|} = \frac{1}{|D|}, \text{ then}$$

(iii) $|D_1|$ is obtained by covering-up the x-column and writing down the remaining coefficients in determinant form in positions corresponding to the positions they occupy in the equations.

(iv) $|D_2|$ is obtained by covering-up the y-column and treating the coefficients as in (iii) above.

(v) $|D|$ is obtained by covering-up the constants-column and treating the coefficients as in (iii) above.

For example, to solve the equations:

$$2x + 3y = 11 \qquad (5)$$
$$4x + 2y = 10 \qquad (6)$$

by using determinants:

(i) the equations are written as:

$$2x + 3y - 11 = 0$$
$$4x + 2y - 10 = 0$$

(ii) $\dfrac{x}{|D_1|} = \dfrac{-y}{|D_2|} = \dfrac{1}{|D|}$

(iii) $|D_1| = \begin{vmatrix} 3 & -11 \\ 2 & -10 \end{vmatrix}$, obtained by covering-up the x-column in (i) above.

(iv) $|D_2| = \begin{vmatrix} 2 & -11 \\ 4 & -10 \end{vmatrix}$, obtained by covering-up the y-column in (i) above.

(v) $|D| = \begin{vmatrix} 2 & 3 \\ 4 & 2 \end{vmatrix}$, obtained by covering-up the constants-column in (i) above.

Thus,

$$\frac{x}{\begin{vmatrix} 3 & -11 \\ 2 & -10 \end{vmatrix}} = \frac{-y}{\begin{vmatrix} 2 & -11 \\ 4 & -10 \end{vmatrix}} = \frac{1}{\begin{vmatrix} 2 & 3 \\ 4 & 2 \end{vmatrix}}$$

i.e. $\dfrac{x}{3 \times (-10) - 2 \times (-11)} = \dfrac{-y}{2 \times (-10) - 4 \times (-11)} = \dfrac{1}{2 \times 2 - 4 \times 3}$

$$\dfrac{x}{-8} = \dfrac{-y}{24} = \dfrac{1}{-8}$$

giving: $x = \dfrac{-8}{-8} = 1$ and $-y = \dfrac{24}{-8}$, i.e. $y = 3$.

Checking in the original equations:

L.H.S. of equation (5) $= 2 \times 1 + 3 \times 3 = 11 =$ R.H.S.
L.H.S. of equation (6) $= 4 \times 1 + 2 \times 3 = 10 =$ R.H.S.

Hence, $x = 1, y = 3$ is the correct solution.

If, in a determinant of the form $D = \begin{vmatrix} a_1 & b_1 \\ a_2 & b_2 \end{vmatrix}$, $a_1 b_2 = a_2 b_1$,

then $a_1 b_2 - a_2 b_1 = 0$, i.e. $D = 0$. This means that in the simultaneous equations on which the determinant is based (say of the form $ax + by = c$), a_1 and b_1 are each multiplied by the same constant to give a_2 and b_2. So essentially there is only one equation with two unknown quantities, which is

not capable of solution. An example is the determinant $\begin{vmatrix} 2 & 1 \\ 10 & 5 \end{vmatrix}$ which

arises when trying to solve the equations, say,

$$2x + y = 3$$
and $10x + 5y = 15$,

and in this case, $D = 2 \times 5 - 10 \times 1 = 0$, i.e. the equations cannot be solved.

The matrix of the coefficients of x and y, i.e. $\begin{pmatrix} 2 & 1 \\ 10 & 5 \end{pmatrix}$, is called a

singular matrix when the determinant of the matrix is equal to 0.

Worked problems on the solution of simultaneous equations having two unknowns using determinants

Problem 1. Solve the simultaneous equations:

$$\tfrac{3}{2}p - 2q = \tfrac{1}{2} \qquad\qquad\qquad (1)$$
$$p + \tfrac{3}{2}q = 6 \qquad\qquad\qquad (2)$$

by using determinants.

(i) Writing the equations in the form $ax + by + c = 0$ gives:

$$\tfrac{3}{2}p - 2q - \tfrac{1}{2} = 0$$
$$p + \tfrac{3}{2}q - 6 = 0$$

(ii) $\dfrac{p}{|D_1|} = \dfrac{-q}{|D_2|} = \dfrac{1}{|D|}$ (note the signs are +, −, +)

(iii) Covering-up the p-column gives: $|D_1| = \begin{vmatrix} -2 & -\frac{1}{2} \\ \frac{3}{2} & -6 \end{vmatrix}$

(iv) Covering-up the q-column gives: $|D_2| = \begin{vmatrix} \frac{3}{2} & -\frac{1}{2} \\ 1 & -6 \end{vmatrix}$

(v) Covering-up the constants-column gives: $|D| = \begin{vmatrix} \frac{3}{2} & -2 \\ 1 & \frac{3}{2} \end{vmatrix}$

Thus,

$$\dfrac{p}{\begin{vmatrix} -2 & -\frac{1}{2} \\ \frac{3}{2} & -6 \end{vmatrix}} = \dfrac{-q}{\begin{vmatrix} \frac{3}{2} & -\frac{1}{2} \\ 1 & -6 \end{vmatrix}} = \dfrac{1}{\begin{vmatrix} \frac{3}{2} & -2 \\ 1 & \frac{3}{2} \end{vmatrix}}$$

i.e. $\dfrac{p}{(-2) \times (-6) - (\frac{3}{2}) \times (-\frac{1}{2})} = \dfrac{-q}{(\frac{3}{2}) \times (-6) - (1) \times (-\frac{1}{2})}$

$$= \dfrac{1}{(\frac{3}{2}) \times (\frac{3}{2}) - (1) \times (-2)}$$

$$\dfrac{p}{12\frac{3}{4}} = \dfrac{-q}{-8\frac{1}{2}} = \dfrac{1}{4\frac{1}{4}}$$

Hence, $p = \dfrac{12\frac{3}{4}}{4\frac{1}{4}} = 3$ and $q = \dfrac{8\frac{1}{2}}{4\frac{1}{4}} = 2.$

Checking in the original equations:

L.H.S. of equation (1) = $\frac{3}{2} \times 3 - 2 \times 2 = \frac{1}{2}$ = R.H.S.

L.H.S. of equation (2) = $3 + \frac{3}{2} \times 2 = 6$ = R.H.S.

Hence $p = 3, q = 2$ is the correct solution.

Problem 2. Use determinants to solve the simultaneous equations:

$$-0.5f + 0.4g = 0.7 \tag{1}$$
$$1.2f - 0.3g = 3.6 \tag{2}$$

Writing the equations in the form $ax + by + c = 0$ gives:

$$-0.5f + 0.4g - 0.7 = 0$$
$$1.2f - 0.3g - 3.6 = 0$$

$$\dfrac{f}{|D_1|} = \dfrac{-g}{|D_2|} = \dfrac{1}{|D|}$$

Covering-up the f-column gives $|D_1|$ $=$ $\begin{vmatrix} 0.4 & -0.7 \\ -0.3 & -3.6 \end{vmatrix}$

$$= (0.4) \times (-3.6) - (-0.3) \times (-0.7)$$
$$= -1.44 - 0.21 = -1.65$$

Covering-up the g-column, gives $|D_2|$ $=$ $\begin{vmatrix} -0.5 & -0.7 \\ 1.2 & -3.6 \end{vmatrix}$

$$= (-0.5) \times (-3.6) - (1.2) \times (-0.7)$$

$$= 1.8 - (-0.84) = 2.64.$$

Covering-up the constants column, gives $|D|$ $=$ $\begin{vmatrix} -0.5 & 0.4 \\ 1.2 & -0.3 \end{vmatrix}$

$$= (-0.5) \times (-0.3) - (1.2) \times (0.4)$$
$$= 0.15 - 0.48 = -0.33$$

Hence, $\dfrac{f}{-1.65} = \dfrac{-g}{2.64} = \dfrac{1}{-0.33}$

i.e. $f = \dfrac{-1.65}{-0.33} = 5$ and $g = \dfrac{-2.64}{-0.33} = 8.$

Checking:

L.H.S. of equation (1) $= -0.5 \times 5 + 0.4 \times 8 = 0.7 =$ R.H.S.
L.H.S. of equation (2) $= 1.2 \times 5 - 0.3 \times 8 = 3.6 =$ R.H.S.

Thus, $f = 5, g = 8$ is the correct solution.

Problem 3. Use determinants to solve the simultaneous equations:

$$\frac{10}{a} - \frac{4}{b} = 3 \tag{1}$$

$$\frac{6}{a} + \frac{8}{b} = 7 \tag{2}$$

Let $x = \dfrac{1}{a}$ and $y = \dfrac{1}{b}$, then

$$10x - 4y = 3$$
$$6x + 8y = 7.$$

Writing in the $ax + by + c = 0$ form gives:

$$10x - 4y - 3 = 0$$
$$6x + 8y - 7 = 0$$

Applying the cover-up rule gives:

$$\frac{x}{\begin{vmatrix} -4 & -3 \\ 8 & -7 \end{vmatrix}} = \frac{-y}{\begin{vmatrix} 10 & -3 \\ 6 & -7 \end{vmatrix}} = \frac{1}{\begin{vmatrix} 10 & -4 \\ 6 & 8 \end{vmatrix}}$$

i.e. $\dfrac{x}{28 + 24} = \dfrac{-y}{-70 + 18} = \dfrac{1}{80 + 24}$

$x = \frac{52}{104} = \frac{1}{2}, y = \frac{52}{104} = \frac{1}{2}$

Since $x = \dfrac{1}{a}$, $a = 2$ and since $y = \dfrac{1}{b}$, $b = 2$.

Checking:

L.H.S. of equation (1) $= \frac{10}{2} - \frac{4}{2} = 3 =$ R.H.S.

L.H.S. of equation (2) $= \frac{6}{2} + \frac{8}{2} = 7 =$ R.H.S.

Hence, $a = 2, b = 2$ is the correct solution.

Problem 4. The forces acting on a bolt are resolved horizontally and vertically, giving the simultaneous equations shown below. Use determinants to find the values of F_1 and F_2, correct to three significant figures.

$$3.4F_1 - 0.83F_2 = 3.9 \tag{1}$$
$$0.7F_1 + 1.47F_2 = -2.05 \tag{2}$$

Writing the equations in the $ax + by + c = 0$ form, gives:

$3.4F_1 - 0.83F_2 - 3.9 = 0$
$0.7F_1 + 1.47F_2 + 2.05 = 0$

Applying the cover-up rule gives:

$$\frac{F_1}{\begin{vmatrix} -0.83 & -3.9 \\ 1.47 & 2.05 \end{vmatrix}} = \frac{-F_2}{\begin{vmatrix} 3.4 & -3.9 \\ 0.7 & 2.05 \end{vmatrix}} = \frac{1}{\begin{vmatrix} 3.4 & -0.83 \\ 0.7 & 1.47 \end{vmatrix}}$$

Hence,

$$\frac{F_1}{(-0.83) \times 2.05 - 1.47 \times (-3.9)} = \frac{-F_2}{3.4 \times 2.05 - 0.7 \times (-3.9)}$$

$$= \frac{1}{3.4 \times 1.47 - 0.7 \times (-0.83)}$$

that is: $\dfrac{F_1}{-1.701\,5 + 5.733} = \dfrac{-F_2}{6.970 + 2.730} = \dfrac{1}{4.998 + 0.581}$

i.e. $\dfrac{F_1}{4.032} = \dfrac{-F_2}{9.700} = \dfrac{1}{5.579}$

Thus, $F_1 = \dfrac{4.032}{5.579} = 0.723$, correct to three significant figures, and $F_2 = \dfrac{-9.700}{5.579} = -1.74$, correct to three significant figures.

Checking:

L.H.S. of equation (1) $= 3.4 \times 0.723 - 0.83 \times (-1.74)$
$= 3.90$ correct to three significant figures.

L.H.S. of equation (2) $= 0.7 \times 0.723 + 1.47 \times (-1.74)$
$= -2.05$, correct to three significant figures.

Hence, $F_1 = 0.723$, $F_2 = -1.74$ is the correct solution.

Further problems on solving simultaneous equations having two unknowns using determinants may be found in Section 4 (Problems 1–15), p. 165.

2 The inverse of a matrix

The inverse or reciprocal of matrix A is the matrix A^{-1}, such that

$A \cdot A^{-1} = I = A^{-1} \cdot A$, where I is the unit matrix, introduced in Chapter 8, Section 3.

The process of inverting a matrix makes division possible. If three matrices, A, B and X, are such that

$$A \cdot X = B$$

then $$X = \frac{B}{A} = A^{-1} \cdot B.$$

Let the inverse of matrix A be $A^{-1} = \begin{pmatrix} a & b \\ c & d \end{pmatrix}$, and let matrix A be, say,

$\begin{pmatrix} 2 & 3 \\ -1 & 1 \end{pmatrix}$. By the definition of the inverse of a matrix,

$$\begin{pmatrix} 2 & 3 \\ -1 & 1 \end{pmatrix} \times \begin{pmatrix} a & b \\ c & d \end{pmatrix} = \begin{pmatrix} 1 & 0 \\ 0 & 1 \end{pmatrix}, \text{ the unit matrix.}$$

Multiplying the matrices on the left-hand side gives:

$$\begin{pmatrix} 2a + 3c & 2b + 3d \\ -a + c & -b + d \end{pmatrix} = \begin{pmatrix} 1 & 0 \\ 0 & 1 \end{pmatrix} \tag{1}$$

Since these two matrices are equal to one another, the corresponding elements are equal to one another, hence

$-a + c = 0$, that is, $a = c$
$2b + 3d = 0$, that is, $b = -\tfrac{3}{2}d$

Substituting for a and b in equation (1) above gives:

$$\begin{pmatrix} 5c & 0 \\ 0 & \dfrac{5d}{2} \end{pmatrix} = \begin{pmatrix} 1 & 0 \\ 0 & 1 \end{pmatrix}$$

Thus, $5c = 1$, that is, $c = \frac{1}{5}$

$\frac{5d}{2} = 1$, that is, $d = \frac{2}{5}$

Since $a = c$, $a = \frac{1}{5}$ and since $b = -\frac{3}{2}d$, $b = -\frac{3}{5}$.

Thus the inverse of matrix $\begin{pmatrix} 2 & 3 \\ -1 & 1 \end{pmatrix}$ is $\begin{pmatrix} \frac{1}{5} & -\frac{3}{5} \\ \frac{1}{5} & \frac{2}{5} \end{pmatrix}$

There is an alternative method of finding the inverse of a matrix. If the inverses of many matrices are determined and the inverses of the matrices are compared with the matrices, a relationship is seen to exist between matrices and their inverses. This relationship for a matrix of the form

$\begin{pmatrix} a & b \\ c & d \end{pmatrix}$ is that in the inverse:

(i) the position of the a and d elements are interchanged,

(ii) the sign of both the b and c elements is changed, and

(iii) the matrix is multiplied by $\dfrac{1}{ad - bc}$, i.e. the reciprocal of the determinant of the matrix.

Thus, the inverse of matrix $\begin{pmatrix} a & b \\ c & d \end{pmatrix}$ is $\dfrac{1}{ad - bc} \begin{pmatrix} d & -b \\ -c & a \end{pmatrix}$

For the matrix $\begin{pmatrix} 2 & 3 \\ -1 & 1 \end{pmatrix}$ considered previously the inverse is

$\dfrac{1}{2 \times 1 - 3 \times (-1)} \begin{pmatrix} 1 & -3 \\ 1 & 2 \end{pmatrix} = \frac{1}{5} \begin{pmatrix} 1 & -3 \\ 1 & 2 \end{pmatrix} = \begin{pmatrix} \frac{1}{5} & -\frac{3}{5} \\ \frac{1}{5} & \frac{2}{5} \end{pmatrix}$ as shown

previously.

Worked problem on the inverse of a matrix

Problem 1. Determine the inverse of the matrix, $A = \begin{pmatrix} 5 & -3 \\ -2 & 1 \end{pmatrix}$

Let the inverse matrix be $A^{-1} = \begin{pmatrix} a & b \\ c & d \end{pmatrix}$

Since $A \cdot A^{-1} = I$, the unit matrix, then

$\begin{pmatrix} 5 & -3 \\ -2 & 1 \end{pmatrix} \times \begin{pmatrix} a & b \\ c & d \end{pmatrix} = \begin{pmatrix} 1 & 0 \\ 0 & 1 \end{pmatrix}$

Applying the multiplication law to the left-hand side gives:

$\begin{pmatrix} 5a - 3c & 5b - 3d \\ -2a + c & -2b + d \end{pmatrix} = \begin{pmatrix} 1 & 0 \\ 0 & 1 \end{pmatrix}$ \hfill (1)

Equating corresponding elements gives.

$-2a + c = 0$, i.e. $a = \dfrac{c}{2}$ and $5b - 3d = 0$, i.e. $b = \tfrac{3}{5}d$.

Substituting in equation (1):

$$\begin{pmatrix} -\dfrac{c}{2} & 0 \\ 0 & -\dfrac{d}{5} \end{pmatrix} = \begin{pmatrix} 1 & 0 \\ 0 & 1 \end{pmatrix}$$

i.e. $-\dfrac{c}{2} = 1, c = -2$ and $-\dfrac{d}{5} = 1, d = -5$.

Since $a = \tfrac{c}{2}$, $a = -1$ and since $b = \tfrac{3}{5}d$, $b = -3$.

Thus the inverse matrix of $\begin{pmatrix} 5 & -3 \\ -2 & 1 \end{pmatrix}$ is $\begin{pmatrix} -1 & -3 \\ -2 & -5 \end{pmatrix}$

The solution may be checked, using $A \cdot A^{-1} = I$. Thus,

$$\begin{pmatrix} 5 & -3 \\ -2 & 1 \end{pmatrix} \times \begin{pmatrix} -1 & -3 \\ -2 & -5 \end{pmatrix} = \begin{pmatrix} -5+6 & -15+15 \\ 2-2 & 6-5 \end{pmatrix}$$

$$= \begin{pmatrix} 1 & 0 \\ 0 & 1 \end{pmatrix}, \text{ the inverse matrix.}$$

Hence the solution $\begin{pmatrix} -1 & -3 \\ -2 & -5 \end{pmatrix}$ is correct.

Alternatively, the relationship that the inverse of matrix

$\begin{pmatrix} a & b \\ c & d \end{pmatrix}$ is $\dfrac{1}{ad - bc} \begin{pmatrix} d & -b \\ -c & a \end{pmatrix}$ could have been applied.

The inverse of $\begin{pmatrix} 5 & -3 \\ -2 & 1 \end{pmatrix} = \dfrac{1}{5 \times 1 - (-2) \times (-3)} \begin{pmatrix} 1 & 3 \\ 2 & 5 \end{pmatrix}$

$$= \dfrac{1}{-1} \begin{pmatrix} 1 & 3 \\ 2 & 5 \end{pmatrix}$$

Applying the law for scalar multiplication gives $\begin{pmatrix} -1 & -3 \\ -2 & -5 \end{pmatrix}$, as obtained

previously. The alternative method of applying a formula is the easiest method of determining the inverse of a matrix.

Further problems on the inverse of a matrix may be found in Section 4 (Problems 16–20), p. 167.

3 The solution of simultaneous equations having two unknowns using matrices

Matrices may be used to solve linear simultaneous equations. For equations having two unknown quantities there is no advantage in using a matrix method. However, for equations having three or more unknown quantities, solution by a matrix method can usually be performed more quickly and accurately.

Two linear simultaneous equations, such as:

$$2x + 3y = 4 \qquad (1)$$
$$x - 5y = 6 \qquad (2)$$

may be written in matrix form, as:

$$\begin{pmatrix} 2 & 3 \\ 1 & -5 \end{pmatrix} \begin{pmatrix} x \\ y \end{pmatrix} = \begin{pmatrix} 4 \\ 6 \end{pmatrix} \qquad (3)$$

The inverse of the matrix $\begin{pmatrix} 2 & 3 \\ 1 & -5 \end{pmatrix}$ is obtained as shown in Section 2

and is $\begin{pmatrix} \frac{5}{13} & \frac{3}{13} \\ \frac{1}{13} & \frac{-2}{13} \end{pmatrix}$. Multiplying both sides of equation (3) by this inversed

matrix gives:

$$\begin{pmatrix} 1 & 0 \\ 0 & 1 \end{pmatrix} \begin{pmatrix} x \\ y \end{pmatrix} = \begin{pmatrix} \frac{5}{13} & \frac{3}{13} \\ \frac{1}{13} & \frac{-2}{13} \end{pmatrix} \begin{pmatrix} 4 \\ 6 \end{pmatrix} = \begin{pmatrix} \frac{20}{13} + \frac{18}{13} \\ \frac{4}{13} - \frac{12}{13} \end{pmatrix}$$

$$= \begin{pmatrix} \frac{38}{13} \\ \frac{-8}{13} \end{pmatrix}$$

i.e. $\begin{pmatrix} x \\ y \end{pmatrix} = \begin{pmatrix} \frac{38}{13} \\ \frac{-8}{13} \end{pmatrix}$

Equating corresponding elements gives:

$x = \frac{38}{13}$ and $y = -\frac{8}{13}$

Check: L.H.S. of equation (1) is $2 \times \frac{38}{13} + 3 \times (-\frac{8}{13}) = 4 = $ R.H.S.

L.H.S. of equation (2) is $\frac{38}{13} - 5(-\frac{8}{13}) = 6 = $ R.H.S.

Hence, $x = \frac{38}{13}$, $y = -\frac{8}{13}$ is the correct solution.

Summary

To solve linear simultaneous equations with two unknown quantities by using matrices:

   (i) write the equations in the standard form

$$ax + by = c$$
$$dx + ey = f$$

(ii) write this in matrix form, i.e.

$$\begin{pmatrix} a & b \\ d & e \end{pmatrix} \begin{pmatrix} x \\ y \end{pmatrix} = \begin{pmatrix} c \\ f \end{pmatrix}$$

(iii) determine the inverse of matrix $\begin{pmatrix} a & b \\ d & e \end{pmatrix}$,

(iv) multiply each side of (ii) by the inversed matrix, and express in the form $\begin{pmatrix} x \\ y \end{pmatrix} = \begin{pmatrix} g \\ h \end{pmatrix}$

(v) solve for x and y by equating corresponding elements,
and (vi) check the solution in the original equations.

Worked problems on solving simultaneous equations having two unknowns using matrices

Problem 1. Use matrices to solve the simultaneous equations:

$$4a - 3b = 18 \qquad \qquad (1)$$
$$a + 2b = -1 \qquad \qquad (2)$$

With reference to the above summary:

(i) The equations are in the standard form.

(ii) The matrices are $\begin{pmatrix} 4 & -3 \\ 1 & 2 \end{pmatrix} \begin{pmatrix} a \\ b \end{pmatrix} = \begin{pmatrix} 18 \\ -1 \end{pmatrix}$

(iii) The inverse matrix of $\begin{pmatrix} 4 & -3 \\ 1 & 2 \end{pmatrix}$ is $\dfrac{1}{4 \times 2 - (-3) \times 1} \begin{pmatrix} 2 & 3 \\ -1 & 4 \end{pmatrix}$

i.e. $\frac{1}{11} \begin{pmatrix} 2 & 3 \\ -1 & 4 \end{pmatrix}$, that is, $\begin{pmatrix} \frac{2}{11} & \frac{3}{11} \\ -\frac{1}{11} & \frac{4}{11} \end{pmatrix}$

(iv) Multiplying each side of (ii) by this inversed matrix, gives:

$$\begin{pmatrix} a \\ b \end{pmatrix} = \begin{pmatrix} \frac{2}{11} & \frac{3}{11} \\ -\frac{1}{11} & \frac{4}{11} \end{pmatrix} \begin{pmatrix} 18 \\ -1 \end{pmatrix}$$

$$\begin{pmatrix} a \\ b \end{pmatrix} = \begin{pmatrix} \frac{36}{11} + (-\frac{3}{11}) \\ -\frac{18}{11} + (-\frac{4}{11}) \end{pmatrix} = \begin{pmatrix} 3 \\ -2 \end{pmatrix}$$

(v) Thus, $a = 3$, $b = -2$.
(vi) Checking: L.H.S. of equation (1) is $4 \times 3 - 3(-2) = 18 =$ R.H.S.
L.H.S. of equation (2) is $3 + 2(-2) \qquad = -1 =$ R.H.S.

Hence $a = 3$, $b = -2$ is the correct solution.

Problem 2. Solve the simultaneous equations:

$$\frac{3}{x} - \frac{2}{y} = 0 \tag{1}$$

$$\frac{1}{x} + \frac{4}{y} = 14 \tag{2}$$

by using matrices.

With reference to the summary:

(i) The equations may be expressed in standard form by letting

$\dfrac{1}{x}$ be p and $\dfrac{1}{y}$ be q. Thus, equations (1) and (2)

become $3p - 2q = 0$
$\qquad\quad p + 4q = 14$

(ii) The matrices are $\begin{pmatrix} 3 & -2 \\ 1 & 4 \end{pmatrix} \begin{pmatrix} p \\ q \end{pmatrix} = \begin{pmatrix} 0 \\ 14 \end{pmatrix}$

(iii) The inverse of $\begin{pmatrix} 3 & -2 \\ 1 & 4 \end{pmatrix}$ is $\frac{1}{14}\begin{pmatrix} 4 & 2 \\ -1 & 3 \end{pmatrix}$

(iv) Multiplying each side of (ii) by (iii) gives:

$$\begin{pmatrix} p \\ q \end{pmatrix} = \frac{1}{14}\begin{pmatrix} 4 & 2 \\ -1 & 3 \end{pmatrix}\begin{pmatrix} 0 \\ 14 \end{pmatrix}$$

i.e. $\begin{pmatrix} p \\ q \end{pmatrix} = \frac{1}{14}\begin{pmatrix} 4\times 0 + 2\times 14 \\ -1\times 0 + 3\times 14 \end{pmatrix} = \frac{1}{14}\begin{pmatrix} 28 \\ 42 \end{pmatrix} = \begin{pmatrix} \frac{1}{14}\times 28 \\ \frac{1}{14}\times 42 \end{pmatrix}$

$$= \begin{pmatrix} 2 \\ 3 \end{pmatrix}$$

(v) Thus $p = 2$ and $q = 3$, i.e. $x = \frac{1}{2}$, $y = \frac{1}{3}$.

(vi) Checking: L.H.S. of equation (1) is $\frac{3}{1/2} - \frac{2}{1/3} = 6-6 = 0 =$ R.H.S.

L.H.S. of equation (2) is $\frac{1}{1/2} + \frac{4}{1/3} = 2+12 = 14 =$ R.H.S.

Hence $x = \frac{1}{2}$, $y = \frac{1}{3}$ **is the correct solution.**

Problem 3. A force system is analysed, and by resolving the forces horizontally and vertically the following equations are obtained:

$$6F_1 - F_2 = 5 \tag{1}$$
$$5F_1 + 2F_2 = 7 \tag{2}$$

Use matrices to solve for F_1 and F_2.

The matrices are $\begin{pmatrix} 6 & -1 \\ 5 & 2 \end{pmatrix}\begin{pmatrix} F_1 \\ F_2 \end{pmatrix} = \begin{pmatrix} 5 \\ 7 \end{pmatrix}$

The inverse of $\begin{pmatrix} 6 & -1 \\ 5 & 2 \end{pmatrix}$ is $\frac{1}{17}\begin{pmatrix} 2 & 1 \\ -5 & 6 \end{pmatrix}$

Hence $\begin{pmatrix} F_1 \\ F_2 \end{pmatrix} = \frac{1}{17}\begin{pmatrix} 2 & 1 \\ -5 & 6 \end{pmatrix}\begin{pmatrix} 5 \\ 7 \end{pmatrix}$

$$= \frac{1}{17}\begin{pmatrix} 10 + 7 \\ -25 + 42 \end{pmatrix} = \begin{pmatrix} 1 \\ 1 \end{pmatrix}$$

Thus, $F_1 = 1, F_2 = 1$.

Checking: L.H.S. of equation (1) is $6 - 1 = 5 =$ R.H.S.
L.H.S. of equation (2) is $5 + 2 = 7 =$ R.H.S.

Thus, $F_1 = 1$ and $F_2 = 1$ is the correct solution.

Any technical problems, such as the equations formed by the resolution of vector quantities or the equations relating load and effort in machines, which were previously solved by using simultaneous equations, may be solved either by using determinants or by using matrices.

Further problems on the solution of simultaneous equations having two unknowns using matrices may be found in the following Section (4) (Problems 21–30), p. 167.

4 Further problems

The solution of simultaneous equations having two unknowns using determinants
In Problems 1 to 11, use determinants to solve the simultaneous equations given.

1. $4v_1 - 3v_2 = 18$
   $v_1 + 2v_2 = -1$ $[v_1 = 3, v_2 = -2]$

2. $3m - 2n = -4.5$
   $4m + 3n = 2.5$ $[m = -\frac{1}{2}, n = 1\frac{1}{2}]$

3. $\dfrac{a}{3} + \dfrac{b}{4} = 8$

   $\dfrac{a}{6} - \dfrac{b}{8} = 1$ $[a = 15, b = 12]$

4. $s + t = 17$

   $\dfrac{s}{5} - \dfrac{t}{7} = 1$ $[s = 10, t = 7]$

5. $\dfrac{c}{5} + \dfrac{d}{3} = \dfrac{43}{30}$

 $\dfrac{c}{9} - \dfrac{d}{6} = -\dfrac{1}{12}$ $[c = 3, d = 2\frac{1}{2}]$

6. $0.5i_1 - 1.2i_2 = -13$
 $0.8i_1 + 0.3i_2 = 12.5$ $[i_1 = 10, i_2 = 15]$

7. $1.25L_1 - 0.75L_2 = 1$
 $0.25L_1 + 1.25L_2 = 17$ $[L_1 = 8.0, L_2 = 12.0]$

8. $\dfrac{1}{2a} + \dfrac{3}{5b} = 7$

 $\dfrac{4}{a} + \dfrac{1}{2b} = 13$ $[a = \frac{1}{2}, b = \frac{1}{10}]$

9. $\dfrac{3}{v_1} - \dfrac{2}{v_2} = \frac{1}{2}$

 $\dfrac{5}{v_1} + \dfrac{3}{v_2} = \dfrac{29}{12}$ $[v_1 = 3, v_2 = 4]$

10. $\dfrac{4}{p_1 - p_2} = \dfrac{16}{21}$

 $\dfrac{3}{p_1 + p_2} = \dfrac{4}{9}$ $[p_1 = 6, p_2 = \frac{3}{4}]$

11. $\dfrac{2x + 1}{5} - \dfrac{1 - 4y}{2} = \dfrac{5}{2}$

 $\dfrac{1 - 3x}{7} + \dfrac{2y - 3}{5} + \dfrac{32}{35} = 0$ $[x = 2, y = 1]$

12. A vector system to determine the shortest distance between two moving bodies is analysed, producing the following equations:

 $11S_1 - 10S_2 = 30$
 $21S_2 - 20S_1 = -40$

 Use determinants to find the values of S_1 and S_2.

 $[S_1 = 7.42, S_2 = 5.16]$

13. The power in a mechanical device is given by $p = aN + \dfrac{b}{N}$ where a and b are constants. Use determinants to find the value of a and b if $p = 13$ when $N = 3$ and $p = 12$ when $N = 2$.

 $[a = 3, b = 12]$

14. The law connecting friction F and load L for an experiment to find the friction force between two surfaces is of the type $F = aL + b$, where a and b are constants.

When $F = 6.0$, $L = 7.5$ and when $F = 2.7$, $L = 2.0$.
Find the values of a and b by using determinants.

$$[a = 0.60, b = 1.5]$$

15. The length L metres of an alloy at temperature $t°C$ is given by:
$L = L_0 (1 + \alpha t)$, where L_0 and α are constants.
Use determinants to find the values of L_0 and α if $L = 20$ m when t is
$52°C$ and $L = 21$ m when $t = 100°C$.

$$[L_0 = 18.92 \text{ m}, \alpha = 0.001\ 1]$$

The inverse of a matrix

In Problems 16 to 20, find the inverse of the matrices given.

16. $\begin{pmatrix} 2 & -1 \\ -5 & -1 \end{pmatrix}$ $\left[\begin{pmatrix} \frac{1}{7} & -\frac{1}{7} \\ -\frac{5}{7} & -\frac{2}{7} \end{pmatrix} \right]$

17. $\begin{pmatrix} 1 & -3 \\ 1 & 7 \end{pmatrix}$ $\left[\begin{pmatrix} \frac{7}{10} & \frac{3}{10} \\ -\frac{1}{10} & \frac{1}{10} \end{pmatrix} \right]$

18. $\begin{pmatrix} 3 & 5 \\ -2 & 1 \end{pmatrix}$ $\left[\begin{pmatrix} \frac{1}{13} & -\frac{5}{13} \\ \frac{2}{13} & \frac{3}{13} \end{pmatrix} \right]$

19. $\begin{pmatrix} -2 & -1 \\ 4 & 3 \end{pmatrix}$ $\left[\begin{pmatrix} -\frac{3}{2} & -\frac{1}{2} \\ 2 & 1 \end{pmatrix} \right]$

20. $\begin{pmatrix} -4 & -3 \\ 5 & 3 \end{pmatrix}$ $\left[\begin{pmatrix} 1 & 1 \\ -\frac{5}{3} & -\frac{4}{3} \end{pmatrix} \right]$

The solution of simultaneous equations having two unknowns using matrices

In Problems 21 to 26, solve the simultaneous equations given by using matrices.

21. $p + 3q = 11$
$p + 2q = 8$ $[p = 2, q = 3]$

22. $3a + 4b - 5 = 0$
$12 = 5b - 2a$ $[a = -1, b = 2]$

23. $\dfrac{m}{3} + \dfrac{n}{4} = 6$

$\dfrac{m}{6} - \dfrac{n}{8} = 0$ $[m = 9, n = 12]$

24. $4a - 6b + 2.5 = 0$
$7a - 5b + 0.25 = 0$ $[a = \frac{1}{2}, b = \frac{3}{4}]$

25. $\dfrac{x}{8} + \dfrac{5}{2} = y$

$13 - \dfrac{y}{3} - 3x = 0$ $[x = 4, y = 3]$

26. $\dfrac{a-1}{3} + \dfrac{b+2}{2} = 3$

$\dfrac{1-a}{6} + \dfrac{4-b}{2} = \frac{1}{2}$ $[a = 4, b = 2]$

27. When determining the relative velocity of a system, the following equations are produced:

$3.0 = 0.10\, v_1 + (v_1 - v_2)$
$-2.0 = 0.05\, v_2 - (v_1 - v_2)$

Use matrices to find the values of v_1 and v_2.

$[v_1 = 7.42, v_2 = 5.16]$

28. Applying Newton's laws of motion to a mechanical system gives the following equations:

$14 = 0.2u + 2u + 8\,(u - v)$
$0 = -8\,(u - v) + 2v + 10v$

Use matrices to find the values of u and v.

$[u = 2.0, v = 0.8]$

29. Equations connecting the lens system in a position transducer are:

$\dfrac{4}{u_1} + \dfrac{6}{v_1} + \dfrac{9}{v_2} = 6$

$\dfrac{15}{u_1} + \dfrac{11}{v_1} + \dfrac{2}{v_2} = 8\tfrac{1}{12}$

If $v_1 = v_2$, use matrices to find the values of u_1, v_1 and v_2.

$[u_1 = 4, v_1 = v_2 = 3]$

30. When an effort E is applied to the gearbox on a diesel motor it is found that a resistance R can be overcome and that E and R are connected by a formula: $E = a + b\,R$ where a and b are constants. An effort of 3.5 newtons overcomes a resistance of 5 newtons and an effort of 5.3 newtons overcomes a resistance of 8 newtons. Use matrices to find the values of a and b.

$[a = 0.50, b = 0.60]$

Chapter 10

Complex numbers

1 Introduction

The solutions of the quadratic equation $ax^2 + bx + c = 0$ may be obtained by using the quadratic formula:

$$x = \frac{-b \pm \sqrt{(b^2 - 4ac)}}{2a}$$

Hence the solutions of $2x^2 + x - 3 = 0$ are

$$x = \frac{-1 \pm \sqrt{[1^2 - 4(2)(-3)]}}{2(2)}$$

$$= \frac{-1 \pm \sqrt{25}}{4} = -\frac{1}{4} \pm \frac{5}{4}$$

i.e. $x = 1$ or $x = -1\frac{1}{2}$.

However, a problem exists if $(b^2 - 4ac)$ in the quadratic formula results in a negative number, since we cannot obtain in real terms the square root of a negative number. The only numbers we have met to date have been real numbers. These are either integers (such as $+1$, $+5$, -7, etc.) or rational numbers (such as $\frac{4}{1}$ or 4.000, $-\frac{7}{9}$ or $-0.7\dot{7}$, $\frac{1}{2}$ or 0.500 0, etc.) or irrational numbers (such as $\pi = 3.141\ 592\ldots$, $\sqrt{3} = 1.732\ldots$, etc.)

If $x^2 - 2x + 5 = 0$, then $x = \dfrac{2 \pm \sqrt{[(-2)^2 - 4(1)(5)]}}{2\,(1)}$

$$= \dfrac{2 \pm \sqrt{-16}}{2}$$

In order to deal with such a problem as determining $\sqrt{-16}$ the concept of complex numbers has been evolved.

2 Definition of a complex number

(a) Imaginary numbers

Let b and c be real numbers. An imaginary number is written in the form jb or jc (i.e. $j \times b$ or $j \times c$) where operator j is defined by the following two rules:

(i) For addition, $jb + jc = j(b + c)$ **(1)**

(ii) For multiplication, $jb \times jc = -bc$ **(2)**

        i.e. $j^2 bc = -bc$

        Thus $j^2 = -1$

        or $j = \sqrt{-1}$.

It is immaterial whether the operator j is placed in front of, or after, the number, i.e. $j4 = 4j$, and so on. An imaginary number $j3$ means $(\sqrt{-1}) \times 3$ and $-j2$ means $-(\sqrt{-1}) \times 2$ or $(-2) \times (\sqrt{-1})$.

Similarly, from equation (1), $j2 + j5 = j7$

and $j5 - j2 = j3$.

(b) Complex numbers

From section 1, $x^2 - 2x + 5 = 0$

and $x = \dfrac{2 \pm \sqrt{-16}}{2}$

$\sqrt{-16}$ can be split into $(\sqrt{-1}) \times \sqrt{16}$, i.e. $j\sqrt{16}$ or $\pm j4$.

Hence $x = \dfrac{2 \pm j4}{2} = 1 \pm j2$

i.e. $x = 1 + j2$ or $x = 1 - j2$.

The solutions of the quadratic equation $x^2 - 2x + 5 = 0$ are of the form $a + jb$, where 'a' is a real number and 'jb' an imaginary number. Numbers in the form $a + jb$ are called complex numbers. Hence $1 + j2$, $5 - j7$, $-2 + j3$ and $-\pi + j\sqrt{2}$ are all examples of complex numbers.

In algebra, if a quantity x is added to a quantity $3y$ the result is written as $x + 3y$ since x and y are separate quantities. Similarly, it is important to appreciate that real and imaginary numbers are different types of numbers and must be kept separate.

When imaginary numbers were first introduced the symbol i (i.e. the first letter of the word imaginary) was used to indicate $\sqrt{-1}$ and this symbol is still used in pure mathematics. However, in engineering, the symbol i indicates electric current, and to avoid any possible confusion the next letter in the alphabet, i.e. j, is used to represent $\sqrt{-1}$.

3 The Argand diagram

A complex number can be represented pictorially on rectangular or cartesian axes. The horizontal (or x) axis is used to represent the real axis and the vertical (or y) axis is used to represent the imaginary axis. Such a diagram is called an **Argand diagram** (named after an eighteenth-century French mathematician), and is shown in Fig. 1(a).

In Fig. 1(b) the point A represents the complex number $2 + j3$ and is obtained by plotting the coordinates $(2, j3)$ as in graphical work. Often an arrow is drawn from the origin to the point as shown. Figure 1(b) also shows the Argand points B, C and D representing the complex numbers $3 - j$, $-2 + j2$ and $-4 - j3$ respectively.

A complex number of the form $a + jb$ is called a **cartesian complex number**.

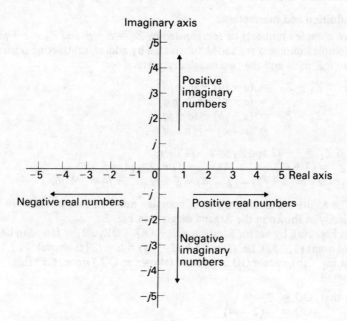

Figure 1(a) The Argand diagram

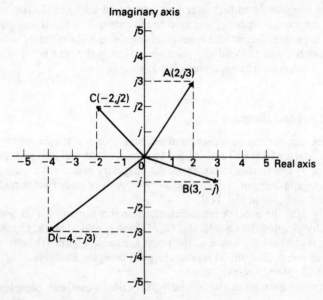

Figure 1(b) The Argand diagram

4 Operations involving cartesian complex numbers

(a) Addition and subtraction

Let two complex numbers be represented by $Z_1 = a + jb$ and $Z_2 = c + jd$.
Two complex numbers are added/subtracted by adding/subtracting separately
the two real parts and the two imaginary parts.

Hence $\quad Z_1 + Z_2 \quad = (a + jb) + (c + jd)$
$$= (a + c) + j(b + d)$$
and $\quad Z_1 - Z_2 \quad = (a + jb) - (c + jd)$
$$= (a - c) + j(b - d)$$

Thus, if $Z_1 = 3 + j2$ and $Z_2 = 2 - j4$ then:
$Z_1 + Z_2 = (3 + j2) + (2 - j4) = 3 + j2 + 2 - j4 = 5 - j2$
and $Z_1 - Z_2 = (3 + j2) - (2 - j4) = 3 + j2 - 2 + j4 = 1 + j6$.

The addition and subtraction of complex numbers may be achieved
graphically as shown in the Argand diagram in Fig. 2.

In Fig. 2(a), by vector addition, OP + OQ = OR$_1$. R$_1$ is found to be the
Argand point $(5, -j2)$, i.e. $(3 + j2) + (2 - j4) = 5 - j2$ (as above).

In Fig. 2(b), vector OQ is reversed (shown as OQ′) since it is being
subtracted.

(Note that $\quad$ OQ $= 2 - j4$
Thus $\quad -$OQ $= -(2 - j4)$
$$= -2 + j4, \text{ shown as OQ}′.)$$

Thus OP $-$ OQ $=$ OP $+$ OQ′ $=$ OR$_2$. R$_2$ is found to be the Argand point

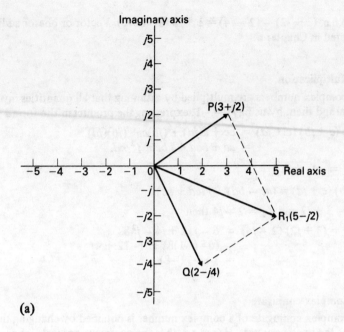

(a)

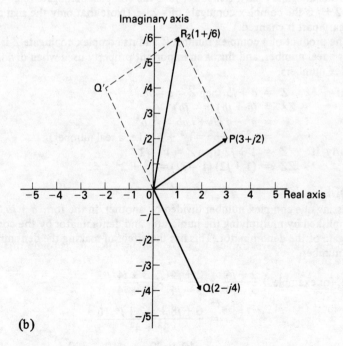

(b)

Figure 2 (a) OP + OQ = OR₁ (b) OP − OQ = OR₂

$(1, j6)$, i.e. $(3 + j2) - (2 - j4) = 1 + j6$ (as above). Vector or phasor addition is covered in Chapter 6.

(b) Multiplication

Two complex numbers are multiplied by assuming that all quantities involved are real and then, by using $j^2 = -1$, expressing the product in the form $a + jb$.

Hence $(a + jb)(c + jd) = ac + a(jd) + (jb)c + (jb)(jd)$
$$= ac + j\,ad + j\,bc + j^2\,bd.$$

But $j^2 = -1$, thus

$(a + jb)(c + jd) = (ac - bd) + j(ad + bc)$.

If $Z_1 = 3 + j2$ and $Z_2 = 2 - j4$ then

$$Z_1 Z_2 = (3 + j2)(2 - j4) = 6 - j12 + j4 - j^2 8$$
$$= (6 - (-1)8) + j(-12 + 4)$$
$$= 14 + j(-8)$$
$$= 14 - j8.$$

(c) Complex conjugate

The complex conjugate of a complex number is obtained by changing the sign of the imaginary part. Hence $a + jb$ is the complex conjugate of $a - jb$ and $-2 + j$ is the complex conjugate of $-2 - j$. (Note that only the sign of the imaginary part is changed.)

The product of a complex number Z and its complex conjugate Z is always a real number, and this is an important property used when dividing complex numbers.

Thus if $\quad Z = a + jb$ then $\bar{Z} = a - jb$
and $\quad\quad Z\bar{Z} = (a + jb)(a - jb)$
$$= a^2 - j\,ab + j\,ab - j^2\,b^2$$
$$= a^2 - -b^2 = a^2 + b^2 \text{ (i.e. a real number).}$$
Similarly, if $\quad Z = 1 + j2$ then $\bar{Z} = 1 - j2$
and $\quad\quad Z\bar{Z} = (1 + j2)(1 - j2) = 1^2 + 2^2 = 5.$

(d) Division

Expressing one complex number divided by another, in the form $a + jb$, is accomplished by multiplying the numerator and denominator by the complex conjugate of the denominator. This has the effect of making the denominator a real number.

Hence, for example, $\quad \dfrac{2 + j4}{3 - j4} = \dfrac{2 + j4}{3 - j4} \times \dfrac{3 + j4}{3 + j4}$

$$= \dfrac{6 + j8 + j12 + j^2\,16}{3^2 + 4^2}$$

$$= \dfrac{-10 + j20}{25} = \dfrac{-10}{25} + j\,\dfrac{20}{25} \text{ or } -0.4 + j\,0.8.$$

(e) Complex equations

If two complex numbers are equal, then their real parts are equal and their imaginary parts are equal.

Hence, if $a + jb = c + jd$
then $a = c$ and $b = d$.

This is a useful property, since equations having two unknown quantities can be solved from one equation (see worked problem 4 following).

Worked problems on operations involving cartesian complex numbers

Problem 1. Solve the following quadratic equations:
  (a) $x^2 + 9 = 0$.
  (b) $4y^2 - 3y + 5 = 0$.

(a) $x^2 + 9 = 0$.
  $x^2 = -9$.
  $x = \sqrt{-9} = (\sqrt{-1})(\sqrt{9}) = (\sqrt{-1})(\pm 3) = (j)(\pm 3) = \pm j3$.
(b) $4y^2 - 3y + 5 = 0$.
Using the quadratic formula:

$$y = \frac{-(-3) \pm \sqrt{[(-3)^2 - 4(4)(5)]}}{2(4)} = \frac{3 \pm \sqrt{(9 - 80)}}{8}$$

$$= \frac{3 \pm \sqrt{-71}}{8} = \frac{3 \pm (\sqrt{-1})(\sqrt{71})}{8} = \frac{3 \pm j\sqrt{71}}{8}$$

$$= \frac{3}{8} \pm j\frac{\sqrt{71}}{8} = 0.375 \pm j1.053, \text{ correct to 3 decimal places.}$$

Problem 2. Evaluate: (a) j^3; (b) j^4; (c) j^5; (d) j^6; (e) j^7; (f) $\dfrac{3}{j^9}$

(a) $j = \sqrt{-1}$
  $j^2 = -1$
  $j^3 = j \times j^2 = (j)(-1) = -j$
(b) $j^4 = j \times j^3 = (j)(-j) = -j^2 = +1$
(c) $j^5 = j \times j^4 = (j) \times (1) = j$
(d) $j^6 = j \times j^5 = (j) \times (j) = j^2 = -1$
(e) $j^7 = j \times j^6 = (j) \times (-1) = -j$
(f) $j^9 = j^2 \times j^7 = (-1) \times (-j) = j$
Hence $\dfrac{3}{j^9} = \dfrac{3}{j} = \dfrac{3}{j} \times \dfrac{(-j)}{(-j)} = \dfrac{-j3}{-j^2} = \dfrac{-j3}{+1} = -j3$.

Problem 3. If $Z_1 = 1 + j2, Z_2 = 2 - j3, Z_3 = -4 + j$ and $Z_4 = -3 - j2$ evaluate in $a + jb$ form the following:

(a) $Z_1 + Z_2 - Z_3$ (d) $\dfrac{Z_2}{Z_4}$

(b) $Z_1 Z_3$

(c) $Z_2 Z_3 Z_4$ (e) $\dfrac{Z_1 - Z_4}{Z_2 + Z_3}$

(a) $\begin{aligned}[t] Z_1 + Z_2 - Z_3 &= (1 + j2) + (2 - j3) - (-4 + j) \\ &= 1 + j2 + 2 - j3 + 4 - j \\ &= 7 - j2. \end{aligned}$

(b) $\begin{aligned}[t] Z_1 Z_3 &= (1 + j2)(-4 + j) \\ &= -4 + j - j8 + j^2 2 \\ &= -6 - j7. \end{aligned}$

(c) $\begin{aligned}[t] Z_2 Z_3 Z_4 &= (2 - j3)(-4 + j)(-3 - j2) \\ &= (-8 + j2 + j12 - j^2 3)(-3 - j2) \\ &= (-5 + j14)(-3 - j2) \\ &= 15 + j10 - j42 - j^2 28 \\ &= 43 - j32. \end{aligned}$

(d)
$$\begin{aligned} \frac{Z_2}{Z_4} &= \frac{2 - j3}{-3 - j2} \\[2mm] &= \frac{2 - j3}{-3 - j2} \times \frac{-3 + j2}{-3 + j2} \\[2mm] &= \frac{-6 + j4 + j9 - j^2 6}{3^2 + 2^2} \\[2mm] &= \frac{0 + j13}{13} \\[2mm] &= 0 + j1 \text{ or } j. \end{aligned}$$

(e)
$$\begin{aligned} \frac{Z_1 - Z_4}{Z_2 + Z_3} &= \frac{(1 + j2) - (-3 - j2)}{(2 - j3) + (-4 + j)} \\[2mm] &= \frac{4 + j4}{-2 - j2} \\[2mm] &= \frac{4(1 + j)}{-2(1 + j)} \\[2mm] &= -2. \end{aligned}$$

Problem 4. Solve the following complex equations:
(a) $3(a + jb) = 9 - j2$
(b) $(2 + j)(-2 + j) = x + jy$
(c) $(a - j2b) + (b - j3a) = 5 + j2.$

(a) $3(a + jb) = 9 - j2$.

$3a + j3b = 9 - j2$.

Equating real parts gives: $3a = 9$, i.e. $a = 3$

Equating imaginary parts gives: $3b = -2$, i.e. $b = -\frac{2}{3}$.

(b) $(2 + j)(-2 + j) = x + jy$

$-4 + j2 - j2 + j^2 = x + jy$

$-5 + j0 = x + jy$

Equating real and imaginary parts gives:

$x = -5, y = 0$.

(c) $(a - j2b) + (b - j3a) = 5 + j2$

$(a + b) + j(-2b - 3a) = 5 + j2$

Hence $a + b = 5$ (1)

and $-2b - 3a = 2$ (2)

We have two simultaneous equations to solve.

Multiplying equation (1) by 2 gives:

$2a + 2b = 10$ (3)

Adding equations (2) and (3) gives:

$-a = 12$, i.e $a = -12$.

From equation (1) $b = 17$.

Further problems on operations involving cartesian complex numbers may be found in Section 9 (Problems 1–23), p. 192.

5   The polar form of a complex number

Let a complex number Z, in cartesian form, be $x + jy$. This is shown in the Argand diagram of Fig. 3(a). Let r be the distance OZ and θ the angle OZ makes with the positive real axis.

From the trigonometry, $\cos \theta = \dfrac{x}{r}$, i.e. $x = r \cos \theta$

and $\sin \theta = \dfrac{y}{r}$, i.e. $y = r \sin \theta$

$Z = x + jy$

$\quad = r \cos \theta + j r \sin \theta$

$\quad = r(\cos \theta + j \sin \theta)$.

This latter form is usually abbreviated to $Z = r \angle \theta$, and is called the polar form of a complex number. The complex number is now specified in terms of r and θ instead of x and y.

r is called the **modulus** (or magnitude of Z and is written as mod Z or $|Z|$. r is determined from Pythagoras's theorem on triangle OAZ,

i.e. $|Z| = r = \sqrt{(x^2 + y^2)}$.

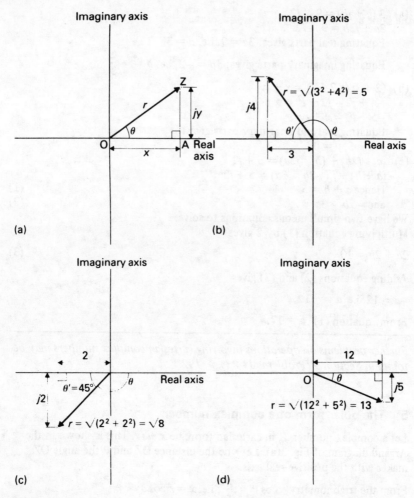

(a)

(b)

(c)

(d)

Figure 3

The modulus is represented on the Argand diagram by the distance OZ. θ is called the **argument** (or amplitude) of Z and is written as arg Z. θ is also deduced from triangle OAZ, giving $\text{arg } Z = \theta = \arctan \dfrac{y}{x}$.

In Fig. 3(a) the Argand point Z is shown in the first quadrant. However, the above results apply to any point in the Argand diagram.

By convention, the principal value of θ is used, i.e. the numerically least value such that $-\pi \leqslant \theta \leqslant \pi$. For example, in Fig. 3(b), $\theta' = \arctan \dfrac{4}{3} = 53° \, 8'$. Hence $\theta = 180° - 53° \, 8' = 126° \, 52'$. Therefore $-3 + j4 = 5 \angle 126° \, 52'$. Similarly, in Fig. 3(c), θ is $180° - 45°$, i.e. $135°$ measured in the negative direction. Hence $-2 - j2 = \sqrt{8} \angle -135°$. (This is the same as $\sqrt{8} \angle 225°$. However, the principal value of $\sqrt{8} \angle -135°$ is normally used.) In Fig. 3(d), $\theta = \arctan \dfrac{5}{12} = 22° \ 37'$. Hence $12 - j5 = 13 \angle -22° \ 37'$.

Whenever changing from a cartesian form of complex number to a polar form, or vice versa, a sketch is invaluable for deciding the quadrant in which the complex number occurs. There are always two possible values of $\theta = \arctan \dfrac{y}{x}$, only one of which is correct for a particular complex number.

6 Multiplication and division using complex numbers in polar form

An important use of the polar form of a complex number is in multiplication and division which is achieved more easily than with cartesian form.

(a) Multiplication

Let $\quad Z_1 = r_1 \angle \theta_1$ and $Z_2 = r_2 \angle \theta_2$

$$
\begin{aligned}
\text{Then } Z_1 Z_2 &= [r_1 \angle \theta_1] \ [r_2 \angle \theta_2] \\
&= [r_1 (\cos \theta_1 + j \sin \theta_1)] \times [r_2 (\cos \theta_2 + j \sin \theta_2)] \\
&= r_1 r_2 (\cos \theta_1 \ \cos \theta_2 + j \sin \theta_2 \ \cos \theta_1 + j \cos \theta_2 \ \sin \theta_1 \\
&\qquad\qquad\qquad\qquad\qquad\qquad\qquad\qquad + j^2 \sin \theta_1 \ \sin \theta_2) \\
&= r_1 r_2 [(\cos \theta_1 \ \cos \theta_2 - \sin \theta_1 \ \sin \theta_2) \\
&\qquad\qquad\qquad\qquad + j (\sin \theta_1 \ \cos \theta_2 + \cos \theta_1 \ \sin \theta_2)] \\
&= r_1 r_2 [\cos (\theta_1 + \theta_2) + j \sin (\theta_1 + \theta_2)] \\
&= r_1 r_2 \angle (\theta_1 + \theta_2).
\end{aligned}
$$

Hence to obtain the product of complex numbers in polar form their moduli are multiplied together and their arguments are added. This result is true for all polar complex numbers.

Thus $3 \angle 25° \times 2 \angle 32° = 6 \angle 57°$,

$4 \angle 11° \times 5 \angle -18° = 20 \angle -7°$,

and $2 \angle \dfrac{\pi}{3} \times 7 \angle \dfrac{\pi}{6} = 14 \angle \dfrac{\pi}{2}$, and so on.

(b) Division

Let $Z_1 = r_1 \angle \theta_1$ and $Z_2 = r_2 \angle \theta_2$.

$$
\begin{aligned}
\text{Then } \frac{Z_1}{Z_2} &= \frac{r_1 \angle \theta_1}{r_2 \angle \theta_2} = \frac{r_1 (\cos \theta_1 + j \sin \theta_1)}{r_2 (\cos \theta_2 + j \sin \theta_2)} \\
&= \frac{r_1 (\cos \theta_1 + j \sin \theta_1)}{r_2 (\cos \theta_2 + j \sin \theta_2)} \times \frac{(\cos \theta_2 - j \sin \theta_2)}{(\cos \theta_2 - j \sin \theta_2)} \\
&= \frac{r_1 (\cos \theta_1 \ \cos \theta_2 - j \sin \theta_2 \ \cos \theta_1 + j \sin \theta_1 \ \cos \theta_2 - j^2 \sin \theta_1 \ \sin \theta_2)}{r_2 (\cos^2 \theta_2 + \sin^2 \theta_2)}
\end{aligned}
$$

$$= \frac{r_1 \left[(\cos\theta_1 \cos\theta_2 + \sin\theta_1 \sin\theta_2) + j(\sin\theta_1 \cos\theta_2 - \sin\theta_2 \cos\theta_1) \right]}{r_2} \quad (1)$$

$$= \frac{r_1}{r_2} \left[\cos(\theta_1 - \theta_2) + j\sin(\theta_1 - \theta_2) \right] \text{ (from compound angle formulae)}$$

$$= \frac{r_1}{r_2} \angle (\theta_1 - \theta_2)$$

Hence to obtain the ratio of two complex numbers in polar form their moludi are divided and their arguments subtracted. This result is true for all polar complex numbers.

Thus $\dfrac{8 \angle 58°}{2 \angle 11°} = 4 \angle 47°,$

$$\frac{9 \angle 136°}{3 \angle -60°} = 3 \angle (136° - -60°) = 3 \angle 196° = 3 \angle -164°,$$

and $\dfrac{10 \times \frac{\pi}{2}}{5 \angle -\frac{\pi}{4}} = 2 \angle \dfrac{3\pi}{4}$, and so on.

Worked problems on the polar form of complex numbers

Problem 1. Determine the moludus and argument of the complex number $Z = -5 + j8$ and express Z in polar form.

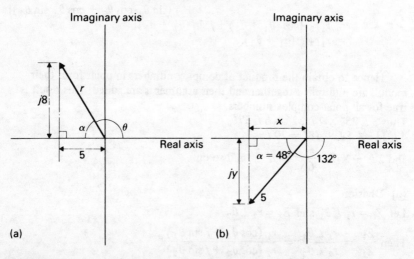

(a) (b)

Figure 4

A sketch, shown in Fig. 4(a), indicates that the complex number $-5 + j8$ lies in the second quadrant of the Argand diagram.

Modulus, $|Z| = r = \sqrt{[(-5)^2 + (8)^2]} = \mathbf{9.434}$, correct to 4 significant figures.

$\alpha = \arctan \dfrac{8}{5} = \mathbf{58°}$.

Argument, arg $Z = \theta = 180° - 58° = 122°$.

In polar form $-5 + j8$ is written as $\mathbf{9.434 \angle 122°}$.

Problem 2. Convert $5 \angle -132°$ into $a + jb$ form correct to 4 significant figures.

A sketch, shown in Fig. 4(b), indicates that the polar complex number $5 \angle -132°$ lies in the third quadrant of the Argand diagram.

Using trigonometrical ratios, $x = 5 \cos 48° = 3.346$
and $\quad y = 5 \sin 48° = 3.716$.

Hence $5 \angle -132° = \mathbf{-3.346 - j3.716}$.

Problem 3. Evaluate (a) $\dfrac{15 \angle 30° \times 8 \angle 45°}{4 \angle 60°}$

and (b) $4 \angle 30° + 3 \angle -60° - 5 \angle -135°$

giving answers in polar and in cartesian forms, correct to 3 significant figures.

(a) $\dfrac{15 \angle 30° \times 8 \angle 45°}{4 \angle 60°} = \dfrac{15 \times 8}{4} \angle (30° + 45° - 60°)$

$$= \mathbf{30.0 \angle 15°} \quad \text{polar form}$$
$$= 30.0 (\cos 15° + j \sin 15°)$$
$$= \mathbf{29.0 + j7.76} \quad \text{cartesian form.}$$

(b) $4 \angle 30° + 3 \angle -60° - 5 \angle -135°$.

The advantages of polar form are seen when multiplying and dividing complex numbers. Addition or subtraction in polar form is not possible. Each polar complex number has to be converted into cartesian form first. Thus

$4 \angle 30° = 4 (\cos 30° + j \sin 30°) = 4 \cos 30° + j 4 \sin 30° = 3.464 + j2.000$
$3 \angle 60° = 3 [\cos (-60°) + j \sin (-60°)] = 3 \cos 60° - j 3 \sin 60°$
$\qquad\qquad = 1.500 - j2.598$
$5 \angle -135° = 5 [\cos (-135°) + j \sin (-135°)] = 5 \cos (-135°) + j 5 \sin (-135°)$
$\qquad\qquad = -5 \cos 45° - j 5 \sin 45° = -3.536 - j3.536$
Hence $4 \angle 30° + 3 \angle -60° - 5 \angle -135° = (3.464 + j2.000) + (1.500 - j2.598)$
$\qquad\qquad\qquad\qquad\qquad\qquad\qquad\qquad\qquad - (-3.536 - j3.536)$

$= \mathbf{8.50 + j2.94} \quad \text{cartesian form}$

$= \sqrt{[(8.50)^2 + (2.94)^2]} \angle \arctan \dfrac{2.94}{8.50}$,

since the complex number is in the first quadrant

$= \mathbf{8.99 \angle 19° 5'} \quad \text{polar form}$

---

*Further problems on the polar form of complex numbers may be found in
Section 9 (Problems 24–38), p. 193.*

7 De Moivre's theorem – powers and roots of complex numbers

From Section 6, $r \angle \theta \times r \angle \theta = r^2 \angle 2\theta$
$r \angle \theta \times r \angle \theta \times r \angle \theta = r^3 \angle 3\theta$, and so on.

Such results are generally stated in de Moivre's theorem, which may be
stated as:

$$[r \angle \theta]^n = r^n \angle n\theta \; (= r^n (\cos n\theta + j \sin n\theta)).$$

This result is true for all positive, negative or fractional values of n. De
Moivre's theorem is thus useful in determining powers and roots of complex
numbers.

For example, $[2 \angle 15°]^6 = 2^6 \angle (6 \times 15°) = 64 \angle 90° = 0 + j\,64$.

A square root of a complex number is determined as follows:

$$\sqrt{[r \angle \theta]} = [r \angle \theta]^{\frac{1}{2}} = r^{\frac{1}{2}} \angle \tfrac{1}{2}\theta.$$

However, it is important to realise that a real number has two square
roots, equal in size but opposite in sign. On an Argand diagram the roots are
180° apart (see worked problem 3).

Worked problems on powers and roots of complex numbers

Problem 1. Determine the square of the complex number $3 - j4$ (a) in cartesian
form and (b) in polar form, using de Moivre's theorem. Compare the results
obtained and show the roots on an Argand diagram.

(a) In cartesian form, $(3 - j4)^2 = (3-j4)(3-j4) = 9 - j12 - j12 + j^2 16$
$$= -7 - j24.$$

(b) In polar form, $(3-j4) = \sqrt{[(3)^2 + (4)^2]} \angle \arctan \dfrac{4}{3}$ (see Fig. 5)
$$= 5 \angle -53° \, 8'.$$
$[5 \angle -53° \, 8']^2 = 5^2 \angle (2 \times -53° \, 8') = 25 \angle -106° \, 16'$

The complex number $(3 - j4)$, together with its square, i.e. $(3-j4)^2$, is
shown in Fig. 5.
$25 \angle -106° \, 16'$ in cartesian form is
$25 \cos (-106° \, 16') + j\, 25 \sin (-106° \, 16')$, i.e. $-7 - j24$, as in part (a).

Problem 2. Determine $(-2 + j3)^5$ in polar and in cartesian form.

$Z = -2 + j3$ is situated in the second quadrant of the Argand diagram.
Thus $r = \sqrt{[(2)^2 + (3)^2]} = \sqrt{13}$

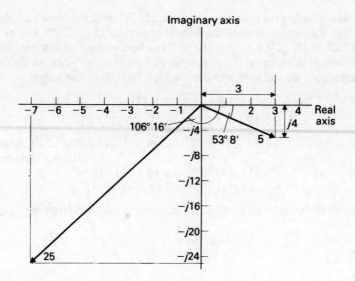

Figure 5

and $\alpha = \arctan \dfrac{3}{2} = 56° \ 19'$

Hence the argument $\theta = 180° - 56° \ 19' = 123° \ 41'$.
Thus $2 - j3$ in polar form is $\sqrt{13} \angle 123° \ 41'$.

$(-2 + j3)^5 = [\sqrt{13} \angle 123° \ 41']^5 = (\sqrt{13})^5 \angle (5 \times 123° \ 41')$, from de

Moivre's theorem

$\qquad = 13^{\frac{5}{2}} \angle 618° \ 25'$

$\qquad = 13^{\frac{5}{2}} \angle 258° \ 25'$
$\qquad$ (since $618° \ 25' = 618° \ 25' - 360°$)

$\qquad = 13^{\frac{5}{2}} \angle -101° \ 35'$
$\qquad = \mathbf{609.3 \angle -101° \ 35'}$.

In cartesian form

$609.3 \angle -101° \ 35' = 609.3 \cos (-101° \ 35') + j \ 609.3 \sin (-101° \ 35')$
$\qquad\qquad\qquad = \mathbf{-122.3 - j \ 596.9}$.

Problem 3. Determine the two square roots of the complex number $12 + j5$ in cartesian and polar form, correct to 3 significant figures. Show the roots on an Argand diagram.

In polar form $12 + j5 = \sqrt{(12^2 + 5^2)} \angle \arctan \dfrac{5}{12}$, since $12 + j5$ is in the

first quadrant of the Argand diagram,

i.e. $12 + j5 = 13 \angle 22° \ 37'$.

184

Since we are finding the square roots of $13 \angle 22° 37'$ there will be two solutions. To obtain the second solution it is helpful to express $13 \angle 22° 37'$ also as $13 \angle (360° + 22° 37')$, i.e. $13 \angle 382° 37'$ (we have merely rotated one revolution to obtain this result). The reason for doing this is that when we divide the angles by 2 we still obtain angles less than $360°$, as shown bleow.

$$
\begin{aligned}
\text{Hence } \sqrt{(12 + j5)} &= \sqrt{[13 \angle 22° 37']} \text{ or } \sqrt{[13 \angle 382° 37']} \\
&= [13 \angle 22° 37']^{\frac{1}{2}} \text{ or } [13 \angle 382° 37']^{\frac{1}{2}} \\
&= 13^{\frac{1}{2}} \angle (\tfrac{1}{2} \times 22° 37') \text{ or } 13^{\frac{1}{2}} \angle (\tfrac{1}{2} \times 382° 37'), \text{ from de} \\
&\qquad\qquad\qquad\qquad\qquad\qquad\qquad\qquad\qquad\quad \text{Moivre's theorem,} \\
&= \sqrt{13} \angle 11° 19' \text{ or } \sqrt{13} \angle 191° 19' \\
&= 3.61 \angle 11° 19' \text{ or } 3.61 \angle -168° 41'.
\end{aligned}
$$

These two solutions of $\sqrt{(12 + j5)}$ are shown in the Argand diagram of Fig. 6.

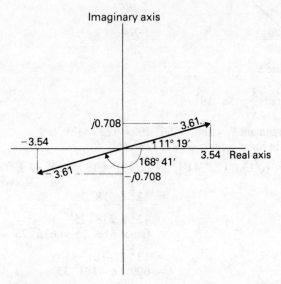

Figure 6

$3.61 \angle 11° 19'$ is in the first quadrant of the Argand diagram.
Thus $3.61 \angle 11° 19' = 3.61 (\cos 11° 19' + j \sin 11° 19') = 3.54 + j\, 0.708$
$3.61 \angle -168° 41'$ is in the third quadrant of the Argand diagram.
Thus $3.61 \angle -168° 41' = 3.61 [\cos (-168° 41') + j \sin (-168° 41')]$
$$= -3.54 - j0.708.$$
Thus in cartesian form the two roots are $\pm\ (\mathbf{3.54 + j\ 0.708}).$

From the Argand diagram the roots are seen to be $180°$ apart, i.e. they lie on a straight line. This is always true when finding square roots of complex numbers.

8. Applications of complex numbers

Complex numbers are widely used in the analysis of electrical circuits supplied by an alternating voltage and can also be used for solving problems involving coplanar vectors.

(a) Phasor applications to series connected circuits

In an electrical circuit containing resistance only (R ohms), the current (I amperes) is in phase with the applied voltage (V volts) and the ratio of voltage to current is given by $\frac{V}{I} = R$. When an electrical circuit contains inductance only (L henrys), the ratio of voltage to current is called the inductive reactance, (X_L ohms), and

$$\frac{V}{I} = X_L = 2\pi f L \text{ ohms} \tag{1}$$

where f is the frequency in hertz of the applied voltage. The current in a purely inductive circuit lags 90° behind the applied voltage.

When both resistance and inductance are present, as shown in Fig. 7(a), the phasor diagram, (a phasor is a rotating vector), is as shown in Fig. 7(b).

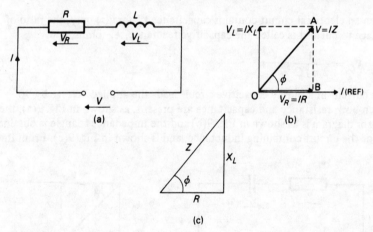

Figure 7

The ratio of $\frac{V}{I}$ in any a.c. electrical circuit containing both resistance and reactance is called the **impedance** Z of the circuit and is measured in ohms. With reference to triangle OAB in Fig. 7(b), the impedance triangle shown in Fig. 7(c) is produced by dividing each quantity by current I. From the impedance triangle, it can be seen that:

modulus of impedance, $\qquad |Z| = \sqrt{(R^2 + X_L^2)} \text{ ohms} \tag{2}$

and circuit phase angle, $\phi = \arctan \dfrac{X_L}{R}$ (3)

If the impedance triangle is superimposed on an Argand diagram as shown in Fig. 8, then:

impedance, $Z = (R + j X_L)$ ohms (4)

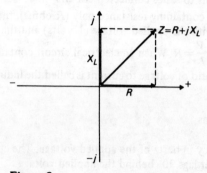

Figure 8

When an electrical circuit contains capacitance (C farads) only, the ratio of voltage to current is called the capacitive reactance, X_C ohms, and

$$\frac{V}{I} = X_C = \frac{1}{2 \pi f C} \text{ ohms}$$ (5)

The current in a purely capacitive circuit leads the applied voltage by $90°$. When both resistance and capacitance are present, as shown in Fig. 9(a), the phasor diagram is as shown in Fig. 9(b) and the impedance triangle is obtained, as for the circuit containing inductance, and is shown in Fig. 9(c). From the

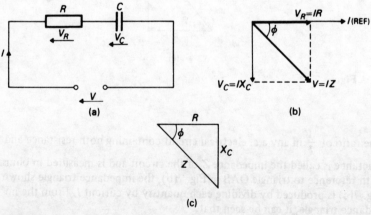

Figure 9

impedance triangle, it can be seen that:

modulus of impedance, $\quad |Z| = (R^2 + X_C^2)$ ohms $\qquad$ (6)

and circuit phase angle, $\quad \phi = \arctan \dfrac{X_C}{R}$ $\qquad$ (7)

If the impedance triangle is superimposed on an Argand diagram, as shown in Fig. 10:

impedance, $Z = R - j X_C$ $\qquad$ (8)

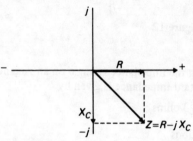

Figure 10

For an electrical circuit containing resistance, inductance and capacitance connected in series, the circuit diagram is as shown in Fig. 11(a), the phasor diagram is as shown in Fig. 11(b) and the impedance triangle is as shown in Fig. 11(c).

From the impedance triangle, it can be seen that:

modulus of impedance, $\quad |Z| = \sqrt{[R^2 + (X_L - X_C)^2]}$ ohms $\qquad$ (9)

and circuit phase angle, $\quad \phi = \arctan \dfrac{X_L - X_C}{R}$ $\qquad$ (10)

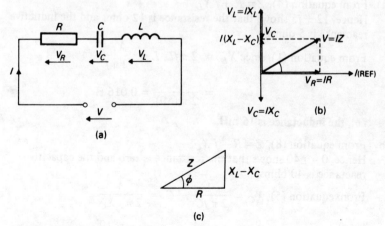

Figure 11

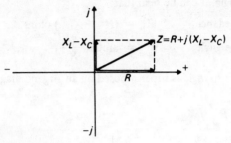

Figure 12

When superimposing the impedance triangle on an Argand diagram, as shown in Fig. 12, the resultant impedance is given by

$$Z = R + j(X_L - X_C) \text{ ohms} \tag{11}$$

(b) Vector applications

Problems involving coplanar vector quantities, such as those dealing with displacement, velocity, acceleration, force, moment and momentum may be resolved using complex number theory. Examples of the application of complex number theory to such problems are shown in worked Problems 5 to 7.

Worked problems on the applications of complex numbers

Problem 1. Determine the resistance and the series connected inductance or capacitance for each of the following impedances:
(a) $12 + j5$, (b) $-j40$ and (c) $30 \angle 60°$.
Assume a frequency of 50 Hz.

(a) From equation (4), $Z = R + jX_L$
Hence, $12 + j5$ shows that the **resistance is 12 ohms** and the inductive reactance is 5 ohms.

From equation (1), since $X_L = 2\pi fL$, $L = \dfrac{X_L}{2\pi f}$

$$= \frac{5}{2\pi(50)} = 0.016 \text{ H}$$

i.e., **the inductance is 16 mH.**

(b) From equation (8), $Z = R - jX_C$
Hence, $0 - j40$ shows that the **resistance is zero** and the capacitive reactance is 40 ohms.

From equation (5), $X_C = \dfrac{1}{2\pi fC}$, $C = \dfrac{1}{2\pi f X_C}$

$$= \frac{1}{2\pi(50)(40)} \text{ F} = \frac{10^6}{2\pi(50)(40)} \,\mu\text{F}$$

$$= 79.6 \ \mu F$$

i.e., **the capacitance is 79.6 μF.**

(c) $30 \angle 60° = 30 (\cos 60° + j \sin 60°) = 15 + j \ 25.98$
From equation (4), $15 + j \ 25.98$ shows that the **resistance is 15 ohms** and the inductive reactance is 25.98 ohms.

From equation (1), the inductance, $L = \dfrac{X_L}{2 \pi f}$

$$= \dfrac{25.98}{2 \pi (50)} = 0.0827 \text{ H,}$$

i.e., **the inductance is 82.7 mH.**

Problem 2. The impedance of an electrical circuit is $30 - j \ 50$ ohms. Determine (a) the resistance, (b) the capacitance, (c) the modulus of the impedance and (d) the current flowing, when the circuit is connected to a 240 V, 50 Hz supply.

(a) Since $Z = R - j \ X_C$, the **resistance is 30 ohms.**
(b) Since $Z = R - j \ X_C$, the capacitance reactance is 50 ohms.

From equation (5), capacitance, $C = \dfrac{1}{2 \pi f X_C} = \dfrac{10^6}{2 \pi (50)(50)} \mu F$

$$= 63.7 \ \mu F.$$

(c) The modulus of the impedance, $|Z| = \sqrt{[R^2 + (X_C)^2]} = \sqrt{[30^2 + (-50)^2]}$
$= \mathbf{58.31}$ **ohms.**

(d) From equation (7), the circuit phase angle, $\phi = \arctan \dfrac{X_C}{R} = \arctan \dfrac{50}{30}$
$= 59° \ 2'$. Since $Z = R - j \ X_C$, this angle is in the fourth quadrant, i.e., $-59° \ 2'$. Thus an alternative way of expressing the impedance is $Z = 58.31 \angle -59° \ 2'$.

The current flowing, $I = \dfrac{V}{Z} = \dfrac{240 \angle 0°}{58.31 \angle -59° \ 2'}$

$$= 4.116 \angle 59° \ 2'.$$

[Since the voltage is given as 240 volts, it is $240 + j \ 0$ volts in rectangular form and $240 \angle 0°$ volts in polar form.]

Problem 3. A series connected electrical circuit has a resistance of 32 ohms and an inductance of 0.15 H. It is connected to a 200 V, 50 Hz supply. Determine (a) the inductive reactance, (b) the impedance in rectangular and polar forms, (c) the current and the circuit phase angle, (d) the voltage drop across the resistor and (e) the voltage drop across the inductor.

(a) From equation (1), inductive reactance $X_L = 2 \pi fL$
$= 2 \pi (50)(0.15) = \mathbf{47.1}$ **ohms.**
(b) From equation (4), impedance, $Z = R + j \ X_L$

i.e., $Z = 32 + j\,47.1$.

Thus, from equation (2), $|Z| = \sqrt{(32^2 + 47.1^2)} = 57$ and from equation (3), circuit phase angle, $\phi = \arctan \dfrac{47.1}{32} = 55°\,48'$

Thus $Z = 57 \angle 55°\,48'$ **ohms**, in polar form.

(c) Current $I = \dfrac{V}{Z} = \dfrac{200 \angle 0°}{57 \angle 55°\,48'} = 3.51 \angle -55°\,48'$

i.e., **the current is 3.51 A lagging V by 55° 48'**.

(d) The voltage crop across the 32 ohm resistor, $V_R = IR$
$= (3.51 \angle -55°\,48')\,(32)$
$= 112.3 \angle -55°\,48'$ **volts**.

(e) The voltage crop across the 0.15 H inductor, $V_L = I X_L$
$= (3.51 \angle -55°\,48')\,(47.1 \angle 90°)$
$= 165.3 \angle 34°\,12'$ **volts**.

Problem 4. A 240 V, 50 Hz voltage is applied across a series connected circuit having a resistance of 12 Ω, an inductance of 0.10 H and a capacitance of 120 μF. Determine the current flowing in the circuit.

From equation (1), inductive reactance, $X_L = 2\,\pi\,fL$
$= 2\,\pi\,(50)\,0.10 = 31.4\,\Omega$

From equation (5), capacitance reactance, $X_C = \dfrac{1}{2\,\pi\,fC}$

$= \dfrac{10^6}{2\,\pi\,(50)(120)} = 26.5\,\Omega$

From equation (11), the impedance, $Z = R + j\,(X_L - X_C)$
$= 12 + j\,(31.4 - 26.5)$
$= 12 + j\,4.9$

In polar form $Z = \sqrt{(12^2 + 4.9^2)} \angle \arctan \dfrac{4.9}{12}$

$= 13 \angle 22°\,13'$ ohms.

Hence, current $I = \dfrac{V}{Z} = \dfrac{240 \angle 0°}{13 \angle 22°\,13'}$

$= 18.5 \angle -22°\,13'$ amperes.

i.e., **the current flowing is 18.5 amperes, lagging the voltage by 22° 13'**.

Problem 5. Coplanar forces of $(7 + jx)$ newtons, $(3 - j5)$ newtons and $(y + j3)$ newtons act on a body which is in equilibrium. Determine the values of the three forces, both in rectangular and polar co-ordinate forms.

Since the body is in equilibrium, the algebraic sum of the forces is zero, i.e.,

$(7 + jx) + (3 - j5) + (y + j3) = 0$ (1)

Also, since the resultant force is zero, then the horizontal and vertical components of the force are zero. It follows that the real and imaginary parts of equation (1) are zero. Thus:

$7 + 3 + y = 0$, i.e., $y = -10$

and $j(x - 5 + 3) = j(0)$, i.e., $x = 2$

Thus, the three forces are $(7 + j2)$, $(3 - j5)$ and $(-10 + j3)$.

In polar form, $(7 + j2) = \sqrt{(7^2 + 2^2)} \angle \arctan \frac{2}{7} = 7.280 \angle 15° \, 57'$

$$(3 - j5) = \sqrt{(3^2 + 5^2)} \angle \arctan -\frac{5}{3} = 5.831 \angle -59° \, 2'$$

$$(-10 + j3) = \sqrt{(10^2 + 3^2)} \angle \arctan -\frac{3}{10} = 10.440 \angle 163° \, 18'$$

Problem 6. The velocity of ship A is $(4 - j5)$ knots and that of ship B is $(-6 - j6)$ knots. Find the magnitude and direction of the velocity of ship B relative to ship A.

Let v_A be the velocity of ship A, i.e., $v_A = (4 - j5)$ and let v_B be the velocity of ship B, i.e., $v_B = (-6 - j6)$. The velocity of B relative to A is $v_B - v_A$.

$v_B - v_A = (-6 - j6) - (4 - j5)$

$= -10 - j = \sqrt{(10^2 + 1^2)} \angle \arctan \frac{-1}{-10} = 10.05 \angle 185° \, 43'$

Thus, the magnitude of the velocity of B relative to A is **10.05 knots** and the direction of B relative to A is **185° 43'**.

Problem 7. A projectile is given an initial velocity of $u = (21 + j8)$ m/s. Determine, (a) the magnitude and direction of its velocity and (b) the distance and direction relative to the origin after 1.5 seconds. [Take g as 9.81 m/s², velocity as $v = u - jgt$ and displacement as $s = ut - j\frac{1}{2}gt^2$, where t is the time in seconds.]

(a) The velocity at time t seconds is $v = u - jgt$, (since g acts vertically downwards), hence $v = (21 + j8) - jgt$

$= 21 + j(8 - 9.81\,t)$

When $t = 1.5$s, $v = 21 + j[8 - (9.81)(1.5)] = 21 - j\,6.715$

In polar form, $v = \sqrt{(21^2 + 6.715^2)} \angle \arctan \frac{-6.715}{21}$

$= 22.05 \angle -17° \, 44'$.

Thus the magnitude of the velocity after 1.5 seconds is **22.05 m/s** and the direction is **-17° 44'**.

(b) The displacement, $s = ut - j\,\frac{1}{2}\,gt^2$

$$= (21 + j8)t - j\,(\tfrac{1}{2})(9.81)\,t^2$$

$$= 21 + j\,(8t - (\tfrac{1}{2})\,(9.81)\,t^2$$

When $t = 1.5$s, $\quad s = 21 + j\,[(8)(1.5) - (\tfrac{1}{2})\,(9.81)(1.5)^2]$

$$= 21 + j\,0.9638$$

In polar form, $\quad s = \sqrt{[(21)^2 + (0.9638)^2]} \angle \arctan \dfrac{0.9638}{21}$

$$= 21.02 \angle 2° 38'.$$

Thus the distance from the origin is **21.02 m** and the direction is **2° 38'.**

Further problems on the applications of complex numbers may be found in the following Section (9) (Problems 49–59), p. 195.

9 Further problems

Operations on cartesian complex numbers

In problems 1 to 5 solve the quadratic equations.
1. $x^2 + 16 = 0$ $\quad [x = \pm j4]$
2. $x^2 - 2x + 2 = 0$ $\quad [x = 1 \pm j]$
3. $2x^2 + 3x + 4 = 0$ $\quad [x = -\dfrac{3}{4} \pm j\,\dfrac{\sqrt{23}}{4}]$
4. $5y^2 + 2y = -3$ $\quad [y = -\dfrac{1}{5} \pm j\,\dfrac{\sqrt{14}}{5}]$
5. $4t^2 = t - 1$ $\quad [t = \dfrac{1}{8} \pm j\,\dfrac{\sqrt{15}}{8}]$
6. Show on an Argand diagram the following complex numbers:
   (a) $3 + j6$ $\quad$ (b) $2 - j3$ $\quad$ (c) $-3 + j4$ $\quad$ (d) $-1 - j5$
7. Write down the complex conjugates of the following complex numbers:
   (a) $4 + j$ $\qquad$ (a) $[4 - j]$
   (b) $3 - j2$ $\qquad$ (b) $[3 + j2]$
   (c) $-5 - j$ $\qquad$ (c) $[-5 + j]$

In problems 8 to 12, evaluate in $a + jb$ form assuming that $Z_1 = 2 + j3$, $Z_2 = 3 - j4$, $Z_3 = -1 + j2$ and $Z_4 = -2 - j5$.

8. (a) $Z_1 - Z_2$ $\quad$ (b) $Z_2 + Z_3 - Z_4$ $\quad$ (a) $[-1 + j7]$ $\quad$ (b) $[4 + j3]$
9. (a) $Z_1 Z_2$ $\quad$ (b) $Z_3 Z_4$ $\quad$ (a) $[18 + j]$ $\quad$ (b) $[12 + j]$
10. (a) $Z_1 Z_3 Z_4$ $\quad$ (b) $Z_2 Z_3 + Z_4$ $\quad$ (a) $[21 + j38]$ $\quad$ (b) $[3 + j5]$
11. (a) $\dfrac{Z_1}{Z_2}$ $\quad$ (b) $\dfrac{Z_1 + Z_2}{Z_3 + Z_4}$ $\quad$ (a) $[-\dfrac{6}{25} + j\,\dfrac{17}{25}]$ $\quad$ (b) $[-\dfrac{2}{3} + j]$

12. (a) $\dfrac{Z_1 Z_2}{Z_1 + Z_2}$ (b) $Z_1 + \dfrac{Z_2}{Z_3} + Z_4$ (a) $[\ \dfrac{89}{26} + j\dfrac{23}{26}\ ]$ (b) $[-\dfrac{11}{5} - j\dfrac{12}{5}\ ]$

13. Evaluate $[\ \dfrac{(1+j)^2 - (1-j)^2}{j}\ ]$ [4]

14. If $Z_1 = 4 - j3$ and $Z_2 = 2 + j$ evaluate x and y given

$x + jy = \dfrac{1}{Z_1 - Z_2} + \dfrac{1}{Z_1 Z_2}$ $[x = 0.188, y = 0.216]$

15. Evaluate (a) j^8 (b) j^{11} (c) $\dfrac{3}{j^3}$ (d) $\dfrac{5}{j^6}$

   (a) [1]   (b) $[-j]$ (c) $[j3]$ (d) $[-5]$

16. Evaluate (a) $(1 + j)^4$ (b) $\dfrac{2 - j}{2 + j}$ (c) $\dfrac{1}{2 + j3}$

   (a) $[-4]$ (b) $[\ \dfrac{3}{5} - j\dfrac{4}{5}\ ]$ (c) $[\ \dfrac{2}{13} - j\dfrac{3}{13}\ ]$

17. If $Z = \dfrac{1 + j3}{1 - j2}$, evaluate Z^2 in $a + jb$ form $[0 - j2]$

18. Evaluate (a) j^{33} (b) $\dfrac{1}{(2 - j2)^4}$ (c) $\dfrac{1 + j3}{2 + j4} + \dfrac{3 - j2}{5 - j}$

   (a) $[j]$ (b) $[\ -\dfrac{1}{64}\ ]$ (c) $[1.354 - j0.169]$

In problems 19 to 23 solve the given complex equations:

19. $4(a + jb) = 7 - j3$ $[a = \dfrac{7}{4}, b = -\dfrac{3}{4}]$

20. $(3 + j4)(2 - j3) = x + jy$ $[x = 18, y = -1]$
21. $(1 + j)(2 - j) = j(p + jq)$ $[p = 1, q = -3]$
22. $(a - j3b) + (b - j2a) = 4 + j6$ $[a = 18, b = -14]$
23. $5 + j2 = \sqrt{(e + jf)}$ $[e = 21, f = 20]$

Polar form of complex numbers
In problems 24 to 26 determine the modulus and the argument of each of the complex numbers given.

24. (a) $3 + j4$ (b) $2 - j5$ (a) $[5, 53° 8']$ (b) $[5.385, -68° 12']$
25. (a) $-4 + j$ (b) $-5 - j3$ (a) $[4.123, 165° 58']$
   (b) $[5.831, -149° 2']$
26. (a) $(2 + j)^2$ (b) $j(3 - j)$ (a) $[5, 53° 8']$ (b) $[3.162, 71° 34']$

In Problems 27 to 29 express the given cartesian complex numbers in polar form, leaving answers in surd form.

27. (a) $6 + j5$ (b) $3 - j2$ (c) -3
   (a) $[\sqrt{61} \angle 39° 48']$ (b) $[\sqrt{13} \angle -33° 41']$ (c) $[3 \angle 180°$ or $3 \angle \pi]$
28. (a) $-5 + j$ (b) $-4 - j3$ (c) $-j2$

   (a) $[\sqrt{26} \angle 168° 41']$ (b) $[5 \angle -143° 8']$ (c) $[2 \angle -90°$ or $2 \angle -\dfrac{\pi}{2}]$

29. (a) $(-1 + j)^3$ (b) $-j(1 - j)$ (c) $j^3(2 - j3)$
   (a) $[\sqrt{8} \angle 45°]$ (b) $[\sqrt{2} \angle -135°]$ (c) $[\sqrt{13} \angle -146° 19']$

In Problems 30 to 32 convert the given polar complex numbers into $(a + jb)$ form, giving answers correct to 4 significant figures.

30. (a) $6 \angle 30°$ (b) $4 \angle 60°$ (c) $3 \angle 45°$
(a) $[5.196 + j3.000]$ (b) $[2.000 + j3.464]$ (c) $[2.121 + j2.121]$

31. (a) $2 \angle \dfrac{\pi}{2}$ (b) $3 \angle \pi$ (c) $5 \angle \dfrac{5\pi}{6}$
(a) $[0 + j2.000]$ (b) $[-3.000 + j0]$ (c) $[-4.330 + j2.500]$

32. (a) $8 \angle 150°$ (b) $4.2 \angle -120°$ (c) $3.6 \angle -25°$
(a) $[-6.928 + j4.000]$ (b) $[-2.100 - j3.637]$
(c) $[3.263 - j1.521]$

33. Using an Argand diagram evaluate in polar form
(a) $2 \angle 30° + 3 \angle 40°$ (b) $5.5 \angle 120° - 2.5 \angle -50°$
(a) $[4.982 \angle 36°]$ (b) $[7.974 \angle 123° \, 7']$

In Problems 34 to 36 evaluate in polar form.

34. (a) $2 \angle 40° \times 5 \angle 20°$ (b) $2.6 \angle 72° \times 4.3 \angle 45°$
(a) $[10 \angle 60°]$ (b) $[11.18 \angle 117°]$

35. (a) $5.8 \angle 35° + 2 \angle -10°$ (b) $4 \angle 30° \times 3 \angle 70° \div 2 \angle -15°$
(a) $[2.9 \angle 45°]$ (b) $[6 \angle 115°]$

36. (a) $\dfrac{4.1 \angle 20° \times 3.2 \angle -62°}{1.2 \angle 150°}$ (b) $6 \angle 25° + 3 \angle -36° - 4 \angle 72°$
(a) $[10.93 \angle 168°]$ (b) $[7.289 \angle 24° \, 35']$

37. Solve the complex equations, giving answers correct to 4 significant figures.

(a) $\dfrac{12 \angle \dfrac{\pi}{2} \times 3 \angle \dfrac{3\pi}{4}}{2 \angle -\dfrac{\pi}{3}} = x + jy$ (b) $15 \angle \dfrac{\pi}{3} + 12 \angle \dfrac{\pi}{2} - 6 \angle -\dfrac{\pi}{3} = r \angle \theta$

(a) $[x = 4.659, y = -17.39]$ (b) $[r = 30.52, \theta = 81° \, 31']$

38. Three vectors are represented by P, $2 \angle 30°$, Q, $3 \angle 90°$ and R, $4 \angle -60°$. Determine in polar form the vectors represented by (a)$P + Q + R$ and (b)$P - Q - R$ (a) $[3.770 \angle 8° \, 10']$ (b) $[1.488 \angle 100° \, 22']$

Powers and roots of complex numbers

In Problems 39 to 42 evaluate in cartesian and in polar form.

39. (a) $(2 + j3)^2$ (b) $(4 - j5)^2$
(a) $[-5 + j12; 13 \angle 112° \, 37']$ (b) $[-9 - j40; 41 \angle -102° \, 41']$

40. (a) $(-3 + j2)^5$ (b) $(-2 - j)^3$
(a) $[597 + j122; 609.3 \angle 11° \, 33']$ (b) $[-2 - j11; 11.18 \angle -100° \, 18']$

41. (a) $[4 \angle 32°]^4$ (b) $[2 \angle 125°]^5$
(a) $[-157.6 + j201.7; 256 \angle 128°]$ (b) $[-2.789 - j31.88; 32 \angle -95°]$

42. (a) $[3 \angle -\dfrac{\pi}{3}]^3$ (b) $[1.5 \angle -160°]^4$
(a) $[-27 + j0; 27 \angle -\pi]$ (b) $[0.879 \, 2 + j4.986; 5.063 \angle 80°]$

In Problems 43 to 45 determine the two square roots of the given complex numbers in cartesian form and show the results on an Argand diagram.

43. (a) $2 + j$ (b) $3 - j2$
     (a) $[\pm (1.455 + j0.344)]$ (b) $[\pm (1.817 - j0.550)]$

44. (a) $-3 + j4$ (b) $-1 - j3$
     (a) $[\pm (1 + j2)]$ (b) $[\pm (1.040 - j1.443)]$

45. (a) $5 \angle 36°$ (b) $14 \angle \dfrac{3\pi}{2}$
     (a) $[\pm (2.127 + j0.691)]$ (b) $[\pm (-2.646 + j2.646)]$

46. If $Z = 3 \angle 30°$ evaluate in polar form (a) Z^2 (b) $\sqrt{Z}$
     (a) $[9 \angle 60°]$ (b) $[\sqrt{3} \angle 15°$ and $\sqrt{3} \angle -165°]$

47. Convert $2 - j$ into polar form and hence evaluate $(2 - j)^7$ in polar form
     $[\sqrt{5} \angle -26° \, 34'; 279.5 \angle 174° \, 3']$

48. Simplify, without the use of tables $\dfrac{(\cos \dfrac{\pi}{9} - j \sin \dfrac{\pi}{9})^4}{(\cos \dfrac{\pi}{9} + j \sin \dfrac{\pi}{9})^5}$ $[-1]$

Application of complex numbers

49. Determine the resistance R and series inductance L (or capacitance C) for each of the following impedances, assuming the frequency to be 50 Hz.
     (a) $4 + j7$ (b) $3 - j2$ (c) $j10$ (d) $-j200$ (e) $15 \angle \dfrac{\pi}{3}$
     (f) $6 \angle -45°$ (a) $[R = 4\Omega, L = 22.3 \text{ mH}]$ (b) $[R = 3\Omega, C = 1\,592 \; \mu\text{F},]$
     (c) $[R = 0, L = 31.8 \text{ mH}]$ (d) $[R = 0, C = 15.92 \; \mu\text{F},]$
     (e) $[R = 7.5\Omega, L = 41.3 \text{ mH}]$ (f) $[R = 4.243 \; \Omega, C = 750.3 \; \mu\text{F}]$

50. An alternating voltage of 100 V, 50 Hz is applied across an impedance of $(20 - j30)$ ohms. Calculate: (a) the resistance, (b) the capacitance; (c) the current; and (d) the phase angle between current and voltage.
     (a) $[20 \; \Omega]$ (b) $[106.1 \; \mu\text{F}]$ (c) $[2.774 \text{ A}]$ (d) $[56° \, 19']$

51. Two voltages are represented by $(15 + j10)$ and $(12 - j4)$ volts. Determine the magnitude of the resultant voltage when these voltages are added.
     $[27.66 \text{ V}]$

52. Two impedances, $Z_1 = (2 + j6)$ ohms and $Z_2 = (5 - j2)$ ohms are connected in series to a supply voltage of 100 V. Determine the magnitude of the current and its phase angle relative to the voltage.
     $[12.40 \text{ A}; 29° \, 45' \text{ lagging}]$

53. A resistance of 45 ohms is connected in series with a capacitor of 42 μF. If the applied voltage is 250 V, 50 Hz determine: (a) the capacitance reactance; (b) the impedance; (c) the current, and its phase relative to the applied voltage; (d) the voltage across the resistance; and (e) the voltage across the capacitance.   (a) $[75.79 \; \Omega]$ (b) $[88.14 \; \Omega]$
     (c) $[2.836 \text{ A at } 59° \, 18' \text{ leading}]$ (d) $[127.6 \text{ V}]$ (e) $[214.9 \text{ V}]$

54. Forces of $(-3 - j5)$N, $(13 + j2)$N, $(-8 + j4)$N and $(x + jy)$N are in equilibrium. Find x and y. $[x = -2\text{N}, y = -1\text{N}]$

55. Find the resultant of forces $F_1 = (3 - j17)$ newtons, $F_2 = (10 - j2)$ newtons and $F_3 = (-8 + j2)$ newtons. Express the resultant force in polar form.   [$17.72\ N \angle -73° 37'$]

56. A body moves from $(0 + j0)$ to point A at $(9 - j10)$. It then moves to points B and C at $(22 + j4)$ and $(-7 - j)$ respectively. Determine its distance from the origin and its angle relative to the real positive axis.
    [$25, \angle -16° 16'$]

57. An aircraft, A, flying at a constant height, has a velocity of $(380 + j270)$ km/h. Another aircraft, B, at the same height, has a velocity of $290 - j\,417$ km/h. Determine (a) the velocity of A relative to B, and (b) the velocity of B relative to A, expressing the results in polar form.
    (a) [692.9 km/h at $82° 32'$]   (b) [692.9 km/h at $-97° 28'$]

58. A projectile is given an initial velocity, u, of $(24 + j\,27)$ m/s. A second projectile launched from the same place in the same vertical plane at the same time has a velocity of $(31 + j\,17)$ m/s. After launching, both projectiles move freely under gravity. Determine the magnitude and direction of the velocity of the second projectile relative to the first.
    ($v = u - jgt$)   [12.21 m at $\angle -55° 0'$]

59. In the hydrogen atom, the angular momentum, (p), of the de Broglie wave is given by:

$$p\,\Psi = -(jh/2\,\pi)(\pm jm\,\Psi).\ \text{Find } p. \qquad [\,p = \pm\,\frac{mh}{2\pi}\,]$$

Section 2

Calculus

Chapter 11

Introduction to differentiation

1 Introduction

Calculus is a branch of mathematics involving or leading to calculations dealing with continuously varying functions. The subject falls into two parts, namely **differential calculus** (usually abbreviated to **differentiation**) and **integral calculus** (usually abbreviated to **integration**).

The central problem of the differential calculus is the investigation of the rate of change of a function with respect to changes in the variables on which it depends.

The two main uses of integral calculus are firstly, finding such quantities as the length of a curve, the area enclosed by a curve, or the volume enclosed by a surface, and secondly, the problem of determining a variable quantity given its rate of change.

There is a close relationship between the processes of differentiation and integration, the latter being considered as the inverse of the former.

Calculus is a comparatively young branch of mathematics; its systematic development started in the middle of the 17th century. Since then there has been an enormous expansion in the scope of calculus and it is now used in every field of applied science as an instrument for the solution of problems of the most varied nature.

Before such uses can be investigated it is essential to grasp the basic concepts and to understand the notations used. The following text deals with this necessary preparatory work.

2 Functional notation

An expression such as $y = 4x^2 - 4x - 3$ contains two variables. For every value of x there is a corresponding value of y. The variable x is called the **independent variable** and y is called the **dependent variable**. y is said to be a function of x and is written as $y = f(x)$. Hence from above $f(x) = 4x^2 - 4x - 3$.

The value of the function $f(x)$ when $x = 0$ is denoted by $f(0)$. Similarly when $x = 1$ the value of the function is denoted by $f(1)$ and so on.

If $f(x) = 4x^2 - 4x - 3$

then
$$f(0) = 4(0)^2 - 4(0) - 3 \quad = -3$$
$$f(1) = 4(1)^2 - 4(1) - 3 \quad = -3$$
$$f(2) = 4(2)^2 - 4(2) - 3 \quad = 5$$
$$f(3) = 4(3)^2 - 4(3) - 3 \quad = 21$$
$$f(-1) = 4(-1)^2 - 4(-1) - 3 \quad = 5$$
and
$$f(-2) = 4(-2)^2 - 4(-2) - 3 \quad = 21$$

Figure 1 shows the curve $f(x) = 4x^2 - 4x - 3$ for values of x between $x = -2$ and $x = 3$. The lengths represented by $f(0)$, $f(1)$, $f(2)$, etc. are also shown.

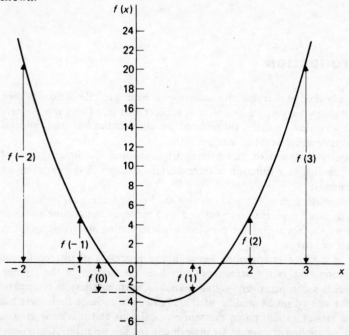

Fig. 1   Graph of $f(x) = 4x^2 - 4x - 3$

201

Worked problems on functional notation

Problem 1. If $f(x) = 5x^2 - 3x + 1$ find $f(0), f(3), f(-1), f(-2)$ and $f(3) - f(-2)$.

$$f(x) = 5x^2 - 3x + 1$$
$$f(0) = 5(0)^2 - 3(0) + 1 \quad = 1$$
$$f(3) = 5(3)^2 - 3(3) + 1 \quad = 37$$
$$f(-1) = 5(-1)^2 - 3(-1) + 1 \quad = 9$$
$$f(-2) = 5(-2)^2 - 3(-2) + 1 \quad = 27$$
$$f(3) - f(-2) = 37 - 27 \quad = 10$$

Problem 2. For the curve $f(x) = 3x^2 + 2x - 9$ evaluate $f(2) \div f(1)$, $f(2 + a)$, $f(2 + a) - f(2)$ and $\dfrac{f(2 + a) - f(2)}{a}$.

$$f(x) = 3x^2 + 2x - 9$$
$$f(1) = 3(1)^2 + 2(1) - 9 = -4$$
$$f(2) = 3(2)^2 + 2(2) - 9 = 7$$
$$\begin{aligned} f(2 + a) &= 3(2 + a)^2 + 2(2 + a) - 9 \\ &= 3(4 + 4a + a^2) + 4 + 2a - 9 \\ &= 12 + 12a + 3a^2 + 4 + 2a - 9 \\ &= 7 + 14a + 3a^2 \end{aligned}$$

$$f(2) \div f(1) = \frac{f(2)}{f(1)} = \frac{7}{-4} = -1\tfrac{3}{4}$$

$$\begin{aligned} f(2 + a) - f(2) &= 7 + 14a + 3a^2 - 7 \\ &= 14a + 3a^2 \end{aligned}$$

$$\frac{f(2 + a) - f(2)}{a} = \frac{14a + 3a^2}{a} = 14 + 3a$$

Further problems on functional notation may be found in Section 5, problems 1 to 5, page 213.

3 The gradient of a curve

If a tangent is drawn at a point A on a curve then the gradient of this tangent is said to be the gradient of the curve at A.

In Fig. 2 the gradient of the curve at A is equal to the gradient of the tangent AB.

Consider the graph of $f(x) = 2x^2$, part of which is shown in Fig. 3.

The gradient of the chord PQ is given by:

$$\frac{QR}{PR} = \frac{QS - RS}{PR} = \frac{QS - PT}{PR}$$

At point P, $x = 1$ and at point Q, $x = 3$.

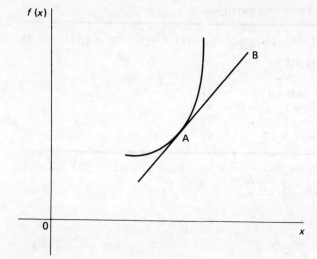

Fig. 2

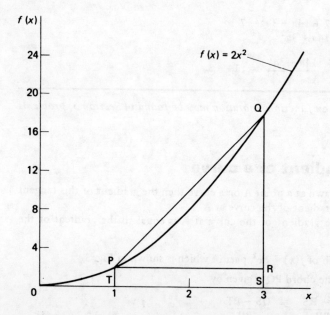

Fig. 3

Hence the gradient of the chord PQ $= \dfrac{f(3) - f(1)}{3 - 1}$

$$= \frac{18 - 2}{2}$$

$$= \frac{16}{2} = 8$$

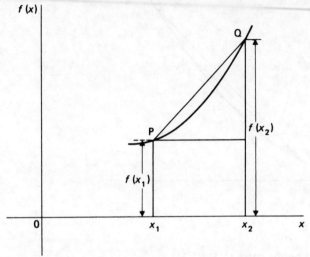

Fig. 4

More generally, for any curve (as shown in Fig. 4):

Gradient of PQ $= \dfrac{f(x_2) - f(x_1)}{x_2 - x_1}$

For the part of the curve $f(x) = 2x^2$ shown in Fig. 5 let us consider what happens as the point Q, at present at $(3, f(3))$, moves closer and closer to point P, which is fixed at $(1, f(1))$.

Let Q_1 be the point on the curve $(2.5, f(2.5))$.

Gradient of chord $PQ_1 = \dfrac{f(2.5) - f(1)}{2.5 - 1}$

$$= \frac{12.5 - 2}{1.5} = 7$$

Let Q_2 be the point on the curve $(2, f(2))$.

Gradient of chord $PQ_2 = \dfrac{f(2) - f(1)}{2 - 1}$

$$= \frac{8 - 2}{1} = 6$$

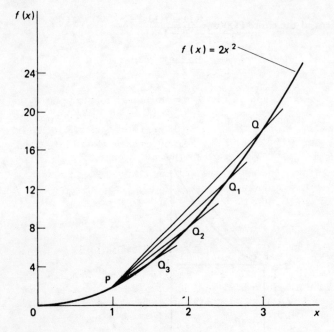

Fig. 5

Let Q_3 be the point on the curve $(1.5, f(1.5))$.

$$\text{Gradient of chord } PQ_3 = \frac{f(1.5) - f(1)}{1.5 - 1}$$

$$= \frac{4.5 - 2}{0.5} = 5$$

The following points, i.e. Q_4, Q_5 and Q_6, are not shown on Fig. 5.
Let Q_4 be the point on the curve $(1.1, f(1.1))$.

$$\text{Gradient of chord } PQ_4 = \frac{f(1.1) - f(1)}{1.1 - 1}$$

$$= \frac{2.42 - 2}{0.1} = 4.2$$

Let Q_5 be the point on the curve $(1.01, f(1.01))$.

$$\text{Gradient of chord } PQ_5 = \frac{f(1.01) - f(1)}{1.01 - 1}$$

$$= \frac{2.040\ 2 - 2}{0.01} = 4.02$$

Let Q_6 be the point on the curve $(1.001, f(1.001))$.

$$\text{Gradient of chord } PQ_6 = \frac{f(1.001) - f(1)}{1.001 - 1}$$

$$= \frac{2.004\,002 - 2}{0.001} = 4.002$$

Thus as the point Q approaches closer and closer to the point P the gradients of the chords approach nearer and nearer to the value 4. This is called the **limiting value** of the gradient of the chord and **at P the chord becomes the tangent to the curve.** Thus the limiting value of 4 is the gradient of the tangent at P.

It can be seen from the above example that deducing the gradient of the tangent to a curve at a given point by this method is a lengthy process. A much more convenient method is shown below.

4 Differentiation from first principles

Let P and Q be two points very close together on a curve as shown in Fig. 6.

Let the length PR be δx (pronounced delta x), representing a small increment (or increase) in x, and the length QR, the corresponding increase in y,

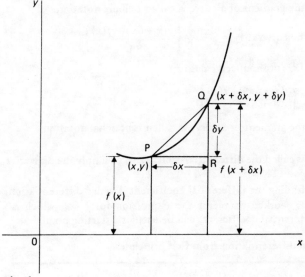

Fig. 6

be δy (pronounced delta y). It is important to realise that δ and x are inseparable, i.e. δx does not mean δ times x. Let P be any point on the curve with coordinates (x, y). Then Q will have the coordinates $(x + \delta x, y + \delta y)$.

The slope of the chord $PQ = \dfrac{\delta y}{\delta x}$

But from Fig. 6, $\delta y = (y + \delta y) - y = f(x + \delta x) - f(x)$

Hence $\dfrac{\delta y}{\delta x} = \dfrac{f(x + \delta x) - f(x)}{\delta x}$

The smaller δx becomes, the closer the gradient of the chord PQ approaches the gradient of the tangent at P. That is, as $\delta x \to 0$, the gradient of the chord→ the gradient of the tangent. (Note '→' means 'approaches'). As δx approaches zero, the value of $\dfrac{\delta y}{\delta x}$ approaches what is called a **limiting value**. There are two notations commonly used when finding the gradient of a tangent drawn to a curve.

1. The gradient of the curve at P is represented as $\displaystyle\lim_{\delta x \to 0} \dfrac{\delta y}{\delta x}$

This is written as $\dfrac{dy}{dx}$ (pronounced dee y by dee x), i.e.

$$\dfrac{dy}{dx} = \lim_{\delta x \to 0} \dfrac{\delta y}{\delta x}$$

This way of stating the gradient of a curve is called **Leibniz notation**.

2. The gradient of the curve at P $= \displaystyle\lim_{\delta x \to 0} \left\{ \dfrac{f(x + \delta x) - f(x)}{\delta x} \right\}$

This is written as $f'(x)$ (pronounced f dash x)

i.e. $f'(x) = \displaystyle\lim_{\delta x \to 0} \left\{ \dfrac{f(x + \delta x) - f(x)}{\delta x} \right\}$

This way of stating the gradient of a curve is called **functional notation**.

$\dfrac{dy}{dx}$ equals $f'(x)$ and is called the **differential coefficient**, or simply the **derivative**.

The process of finding the differential coefficient is called **differentiation**.

In the following worked problems the expression for $f'(x)$, which is a definition of the differential coefficient, will be used as a starting point.

Worked problems on differentiation from first principles

Problem 1. Differentiate from first principles $f(x) = x^2$ and find the value of the gradient of the curve at $x = 3$.

To 'differentiate from first principles' means 'to find $f'(x)$' by using the expression:

$$f'(x) = \lim_{\delta x \to 0} \left\{ \dfrac{f(x + \delta x) - f(x)}{\delta x} \right\}$$

$$f(x) = x^2$$
$$f(x + \delta x) = (x + \delta x)^2 = x^2 + 2x\,\delta x + \delta x^2$$

$$f(x + \delta x) - f(x) = x^2 + 2x\,\delta x + \delta x^2 - x^2$$
$$= 2x\,\delta x + \delta x^2$$

$$\frac{f(x + \delta x) - f(x)}{\delta x} = \frac{2x\,\delta x + \delta x^2}{\delta x}$$

$$= 2x + \delta x$$

As $\delta x \to 0$, $\dfrac{f(x + \delta x) - f(x)}{\delta x} \to 2x + 0$

Therefore $f'(x) = \displaystyle\lim_{\delta x \to 0} \left\{ \frac{f(x + \delta x) - f(x)}{\delta x} \right\} = 2x$

At $x = 3$, the gradient of the curve, i.e. $f'(x) = 2(3) = 6$
Hence if $f(x) = x^2$, $f'(x) = 2x$. **The gradient at $x = 3$ is 6.**

Problem 2. Find the differential coefficient of $f(x) = 3x^3$, from first principles.

To 'find the differential coefficient' means 'to find $f'(x)$' by using the expression:

$$f'(x) = \lim_{\delta x \to 0} \left\{ \frac{f(x + \delta x) - f(x)}{\delta x} \right\}$$

$$f(x) = 3x^3$$
$$\begin{aligned} f(x + \delta x) &= 3(x + \delta x)^3 \\ &= 3(x + \delta x)(x^2 + 2x\,\delta x + \delta x^2) \\ &= 3(x^3 + 3x^2\delta x + 3x\delta x^2 + \delta x^3) \\ &= 3x^3 + 9x^2\delta x + 9x\delta x^2 + 3\delta x^3. \end{aligned}$$
$$\begin{aligned} f(x + \delta x) - f(x) &= 3x^3 + 9x^2\delta x + 9x\delta x^2 + 3\delta x^3 - 3x^3 \\ &= 9x^2\,\delta x + 9x\delta x^2 + 3\delta x^3 \end{aligned}$$

$$\frac{f(x + \delta x) - f(x)}{\delta x} = \frac{9x^2\delta x + 9x\delta x^2 + 3\delta x^3}{\delta x}$$

$$= 9x^2 + 9x\delta x + 3\delta x^2$$

As $\delta x \to 0$, $\dfrac{f(x + \delta x) - f(x)}{\delta x} \to 9x^2 + 9x(0) + 3(0)^2$

i.e. $f'(x) = \displaystyle\lim_{\delta x \to 0} \left\{ \frac{f(x + \delta x) - f(x)}{\delta x} \right\} = 9x^2$

Problem 3. By differentiation from first principles determine $\dfrac{dy}{dx}$ for $y = 3x$.

The object is to find $\dfrac{dy}{dx}$

$$\frac{dy}{dx} = f'(x) = \lim_{\delta x \to 0}\left\{\frac{f(x + \delta x) - f(x)}{\delta x}\right\}$$

$y = f(x) = 3x$

$f(x + \delta x) = 3(x + \delta x) = 3x + 3\delta x$

$f(x + \delta x) - f(x) = 3x + 3\delta x - 3x$

$\qquad\qquad\qquad = 3\delta x$

$$\frac{f(x + \delta x) - f(x)}{\delta x} = \frac{3\delta x}{\delta x} = 3$$

Hence $\dfrac{dy}{dx} = \lim\limits_{\delta x \to 0}\left\{\dfrac{f(x + \delta x) - f(x)}{\delta x}\right\} = 3.$

Another way of writing $\dfrac{dy}{dx} = 3$ is $f'(x) = 3$

or $\dfrac{d}{dx}(3x) = 3$ since $y = 3x$.

Problem 4. Find the derivative of $y = \sqrt{x}$.

Let $y = f(x) = \sqrt{x}$
To 'find the derivative' means 'to find $f'(x)$'.

$$f'(x) = \lim_{\delta x \to 0}\left\{\frac{f(x + \delta x) - f(x)}{\delta x}\right\}$$

$f(x) = \sqrt{x} = x^{\frac{1}{2}}$

$f(x + \delta x) = (x + \delta x)^{\frac{1}{2}}$

$f(x + \delta x) - f(x) = (x + \delta x)^{\frac{1}{2}} - x^{\frac{1}{2}}$

$$\frac{f(x + \delta x) - f(x)}{\delta x} = \frac{(x + \delta x)^{\frac{1}{2}} - x^{\frac{1}{2}}}{\delta x}$$

Now from algebra, $(a - b)(a + b) = a^2 - b^2$, i.e. the difference of two squares. Therefore, in this case, multiplying both the numerator and the denominator by $[(x + \delta x)^{\frac{1}{2}} + x^{\frac{1}{2}}]$, to make the numerator of the fraction of $(a+b)(a-b)$ form, gives:

$$\frac{f(x + \delta x) - f(x)}{\delta x} = \frac{[(x + \delta x)^{\frac{1}{2}} - x^{\frac{1}{2}}]\,[(x + \delta x)^{\frac{1}{2}} + x^{\frac{1}{2}}]}{\delta x\,[(x + \delta x)^{\frac{1}{2}} + x^{\frac{1}{2}}]}$$

$$= \frac{[(x + \delta x)^{\frac{1}{2}}]^2 - [x^{\frac{1}{2}}]^2}{\delta x\,[(x + \delta x)^{\frac{1}{2}} + x^{\frac{1}{2}}]}$$

$$= \frac{(x + \delta x) - (x)}{\delta x\,[(x + \delta x)^{\frac{1}{2}} + x^{\frac{1}{2}}]}$$

$$= \frac{\delta x}{\delta x \left[(x + \delta x)^{\frac{1}{2}} + x^{\frac{1}{2}}\right]}$$

$$= \frac{1}{(x + \delta x)^{\frac{1}{2}} + x^{\frac{1}{2}}}$$

As $\delta x \to 0$, $\dfrac{f(x + \delta x) - f(x)}{\delta x} \to \dfrac{1}{(x + 0)^{\frac{1}{2}} + x^{\frac{1}{2}}}$

Therefore $f'(x) = \displaystyle\lim_{\delta x \to 0} \left\{ \frac{f(x + \delta x) - f(x)}{\delta x} \right\} = \dfrac{1}{x^{\frac{1}{2}} + x^{\frac{1}{2}}} = \dfrac{1}{2\,x^{\frac{1}{2}}}$

Hence if $f(x) = \sqrt{x}$, $f'(x) = \dfrac{1}{2\sqrt{x}}$ or $\frac{1}{2} x^{-\frac{1}{2}}$

Another way of writing this is:

If $y = \sqrt{x}, \dfrac{dy}{dx} = \dfrac{1}{2\sqrt{x}}$,

or $\dfrac{d}{dx} (\sqrt{x}) = \dfrac{1}{2\sqrt{x}}$

Problem 5. Differentiate from first principles $f(x) = \dfrac{1}{2x}$

$$f'(x) = \lim_{\delta x \to 0} \left\{ \frac{f(x + \delta x) - f(x)}{\delta x} \right\}$$

$$f(x) = \frac{1}{2x}$$

$$f(x + \delta x) = \frac{1}{2(x + \delta x)}$$

$$f(x + \delta x) - f(x) = \frac{1}{2(x + \delta x)} - \frac{1}{2x}$$

$$= \frac{x - (x + \delta x)}{2x\,(x + \delta x)}$$

$$= \frac{-\delta x}{2x\,(x + \delta x)}$$

$$\frac{f(x + \delta x) - f(x)}{\delta x} = \frac{-\delta x}{2x\,(x + \delta x)\,\delta x}$$

$$= \frac{-1}{2x\,(x + \delta x)}$$

As $\delta x \to 0$, $\dfrac{f(x + \delta x) - f(x)}{\delta x} \to \dfrac{-1}{2x\,(x + 0)}$

Therefore $f'(x) = \lim\limits_{\delta x \to 0} \left\{ \dfrac{f(x + \delta x) - f(x)}{\delta x} \right\} = \dfrac{-1}{2x\,(x)} = -\dfrac{1}{2x^2}$

Problem 6. Find the differential coefficient of $y = 5$.

The differential coefficient of $y = 5$ may be deduced as follows:
If a graph is drawn of $y = 5$ a straight horizontal line results and the gradient or slope of a horizontal line is zero. Finding the differential coefficient is, in fact, finding the slope of a curve, or, as in this case, of a horizontal straight line.

Hence $\dfrac{dy}{dx} = 0$

This may also be shown by the conventional method since:

$\dfrac{dy}{dx} = f'(x) = \lim\limits_{\delta x \to 0} \left\{ \dfrac{f(x + \delta x) - f(x)}{\delta x} \right\}$

$y = f(x) = 5$
$\therefore f(x + \delta x) = 5$

$\therefore \dfrac{dy}{dx} = f'(x) = \lim\limits_{\delta x \to 0} \left\{ \dfrac{5 - 5}{\delta x} \right\}$

$\qquad\qquad = \dfrac{0}{\delta x} = 0$

More generally, if C is any constant, then if
$f(x) = C, f'(x) = 0$

i.e. If $y = C$ then $\dfrac{dy}{dx} = 0$

Problem 7. Differentiate from first principles $f(x) = 3x^2 + 6x - 3$ and find the gradient of the curve at $x = -2$.

$f'(x) = \lim\limits_{\delta x \to 0} \left\{ \dfrac{f(x + \delta x) - f(x)}{\delta x} \right\}$

$f(x) = 3x^2 + 6x - 3$
$\therefore f(x + \delta x) = 3(x + \delta x)^2 + 6(x + \delta x) - 3$
$\qquad\qquad\quad = 3(x^2 + 2x\,\delta x + \delta x^2) + 6x + 6\delta x - 3$
$\qquad\qquad\quad = 3x^2 + 6x\delta x + 3\delta x^2 + 6x + 6\delta x - 3$
$\therefore f(x + \delta x) - f(x) = (3x^2 + 6x\delta x + 3\delta x^2 + 6x + 6\delta x - 3) - (3x^2 + 6x - 3)$
$\qquad\qquad\qquad\quad = 6x\,\delta x + 3\delta x^2 + 6\delta x$

$\therefore \dfrac{f(x + \delta x) - f(x)}{\delta x} = \dfrac{6x\,\delta x + 3\delta x^2 + 6\delta x}{\delta x}$

$$= 6x + 3\delta x + 6$$

As $\delta x \to 0$, $\dfrac{f(x + \delta x) - f(x)}{\delta x} \to 6x + 3\,(0) + 6$

Therefore $f'(x) = \underset{\delta x \to 0}{\lim.} \left\{ \dfrac{f(x + \delta x) - f(x)}{\delta x} \right\} = 6x + 6$

At $x = -2$ the gradient of the curve, i.e. $f'(x)$, is $6(-2) + 6$, i.e. -6.
Hence if $f(x) = 3x^2 + 6x - 3$, $f'(x) = 6x + 6$ and the gradient of the curve at $x = -2$ is -6.

A summary of the results obtained in the above problems is tabulated below:

y or $f(x)$	$\dfrac{dy}{dx}$ or $f'(x)$
x^2	$2x$
$3x^3$	$9x^2$
$3x$	3
$x^{\frac{1}{2}}$	$\frac{1}{2}x^{-\frac{1}{2}}$
$\dfrac{1}{2x}$	$-\dfrac{1}{2x^2}$
5	0
$3x^2 + 6x - 3$	$6x + 6$

Three basic rules of differentiation emerge from these results:
Rule 1. The differential coefficient of a constant is zero.

Rule 2. $\dfrac{d}{dx}(x^n) = nx^{n-1}$.

For example $\dfrac{d}{dx}(x^3) = 3x^{3-1} = 3x^2$ (as in the table)

Rule 3. Constants associated with variables are carried forward.

For example $\dfrac{d}{dx}(3x^2) = 3\dfrac{d}{dx}(x^2)$

Problem 8. Differentiate from first principles $f(x) = \dfrac{1}{5x + 3}$

$f'(x) = \underset{\delta x \to 0}{\lim.} \left\{ \dfrac{f(x + \delta x) - f(x)}{\delta x} \right\}$

$$f(x) = \frac{1}{5x + 3}$$

$$f(x + \delta x) = \frac{1}{5(x + \delta x) + 3}$$

$$f(x + \delta x) - f(x) = \frac{1}{5(x + \delta x) + 3} - \frac{1}{5x + 3}$$

$$= \frac{[5x + 3] - [5(x + \delta x) + 3]}{[5(x + \delta x) + 3][5x + 3]}$$

$$= \frac{5x + 3 - 5x - 5\delta x - 3}{[5(x + \delta x) + 3][5x + 3]}$$

$$= \frac{-5\delta x}{[5(x + \delta x) + 3][5x + 3]}$$

$$\therefore \frac{f(x + \delta x) - f(x)}{\delta x} = \frac{-5\delta x}{[5(x + \delta x) + 3][5x + 3]\delta x}$$

$$= \frac{-5}{[5(x + \delta x) + 3][5x + 3]}$$

As $\delta x \rightarrow 0$, $\dfrac{f(x + \delta x) - f(x)}{\delta x} \rightarrow \dfrac{-5}{[5(x + 0) + 3][5x + 3]}$

Therefore $f'(x) = \underset{\delta x \rightarrow 0}{\text{lim.}} \left\{ \dfrac{f(x + \delta x) - f(x)}{\delta x} \right\} = \dfrac{-5}{(5x + 3)(5x + 3)}$

Hence if $f(x) = \dfrac{1}{5x + 3}$, $f'(x) = \dfrac{-5}{(5x + 3)^2}$

In the above worked problems the questions have been worded in a variety of ways. The important thing to realise is that they all mean the same thing. For example, in worked problem 8, on differentiating from first principles

$f(x) = \dfrac{1}{5x + 3}$ gives $\dfrac{-5}{(5x + 3)^2}$. This result can be expressed in a number of ways.

1. If $f(x) = \dfrac{1}{5x + 3}$ then $f'(x) = \dfrac{-5}{(5x + 3)^2}$

2. If $y = \dfrac{1}{5x + 3}$ then $\dfrac{dy}{dx} = \dfrac{-5}{(5x + 3)^2}$

3. The differential coefficient of $\dfrac{1}{5x + 3}$ is $\dfrac{-5}{(5x + 3)^2}$

4. The derivative of $\dfrac{1}{5x + 3}$ is $\dfrac{-5}{(5x + 3)^2}$

5. $\dfrac{d}{dx} \left(\dfrac{1}{5x + 3} \right) = \dfrac{-5}{(5x + 3)^2}$

Further problems on differentiating from first principles may be found in the following Section (numbers 6 to 34).

5   Further problems

Functional notation

1. If $f(x) = 2x^2 - x + 3$ find $f(0)$, $f(1)$, $f(2)$, $f(-1)$ and $f(-2)$.

$$[3, 4, 9, 6, 13]$$

2. If $f(x) = 6x^2 - 4x + 7$ find $f(1)$, $f(2)$, $f(-2)$ and $f(1) - f(-2)$.

$$[9, 23, 39, -30]$$

3. If a curve is represented by $f(x) = 2x^3 + x^2 - x + 6$ prove that

$$f(1) = \frac{1}{3} f(2).$$

4. If $f(x) = 3x^2 + 2x - 9$ find $f(3)$, $f(3 + a)$ and $\dfrac{f(3+a) - f(3)}{a}$.

$$[24, 3a^2 + 20a + 24, 3a + 20]$$

5. If $f(x) = 4x^3 - 2x^2 - 3x + 1$ find $f(2)$, $f(-3)$ and $\dfrac{f(1 + b) - f(1)}{b}$.

$$[19, -116, 4b^2 + 10b + 5]$$

Differentiation from first principles

6. Sketch the curve $f(x) = 5x^2 - 6$ for values of x from $x = -2$ to $x = +4$. Label the coordinate $(3.5, f(3.5))$ as A. Label the coordinate $(1.5, f(1.5))$ as B. Join points A and B to form the chord AB. Find the gradient of the chord AB. By moving A nearer and nearer to B find the gradient of the tangent of the curve at B.   [25, 15]

In problems 7–27 differentiate from first principles:

7. $y = x$.   [1]
8. $y = 5x$.   [5]
9. $y = x^2$.   [2x]
10. $y = 7x^2$.   [14x]
11. $y = 4x^3$. $[12x^2]$
12. $y = 2x^2 - 3x + 2$.   [4x − 3]

13. $y = 2\sqrt{x}$. $\left[\dfrac{1}{\sqrt{x}} \text{ or } x^{-\frac{1}{2}}\right]$

14. $y = \dfrac{1}{x}$. $\left[-\dfrac{1}{x^2}\right]$

15. $y = \dfrac{5}{6x^2}$. $\left[-\dfrac{5}{3x^3}\right]$

16. $y = 19$.   [0]

17. $f(x) = 3x.$ [3]

18. $f(x) = \dfrac{x}{4}.$ $\left[\dfrac{1}{4}\right]$

19. $f(x) = 3x^2.$ [6x]

20. $f(x) = 14x^3.$ [42x²]

21. $f(x) = x^2 + 16x - 4.$ [2x + 16]

22. $f(x) = 4x^{\frac{1}{2}}.$ $\left[2x^{-\frac{1}{2}} \text{ or } \dfrac{2}{\sqrt{x}}\right]$

23. $f(x) = \dfrac{16}{17x}.$ $\left[-\dfrac{16}{17x^2}\right]$

24. $f(x) = \dfrac{1}{x^3}.$ $\left[-\dfrac{3}{x^4}\right]$

25. $f(x) = 8.$ [0]

26. $f(x) = \dfrac{1}{\sqrt{x}}$ $\left[-\dfrac{1}{2\sqrt{x^3}} \text{ or } -\dfrac{1}{2}x^{-3/2}\right]$

27. $f(x) = \dfrac{1}{3x - 2}$ $\left[\dfrac{-3}{(3x - 2)^2}\right]$

28. Find $\dfrac{d}{dx}(6x^3).$ [18x²]

29. Find $\dfrac{d}{dx}(3\sqrt{x} + 6)$ $\left[\dfrac{3}{2\sqrt{x}}\right]$

30. Find $\dfrac{d}{dx}(2x^{-2} + 7x^2).$ [−4x⁻³ + 14x]

31. Find $\dfrac{d}{dx}\left(13 - \dfrac{3}{2x}\right).$ $\left[\dfrac{3}{2x^2}\right]$

32. If E, F and G are the points $(1, 2)$, $(2, 16)$ and $(3, 54)$ respectively on the graph of $y = 2x^3$, find the gradients of the tangents at the points E, F and G and the gradient of the chord EG.   [6, 24, 54, 26]

33. Differentiate from first principles $f(x) = 5x^2 - 6x + 2$ and find the gradient of the curve at $x = 2$.   [10x − 6, 14]

34. If $y = \dfrac{7}{2}\sqrt{x} + \dfrac{3}{x^2} - 9$ find the differential coefficient of y with respect to x.

$$\left[\dfrac{7}{4\sqrt{x}} - \dfrac{6}{x^3}\right]$$

Chapter 12

Methods of differentiation

1 Differential coefficients of some mathematical functions

(i) Differential coefficient of ax^n.

In the worked problems of Chapter 11 the differential coefficients of certain algebraic functions of the form $y = ax^n$ are derived from first principles and the results are summarised on page 211. The rules stated on page 211 are best remembered by the single statement that

$$\text{when } y = ax^n, \frac{dy}{dx} = anx^{n-1}$$

An analytical proof of this rule is given in Appendix D, (page 351).

(ii) Differential coefficient of $\sin x$

A graph of $y = \sin x$ is shown in Fig. 1(a). The slope or gradient of the curve at any point is given by $\frac{dy}{dx}$ and is continually changing as values of x vary from O to S. By drawing tangents to the curve at many points on the curve

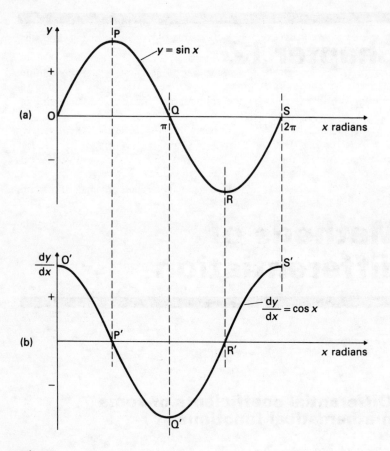

Fig. 1

and measuring the gradient of the tangents, values of $\frac{dy}{dx}$ may be obtained for corresponding values of x and these values are shown graphically in Fig. 1(b). The graph of $\frac{dy}{dx}$ against x so produced (called the derived curve) is a graph of $y = \cos x$. It follows that

$$\text{when } y = \sin x, \frac{dy}{dx} = \cos x$$

An analytical proof of this rule is given in Appendix D (page 351). By applying the principles of differentiation by substitution (see section 3 of this chapter), it may also be proved that

$$\text{when } y = \sin ax, \frac{dy}{dx} = a \cos ax$$

[An alternative method of reasoning the shape of the derived curve of $y = \sin x$ is as follows. By examining the curve of $y = \sin x$ in Fig. 1(a), the following observations can be made:

(i) at point O, the gradient is positive and at its steepest, giving a maximum positive value, shown by O' in Fig. 1(b),

(ii) between O and P, values of the gradient are positive and decreasing in value, as values of x approach P,

(iii) at point P, the tangent is a horizontal line, hence the gradient is zero, shown as P' in Fig. 1(b),

(iv) between P and Q, the gradient is negative and increasing in numerical value as x approaches point Q,

(v) at point Q the gradient is negative and at its steepest, giving a maximum negative value, shown by Q' in Fig. 1(b).

Similarly, points R' and S' may be reasoned out for the negative half cycle of the curve $y = \sin x$.]

(iii) Differential coefficient of cos x

When graphs of $y = \cos x$ and its derived curve ($\frac{dy}{dx}$ against x) are drawn in a similar way to those for $y = \sin x$ shown in (ii) above, the derived curve is a graph of $(-\sin x)$. Thus

$$\text{when } y = \cos x, \frac{dy}{dx} = -\sin x$$

An analytical proof of this rule is given in Appendix D (page 352). By applying the principles of differentiation by substitution (see section 3 of this chapter), it may be proved that

$$\text{when } y = \cos ax, \frac{dy}{dx} = -a \sin ax$$

(iv) Differential coefficient of e^x

A graph of $y = e^x$ is shown in Fig. 2(a). The slope or gradient of the curve at any point is given by $\frac{dy}{dx}$ and is continually changing. By drawing tangents to the curve at many points on the curve and measuring the gradient of the tangents, values of $\frac{dy}{dx}$ for corresponding values of x may be obtained. These values are shown graphically in Fig. 2(b). The graph of $\frac{dy}{dx}$ against x so produced is identical to the original graph of $y = e^x$. It follows that

$$\text{when } y = e^x, \frac{dy}{dx} = e^x$$

218

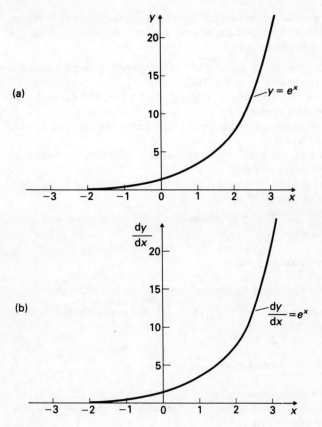

Fig. 2

By applying the principles of differentiation by substitution (see section 3 of this chapter), it may be proved that

$$\text{when } y = e^{ax}, \frac{dy}{dx} = a\,e^{ax}$$

This is as expected since by definition, the exponential function e^x, is a function whose rate of change is proportional to the original function. In the case of $y = e^x$, $a = 1$.

An analytical proof of this rule is given in Appendix D (page 353).

(v) Differential coefficient of ln x.

A graph of $y = \ln x$ is shown in Fig. 3(a). The slope or gradient of the curve at any point is given by $\frac{dy}{dx}$ and is continually changing. By drawing tangents to the curve at many points on the curve and measuring the slope of the

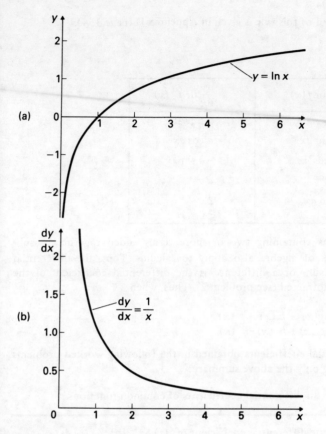

Fig. 3

tangents, values of $\dfrac{dy}{dx}$ for corresponding values of x may be obtained. These values are shown graphically in Fig. 3(b). The graph of $\dfrac{dy}{dx}$ against x so produced is the graph of $\dfrac{dy}{dx} = \dfrac{1}{x}$. It follows that

$$\text{when } y = \ln x, \frac{dy}{dx} = \frac{1}{x}$$

By applying the principles of differentiation by substitution (see section 3 of this chapter), it may be proved that

$$\text{when } y = \ln ax, \frac{dy}{dx} = \frac{1}{x}$$

(note that when $y = \ln ax$, $\dfrac{dy}{dx} \neq \dfrac{1}{ax}$)

220

An analytical proof of this rule is given in Appendix D (page 354).

Summary

y or $f(x)$	$\dfrac{dy}{dx}$ or $f'(x)$
(i) $\quad ax^n$	$a\,n\,x^{n-1}$
(ii) $\quad \sin ax$	$a \cos ax$
(iii) $\quad \cos ax$	$-a \sin ax$
(iv) $\quad e^{ax}$	$a\,e^{ax}$
(v) $\quad \ln ax$	$\dfrac{1}{x}$

For functions containing two or more terms added together or subtracted, the rules of algebra also apply to calculus. Thus, the differential coefficient of a sum or a difference is the differential coefficient of the terms added or subtracted (see problem 2). Thus, when

$$f(x) = g(x) + h(x) - j(x)$$
$$\text{then } f'(x) = g'(x) + h'(x) - j'(x)$$

The differential coefficients obtained in the following worked problems are deduced using only the above summary.

Worked problems on differential coefficients of common functions

---

Problem 1. Find the differential coefficient of: (a) $5x^4$; (b) $\dfrac{3}{x^2}$; (c) $4\sqrt{x}$.

When $f(x) = ax^n$, $f'(x) = an\,x^{n-1}$

(a) $\quad f(x) = 5x^4$

$\quad\quad f'(x) = (5)(4)\,x^{4-1} = 20x^3$

(b) $\quad f(x) = \dfrac{3}{x^2} = 3x^{-2}$

$\quad\quad f'(x) = (3)(-2)\,x^{-2-1} = -6x^{-3}$

i.e. $\quad f'(x) = \dfrac{-6}{x^3}$

(c) $\quad f(x) = 4\sqrt{x} = 4x^{\frac{1}{2}}$

$\quad\quad f'(x) = (4)(\tfrac{1}{2})\,x^{\frac{1}{2}-1} = 2x^{-\frac{1}{2}}$

i.e. $\quad f'(x) = \dfrac{2}{\sqrt{x}}$

Problem 2. Differentiate $2x^3 + 7x + \dfrac{1}{3x^2} - \dfrac{4}{x^3} + \dfrac{4}{3}\sqrt{x^3} - 8$ with respect to x.

$$f(x) = 2x^3 + 7x + \frac{1}{3x^2} - \frac{4}{x^3} + \frac{4}{3}\sqrt{x^3} - 8$$

$$= 2x^3 + 7x + \frac{x^{-2}}{3} - 4x^{-3} + \frac{4}{3}x^{\frac{3}{2}} - 8$$

$$f'(x) = (2)(3)\,x^{3-1} + (7)\,x^{1-1} + \frac{(-2)}{3}\,x^{-2-1} - (4)(-3)\,x^{-3-1}$$

$$+ \left(\frac{4}{3}\right)\left(\frac{3}{2}\right)x^{\frac{3}{2}-1} - 0$$

$$= 6x^2 + 7 - \frac{2}{3}\,x^{-3} + 12\,x^{-4} + 2x^{\frac{1}{2}}$$

i.e. $f'(x) = 6x^2 + 7 - \dfrac{2}{3x^3} + \dfrac{12}{x^4} + 2\sqrt{x}$

Problem 3. (a) If $f(x) = 2\sin x$ find $f'(x)$;

(b) If $y = 5\cos x$ find $\dfrac{dy}{dx}$.

(a) When $f(x) = \sin x, f'(x) = \cos x$
When $f(x) = 2\sin x$
then $f'(x) = 2\cos x$

(b) When $y = \cos x, \dfrac{dy}{dx} = -\sin x$

When $y = 5\cos x$

then $\dfrac{dy}{dx} = -5\sin x$

Problem 4. Differentiate: (a) e^{6t}; (b) $5e^{-3t}$ with respect to t.

When $f(t) = e^{at}, f'(t) = a\,e^{at}$
(a) $f(t) = e^{6t}$
$f'(t) = 6\,e^{6t}$
(b) $f(t) = 5e^{-3t}$
$f'(t) = (5)(-3)\,e^{-3t} = -15\,e^{-3t}$

Problem 5. Find the differential coefficient of: (a) $\ln 4x$; (b) $3\ln 2x$.

When $f(x) = \ln ax, f'(x) = \dfrac{1}{x}$

(a) $f(x) = \ln 4x, f'(x) = \dfrac{1}{x}$

(b) $f(x) = 3\ln 2x, f'(x) = \dfrac{3}{x}$

Problem 6. If $g = 3.2\,b^5 - 3\sin b - 5e^{7b} + \sqrt[3]{b^4} + 6$, find $\dfrac{dg}{db}$.

$$g = 3.2\,b^5 - 3\sin b - 5e^{7b} + b^{\frac{4}{3}} + 6$$

$$\frac{dg}{db} = (3.2)(5)\,b^4 - 3\cos b - (5)(7)\,e^{7b} + \left(\frac{4}{3}\right)b^{\frac{1}{3}} + 0$$

$$= 16\,b^4 - 3\cos b - 35\,e^{7b} + \frac{4}{3}\,b^{\frac{1}{3}}$$

i.e. $\dfrac{dg}{db} = 16\,b^4 - 3\cos b - 35\,e^{7b} + \dfrac{4}{3}\sqrt[3]{b}$

Problem 7. $f(x) = 4\ln(2.6x) - \dfrac{3}{\sqrt[3]{x^2}} + \dfrac{4}{e^{3x}} + \dfrac{1}{5} - 2\cos x$. Find $f'(x)$.

$$f(x) = 4\ln(2.6x) - 3x^{-\frac{2}{3}} + 4e^{-3x} + \frac{1}{5} - 2\cos x$$

$$f'(x) = \frac{4}{x} - (3)\left(-\frac{2}{3}\right)x^{-\frac{5}{3}} + (4)(-3)\,e^{-3x} + 0 - (-2\sin x)$$

i.e. $f'(x) = \dfrac{4}{x} + \dfrac{2}{\sqrt[3]{x^5}} - \dfrac{12}{e^{3x}} + 2\sin x$

Problem 8. Find the gradient of the curve $y = \dfrac{3}{2\sqrt{x}}$ at the point $\left(4, \dfrac{3}{4}\right)$.

$$y = \frac{3}{2\sqrt{x}} = \frac{3}{2}\,x^{-\frac{1}{2}}$$

$$\text{Gradient} = \frac{dy}{dx} = \left(\frac{3}{2}\right)\left(-\frac{1}{2}\right)x^{-\frac{3}{2}} = -\frac{3}{4\sqrt{x^3}}$$

When $x = 4$, gradient $= -\dfrac{3}{4\sqrt{4^3}} = -\dfrac{3}{4(8)}$

i.e. **Gradient** $= -\dfrac{3}{32}$

Problem 9. Find the coordinates of the point on the curve $y = 3\sqrt[3]{x^2}$ where the gradient is 1.

$$y = 3\sqrt[3]{x^2} = 3x^{\frac{2}{3}}$$

$$\text{Gradient} = \frac{dy}{dx} = (3)(\tfrac{2}{3})\,x^{-\frac{1}{3}} = \frac{2}{\sqrt[3]{x}}$$

If the gradient is equal to 1, then $1 = \dfrac{2}{\sqrt[3]{x}}$

i.e. $\sqrt[3]{x} = 2$

$x = 2^3 = 8$

When $x = 8$, $y = 3\sqrt[3]{8^2} = 3(4) = 12$

Hence the gradient is 1 at the point (8, 12)

Problem 10. If $f(x) = \dfrac{4x^3 - 8x^2 + 6x}{2x}$ find the coordinates of the point at which the gradient is: (a) zero; and (b) 4.

$$f(x) = \frac{4x^3 - 8x^2 + 6x}{2x} = \frac{4x^3}{2x} - \frac{8x^2}{2x} + \frac{6x}{2x}$$
$$= 2x^2 - 4x + 3$$

The derivative, $f'(x)$, gives the gradient of the curve.
Hence $f'(x) = (2)(2) x^1 - 4$
$$= 4x - 4$$

    (a) When $f'(x)$ is zero
      $4x - 4 = 0$
i.e. $x = 1$

When $x = 1$, $y = \dfrac{4x^3 - 8x^2 + 6x}{2x} = \dfrac{4(1)^3 - 8(1)^2 + 6(1)}{2(1)}$

i.e. $y = 1$
Hence the coordinates of the point where the gradient is zero are **(1, 1)**

    (b) When $f'(x)$ is 4
      $4x - 4 = 4$
i.e. $x = 2$
When $x = 2$, $y = 2 (2)^2 - 4 (2) + 3 = 3$
Hence the coordinates of the point where the gradient is 4 are **(2, 3)**

Further problems on differential coefficients of common functions may be found in Section 5, Problems 1–30, page 236.

2 Differentiation of products and quotients of two functions

(i) Differentiation of a product

The function $y = 3x^2 \sin x$ is a product of two terms in x, i.e. $3x^2$ and $\sin x$.
    Let $u = 3x^2$ and $v = \sin x$.
    Let x increase by a small increment δx, causing incremental changes in u, v and y of δu, δv and δy respectively.

Then $y = (3x^2)(\sin x)$
            $= (u)(v)$
      $y + \delta y = (u + \delta u)(v + \delta v)$
            $= uv + v\delta u + u\delta v + \delta u \delta v$
$(y + \delta y) - (y) = uv + v\delta u + u\delta v + \delta u \delta v - uv$
        $\delta y = v\delta u + u\delta v + \delta u \delta v$

Dividing both sides by δx gives:

$$\frac{\delta y}{\delta x} = v\frac{\delta u}{\delta x} + u\frac{\delta v}{\delta x} + \frac{\delta u}{\delta x}\,\delta v$$

As $\delta x \to 0$ then $\delta u \to 0$, $\delta v \to 0$ and $\delta y \to 0$

However, the fact that δu and δx, for example, both approach zero does not mean that $\frac{\delta u}{\delta x}$ will approach zero.

Ratios of small quantities, such as $\frac{\delta u}{\delta x}, \frac{\delta v}{\delta x}$ or $\frac{\delta y}{\delta x}$ can be significant.

Consider two lines AB and AC meeting at A and whose intersecting angle (i.e. $\angle$ BAC) is any value.

If AB $= \delta y = 1$ unit, say, and AC $= \delta x = 2$ units, then the ratio

$$\frac{\delta y}{\delta x} = \frac{1}{2}.$$

This ratio of $\frac{1}{2}$ is still the same whether the unit of δy and δx is in, say, kilometres or millimetres. No matter how small δy or δx is made, the ratio is still $\frac{1}{2}$. Thus when $\delta y \to 0$ and when $\delta x \to 0$, the ratio $\frac{\delta y}{\delta x}$ is still a significant value.

As $\delta x \to 0$, $\frac{\delta u}{\delta x} \to \frac{du}{dx}, \frac{\delta v}{\delta x} \to \frac{dv}{dx}, \frac{\delta y}{\delta x} \to \frac{dy}{dx}$ and $\delta v \to 0$

Hence $\dfrac{dy}{dx} = v\dfrac{du}{dx} + u\dfrac{dv}{dx}$

This is known as the **product rule**.

Summary

When $y = uv$ and u and v are functions of x, then

$$\frac{dy}{dx} = v\frac{du}{dx} + u\frac{dv}{dx}$$

Using functional notation: When $F(x) = f(x)\,g(x)$ then:

$$F'(x) = f(x)\,g'(x) + g(x)\,f'(x)$$

Applying the product rule to $y = 3x^2 \sin x$:

let $\qquad u = 3x^2$ and $v = \sin x$

Then $\quad \dfrac{dy}{dx} = (\sin x)\dfrac{d}{dx}(3x^2) + (3x^2)\dfrac{d}{dx}(\sin x)$

$\qquad\qquad = (\sin x)(6x) + (3x^2)(\cos x)$

$\qquad\qquad = 6x \sin x + 3x^2 \cos x$

i.e. $\qquad \dfrac{dy}{dx} = 3x(2\sin x + x\cos x)$

From the above it should be noted that the differential coefficient of a product **cannot** be obtained merely by differentiating each term and multiplying the two answers together. The above formula **must** be used whenever differentiating products.

(ii) Differentiation of a quotient

The function $y = \dfrac{3 \cos x}{5x^3}$ is a quotient of two terms in x, i.e. $3 \cos x$ and $5x^3$.

Let $u = 3 \cos x$ and $v = 5x^3$.

Let x increase by a small increment δx causing incremental changes in u, v and y of δu, δv and δy respectively.

Then
$$y = \frac{3 \cos x}{5x^3}$$

$$= \frac{u}{v}$$

$$y + \delta y = \frac{u + \delta u}{v + \delta v}$$

$$(y + \delta y) - (y) = \frac{u + \delta u}{v + \delta v} - \frac{u}{v}$$

$$= \frac{uv + v\delta u - uv - u\delta v}{v(v + \delta v)}$$

i.e.
$$\delta y = \frac{v\delta u - u\delta v}{v^2 + v\delta v}$$

Dividing both sides by δx gives:

$$\frac{\delta y}{\delta x} = \frac{v\dfrac{\delta u}{\delta x} - u\dfrac{\delta v}{\delta x}}{v^2 + v\delta v}$$

As $\delta x \to 0$, $\dfrac{\delta u}{\delta x} \to \dfrac{du}{dx}$, $\dfrac{\delta v}{\delta x} \to \dfrac{dv}{dx}$, $\dfrac{\delta y}{\delta x} \to \dfrac{dy}{dx}$ and $\delta v \to 0$

Hence
$$\frac{dy}{dx} = \frac{v\dfrac{du}{dx} - u\dfrac{dv}{dx}}{v^2}$$

This is known as the **quotient rule**.

Summary

When $y = \dfrac{u}{v}$ and u and v are functions of x, then

$$\frac{dy}{dx} = \frac{v\dfrac{du}{dx} - u\dfrac{dv}{dx}}{v^2}$$

Using functional notation:

When $F(x) = \dfrac{f(x)}{g(x)}$, then $F'(x) = \dfrac{g(x)\,f'(x) - f(x)\,g'(x)}{[g(x)]^2}$

Applying the quotient rule to $y = \dfrac{3 \cos x}{5x^3}$:

Let $u = 3 \cos x$ and $v = 5x^3$

Then $\dfrac{dy}{dx} = \dfrac{(5x^3)\,\dfrac{d}{dx}(3 \cos x) - (3 \cos x)\,\dfrac{d}{dx}(5x^3)}{(5x^3)^2}$

$= \dfrac{(5x^3)(-3 \sin x) - (3 \cos x)(15x^2)}{25x^6}$

$= \dfrac{-15x^2(x \sin x + 3 \cos x)}{25x^6}$

i.e. $\dfrac{dy}{dx} = \dfrac{-3(x \sin x + 3 \cos x)}{5x^4}$

From above it should be noted that the differential coefficient of a quotient cannot be obtained by merely differentiating each term and dividing the numerator by the denominator. The above formula must be used when differentiating quotients.

The first step when differentiating a product such as $y = uv$ or a quotient such as $y = \dfrac{u}{v}$ is to decide clearly which is the u part and which is the v part. When this has been decided differentiation involves substitution into the appropriate formula.

Worked Problems on differentiating products and quotients

Problem 1. Find the differential coefficient of $5x^2 \cos x$.

Let $y = 5x^2 \cos x$

Also, let $u = 5x^2$ and $v = \cos x$

Then $\dfrac{du}{dx} = 10x$ and $\dfrac{dv}{dx} = -\sin x$

Then $\dfrac{dy}{dx} = v\,\dfrac{du}{dx} + u\,\dfrac{dv}{dx}$

$= (\cos x)(10x) + (5x^2)(-\sin x)$

$= 10x \cos x - 5x^2 \sin x$

i.e. $\dfrac{dy}{dx} = 5x(2 \cos x - x \sin x)$

Problem 2. Differentiate $3e^{2b} \sin b$ with respect to b.

Let $F(b) = 3e^{2b} \sin b$
Let $f(b) = 3e^{2b}$ and $g(b) = \sin b$
then $f'(b) = 6e^{2b}$ and $g'(b) = \cos b$
Then $F'(b) = g(b)\,f'(b) + f(b)\,g'(b)$
$\qquad\qquad = (\sin b)\,(6e^{2b}) + (3e^{2b})\,(\cos b)$
$\qquad\qquad = 6e^{2b} \sin b + 3e^{2b} \cos b$
i.e. $F'(b) = 3e^{2b}\,[2\sin b + \cos b]$

Problem 3. If $y = 7\sqrt{x}\, \ln 4x$ find $\dfrac{dy}{dx}$.

$\qquad y = 7x^{\frac{1}{2}} \ln 4x$
Let $u = 7x^{\frac{1}{2}}$ and $v = \ln 4x$
then $\dfrac{du}{dx} = \dfrac{7}{2} x^{-\frac{1}{2}}$ and $\dfrac{dv}{dx} = \dfrac{1}{x}$

Then $\dfrac{dy}{dx} = v\dfrac{du}{dx} + u\dfrac{dv}{dx}$

$\qquad\qquad = (\ln 4x)\left[\dfrac{7}{2} x^{-\frac{1}{2}}\right] + [7x^{\frac{1}{2}}]\left[\dfrac{1}{x}\right]$

$\qquad\qquad = \dfrac{7}{2\sqrt{x}} \ln 4x + \dfrac{7}{\sqrt{x}}$

i.e. $\dfrac{dy}{dx} = \dfrac{7}{2\sqrt{x}}\,(\ln 4x + 2)$

Problem 4. Find the differential coefficients of: (a) $\tan x$; (b) $\cot x$; (c) $\sec x$; (d) $\operatorname{cosec} x$.

$\qquad$ (a) Let $y = \tan x = \dfrac{\sin x}{\cos x}$

Differentiation of $\tan x$ is treated as a quotient with $u = \sin x$ and $v = \cos x$.

Then $\dfrac{du}{dx} = \cos x$ and $\dfrac{dv}{dx} = -\sin x$

$\dfrac{dy}{dx} = \dfrac{v\dfrac{du}{dx} - u\dfrac{dv}{dx}}{v^2}$

$\qquad = \dfrac{(\cos x)\,(\cos x) - (\sin x)\,(-\sin x)}{(\cos x)^2}$

$$= \frac{(\cos^2 x + \sin^2 x)}{(\cos x)^2}$$

$$= \frac{1}{\cos^2 x} \quad (\text{since } \cos^2 x + \sin^2 x = 1)$$

i.e. $\dfrac{dy}{dx} = \sec^2 x$.

Hence, when $y = \tan x, \dfrac{dy}{dx} = \sec^2 x$

or, when $f(x) = \tan x, f'(x) = \sec^2 x$

(b) Let $y = \cot x = \dfrac{\cos x}{\sin x}$

Differentiation of $\cot x$ is treated as a quotient with $u = \cos x$ and $v = \sin x$.

Then $\dfrac{du}{dx} = -\sin x$ and $\dfrac{dv}{dx} = \cos x$

$$\frac{dy}{dx} = \frac{v\dfrac{du}{dx} - u\dfrac{dv}{dx}}{v^2}$$

$$= \frac{(\sin x)(-\sin x) - (\cos x)(\cos x)}{(\sin x)^2}$$

$$= \frac{-(\sin^2 x + \cos^2 x)}{\sin^2 x}$$

$$= \frac{-1}{\sin^2 x}$$

i.e. $\dfrac{dy}{dx} = -\operatorname{cosec}^2 x$

Hence when $y = \cot x, \dfrac{dy}{dx} = -\operatorname{cosec}^2 x$

or, when $f(x) = \cot x, f'(x) = -\operatorname{cosec}^2 x$

(c) Let $y = \sec x = \dfrac{1}{\cos x}$

Differentiation of $\sec x$ is treated as a quotient with $u = 1$ and $v = \cos x$.

Then $\dfrac{du}{dx} = 0$ and $\dfrac{dv}{dx} = -\sin x$

$$\frac{dy}{dx} = \frac{v\dfrac{du}{dx} - u\dfrac{dv}{dx}}{v^2}$$

$$= \frac{(\cos x)(0) - (1)(-\sin x)}{(\cos x)^2}$$

$$= \frac{\sin x}{\cos^2 x}$$

$$= \left[\frac{1}{\cos x}\right] \left[\frac{\sin x}{\cos x}\right]$$

i.e. $\dfrac{dy}{dx} = \sec x \tan x$

Hence when $y = \sec x$, $\dfrac{dy}{dx} = \sec x \tan x$

or, when $f(x) = \sec x$, $f'(x) = \sec x \tan x$

(d) Let $y = \text{cosec } x = \dfrac{1}{\sin x}$

Differentiation of cosec x is treated as a quotient with $u = 1$ and $v = \sin x$.

Then $\dfrac{du}{dx} = 0$ and $\dfrac{dv}{dx} = \cos x$

$$\frac{dy}{dx} = \frac{v\dfrac{du}{dx} - u\dfrac{dv}{dx}}{v^2}$$

$$= \frac{(\sin x)\,(0) - (1)\,(\cos x)}{(\sin x)^2}$$

$$= \frac{-\cos x}{\sin^2 x}$$

$$= -\left[\frac{1}{\sin x}\right] \left[\frac{\cos x}{\sin x}\right]$$

i.e. $\dfrac{dy}{dx} = -\text{cosec } x \cot x$

Hence when $y = \text{cosec } x$, $\dfrac{dy}{dx} = -\text{cosec } x \cot x$

or, when $f(x) = \text{cosec } x$, $f'(x) = -\text{cosec } x \cot x$

The differential coefficients of the six trigonometrical ratios may thus be summarised as below:

	y or $f(x)$	$\dfrac{dy}{dx}$ or $f'(x)$
1.	$\sin x$	$\cos x$
2.	$\cos x$	$-\sin x$
3.	$\tan x$	$\sec^2 x$
4.	$\sec x$	$\sec x \tan x$
5.	$\text{cosec } x$	$-\text{cosec } x \cot x$
6.	$\cot x$	$-\text{cosec}^2 x$

Problem 5. If $f(t) = \dfrac{4e^{7t}}{\sqrt[3]{t^2}}$ find $f'(t)$

$$f(t) = \frac{4e^{7t}}{t^{\frac{2}{3}}}$$

Let $\quad g(t) = 4e^{7t}$ and $h(t) = t^{\frac{2}{3}}$

then $\quad g'(t) = 28e^{7t}$ and $h'(t) = \frac{2}{3}t^{-\frac{1}{3}}$

$$f'(t) = \frac{h(t)\,g'(t) - g(t)\,h'(t)}{[h(t)]^2} = \frac{(t^{\frac{2}{3}})(28e^{7t}) - (4e^{7t})(\frac{2}{3}t^{-\frac{1}{3}})}{(t^{\frac{2}{3}})^2}$$

$$= \frac{28t^{\frac{2}{3}}e^{7t} - \frac{8}{3}t^{-\frac{1}{3}}e^{7t}}{t^{\frac{4}{3}}} = \frac{28t^{\frac{2}{3}}e^{7t}}{t^{\frac{4}{3}}} - \frac{8t^{-\frac{1}{3}}e^{7t}}{3t^{\frac{4}{3}}}$$

$$= 28t^{-\frac{2}{3}}e^{7t} - \frac{8}{3}t^{-\frac{5}{3}}e^{7t}$$

$$= \frac{4}{3}e^{7t}\,t^{-\frac{5}{3}}(21t - 2)$$

i.e. $\quad f'(t) = \dfrac{4e^{7t}}{3\sqrt[3]{t^5}}(21t - 2)$

(Note that initially, $f(t) = \dfrac{4e^{7t}}{t^{\frac{2}{3}}}$ could have been treated as a product $f(t) = 4e^{7t}\,t^{-\frac{2}{3}}$)

Problem 6. Find the coordinates of the points on the curve $y = \dfrac{\frac{1}{3}(5 - 6x)}{3x^2 + 2}$ where the gradient is zero.

$$y = \frac{\frac{1}{3}(5 - 6x)}{3x^2 + 2}$$

Let $\quad u = \frac{1}{3}(5 - 6x)$ and $v = 3x^2 + 2$

then $\quad \dfrac{du}{dx} = -2$ and $\dfrac{dv}{dx} = 6x$

$$\frac{dy}{dx} = \frac{v\dfrac{du}{dx} - u\dfrac{dv}{dx}}{v^2} = \frac{(3x^2 + 2)(-2) - \frac{1}{3}(5 - 6x)(6x)}{(3x^2 + 2)^2}$$

$$= \frac{-6x^2 - 4 - 10x + 12x^2}{(3x^2 + 2)^2} = \frac{6x^2 - 10x - 4}{(3x^2 + 2)^2}$$

When the gradient is zero, $\dfrac{dy}{dx} = 0$

Hence $\quad 6x^2 - 10x - 4 = 0$

$$2(3x^2 - 5x - 2) = 0$$

$$2(3x + 1)(x - 2) = 0$$

i.e. $x = -\frac{1}{3}$ or $x = 2$

Substituting in the original equation for y:

When $x = -\frac{1}{3}$, $\quad y = \dfrac{\frac{1}{3}[5 - 6(-\frac{1}{3})]}{3(-\frac{1}{3})^2 + 2} = \dfrac{\frac{7}{3}}{\frac{7}{3}} = 1$

When $x = 2$, $y = \dfrac{\frac{1}{3}[5 - 6(2)]}{3(2)^2 + 2} = \dfrac{-\frac{7}{3}}{14} = -\frac{1}{6}$

Hence the coordinates of the points on the curve $y = \dfrac{\frac{1}{3}(5 - 6x)}{3x^2 + 2}$ where the gradient is zero are $(-\frac{1}{3}, 1)$ and $(2, -\frac{1}{6})$.

Problem 7. Differentiate $\dfrac{\sqrt{x}\sin x}{2e^{4x}}$ with respect to x.

The function $\dfrac{\sqrt{x}\sin x}{2e^{4x}}$ is a quotient, although the numerator (i.e. $\sqrt{x}\sin x$) is a product.

Let $\quad y = \dfrac{x^{\frac{1}{2}}\sin x}{2e^{4x}}$

Let $\quad u = x^{\frac{1}{2}}\sin x$ and $v = 2e^{4x}$

then $\quad \dfrac{du}{dx} = (x^{\frac{1}{2}})(\cos x) + (\sin x)(\frac{1}{2}x^{-\frac{1}{2}})$

and $\quad \dfrac{dv}{dx} = 8e^{4x}$

$\dfrac{dy}{dx} = \dfrac{v\dfrac{du}{dx} - u\dfrac{dv}{dx}}{v^2}$

$= \dfrac{(2e^{4x})(x^{\frac{1}{2}}\cos x + \frac{1}{2}x^{-\frac{1}{2}}\sin x) - (x^{\frac{1}{2}}\sin x)(8e^{4x})}{(2e^{4x})^2}$

Dividing throughout by $2e^{4x}$ gives:

$\dfrac{dy}{dx} = \dfrac{x^{\frac{1}{2}}\cos x + \frac{1}{2}x^{-\frac{1}{2}}\sin x - 4x^{\frac{1}{2}}\sin x}{2e^{4x}}$

Hence $\dfrac{dy}{dx} = \dfrac{\sqrt{x}\cos x + \sin x\left(\dfrac{1}{2\sqrt{x}} - 4\sqrt{x}\right)}{2e^{4x}}$

or $\dfrac{dy}{dx} = \dfrac{\sqrt{x}\cos x + \left(\dfrac{1 - 8x}{2\sqrt{x}}\right)\sin x}{2e^{4x}}$

Further problems on differentiating products and quotients may be found in Section 5, Problems 31–64, page 238.

3 Differentiation by substitution

The function $y = (4x - 3)^7$ can be differentiated by firstly multiplying $(4x - 3)$

by itself seven times, and then differentiating each term produced in turn. This would be a long process. In this type of function a substitution is made. Let $u = 4x - 3$, then instead of $y = (4x - 3)^7$ we have $y = u^7$.

An important rule that is used when differentiating by substitution is:

$$\frac{dy}{dx} = \frac{dy}{du} \cdot \frac{du}{dx}$$

This is often known as the **chain rule**.

From above, $y = (4x - 3)^7$

If $u = 4x - 3$ then $y = u^7$

Thus $\dfrac{dy}{du} = 7u^6$ and $\dfrac{du}{dx} = 4$

Hence since $\dfrac{dy}{dx} = \dfrac{dy}{du} \cdot \dfrac{du}{dx}$

$$\frac{dy}{dx} = (7u^6)(4) = 28u^6$$

Rewriting $u = 4x - 3$, $\dfrac{dy}{dx} = 28(4x - 3)^6$

Since y is a function of u, and u is a function of x, then y is a 'function of a function' of x. The method of obtaining differential coefficients by making substitutions is often called the 'function of a function process'.

Worked problems on differentiation by substitution

Problem 1. Differentiate $\sin(6x + 1)$.

Let $\quad y = \sin(6x + 1)$

and $\quad u = 6x + 1$

Then $\quad y = \sin u$, giving $\dfrac{dy}{du} = \cos u$

and $\quad \dfrac{du}{dx} = 6$

Using the 'differentiation by substitution' formula: $\dfrac{dy}{dx} = \dfrac{dy}{du} \cdot \dfrac{du}{dx}$ gives

$\dfrac{dy}{dx} = (\cos u)(6) = 6 \cos u$

Rewriting $u = 6x + 1$ gives:

$$\frac{dy}{dx} = 6 \cos(6x + 1)$$

Note that this result could have been obtained by firstly differentiating the trigonometric function (i.e. differentiating $\sin f(x)$) giving $\cos f(x)$ and then multiplying by the differential coefficient of $f(x)$, i.e. 6.

Problem 2. Find the differential coefficient of $(3t^4 - 2t)^5$.

Let $\quad y = (3t^4 - 2t)^5$

and $\quad u = 3t^4 - 2t$

Then $\quad y = u^5$, giving $\dfrac{dy}{du} = 5u^4$

and $\quad \dfrac{du}{dt} = 12t^3 - 2$

Using the 'chain rule': $\dfrac{dy}{dt} = \dfrac{dy}{du} \cdot \dfrac{du}{dt}$ gives $\dfrac{dy}{dt} = (5u^4)(12t^3 - 2)$

Rewriting $u = 3t^4 - 2t$ gives:

$$\frac{dy}{dt} = 5(3t^4 - 2t)^4 (12t^3 - 2)$$

Note that this result could have been obtained by firstly differentiating the bracket, giving $5[f(x)]^4$ and then multiplying this result by the differential coefficient of $f(x)$ (i.e. $(12t^3 - 2)$).

Problem 3. If $y = 5 \operatorname{cosec}(3\sqrt{x} + 2x)$ find $\dfrac{dy}{dx}$.

$$y = 5 \operatorname{cosec}(3\sqrt{x} + 2x)$$

Let $\quad u = (3\sqrt{x} + 2x)$ then $\dfrac{du}{dx} = \dfrac{3}{2\sqrt{x}} + 2$

Thus $\quad y = 5 \operatorname{cosec} u$ and $\dfrac{dy}{du} = -5 \operatorname{cosec} u \cot u$

Now $\dfrac{dy}{dx} = \dfrac{dy}{du} \cdot \dfrac{du}{dx} = (-5 \operatorname{cosec} u \cot u)\left(\dfrac{3}{2\sqrt{x}} + 2\right)$

Rewriting $u = 3\sqrt{x} + 2x$ gives:

$$\frac{dy}{dx} = -5\left(\frac{3}{2\sqrt{x}} + 2\right) \operatorname{cosec}(3\sqrt{x} + 2x) \cot(3\sqrt{x} + 2x)$$

In a similar way to Problem 1, this result could have been obtained by firstly differentiating $5 \operatorname{cosec} f(x)$ giving $-5 \operatorname{cosec} f(x) \cot f(x)$ and then multiplying this result by the differential coefficient of $f(x)$.

Problem 4. If $p = 2 \tan^5 v$ find $\dfrac{dp}{dv}$.

$$p = 2 \tan^5 v$$

Let $\quad u = \tan v$ then $\dfrac{du}{dv} = \sec^2 v$

Then $\quad p = 2u^5$ and $\dfrac{dp}{du} = 10u^4$

Now $\dfrac{dp}{dv} = \dfrac{dp}{du} \cdot \dfrac{du}{dv} = (10u^4)(\sec^2 v)$

Rewriting $u = \tan v$ gives:

$$\frac{dp}{dv} = 10 \, (\tan v)^4 \sec^2 v$$

$$\frac{dp}{dv} = 10 \, \tan^4 v \, \sec^2 v$$

In a similar way to Problem 2, this result could have been obtained by firstly differentiating the bracket (i.e. differentiating $2[f(v)]^5$) giving $10[f(v)]^4$ and then multiplying this result by the differential coefficient of $f(v)$.

Problem 5. Write down the differential coefficients of the following:
(a) $\sqrt{(4x^2 + x - 3)}$; (b) $2 \sec^3 t$; (c) $4 \cot (5g^2 + 2)$; (d) $\sqrt{(4x^3 + 2)^3} \cos (3x^2 + 2)$.

(a) $f(x) = \sqrt{(4x^2 + x - 3)} = (4x^2 + x - 3)^{\frac{1}{2}}$

$f'(x) = \frac{1}{2} (4x^2 + x - 3)^{-\frac{1}{2}} (8x + 1)$

$$= \frac{8x + 1}{2\sqrt{(4x^2 + x - 3)}}$$

(b) $f(t) = 2 \sec^3 t = 2 (\sec t)^3$

$f'(t) = 6 (\sec t)^2 (\sec t \tan t)$

$= 6 \sec^3 t \tan t$

(c) $f(g) = 4 \cot (5g^2 + 2)$

$f'(g) = 4 [- \operatorname{cosec}^2 (5g^2 + 2)] \, (10g)$

$= - 40g \operatorname{cosec}^2 (5g^2 + 2)$

(d) $f(x) = \sqrt{(4x^3 + 2)^3} \cos (3x^2 + 2)$

$= (4x^3 + 2)^{\frac{3}{2}} \cos (3x^2 + 2)$ (i.e. a product)

$f'(x) = [\cos (3x^2 + 2)] \, [\frac{3}{2} (4x^3 + 2)^{\frac{1}{2}} (12x^2)]$

$\qquad\qquad + [(4x^3 + 2)^{\frac{3}{2}}] \, [(- \sin (3x^2 + 2))(6x)]$

$= 6x\sqrt{(4x^3 + 2)} \, [3x \cos (3x^2 + 2) - (4x^3 + 2) \sin (3x^2 + 2)]$

Further problems on differentiation by substitution may be found in Section 5, Problems 65–128, page 240.

4   Successive differentiation

When a function, say, $y = f(x)$, is differentiated, the differential coefficient is written as $f'(x)$ or $\frac{dy}{dx}$.

If the expression is differentiated again, the second differential coefficient or the second derivative is obtained. This is written as $f''(x)$ (pronounced 'f double-dash x') or $\frac{d^2y}{dx^2}$ (pronounced 'dee two y by dee x squared'). Similarly, if differentiated again the third differential coefficient or third derivative is obtained, and is written as $f'''(x)$ or $\dfrac{d^3y}{dx^3}$, and so on.

Worked problems on successive differentiation

Problem 1. If $f(x) = 3x^4 + 2x^3 + x - 1$, find $f'(x)$ and $f''(x)$.

$$f(x) = 3x^4 + 2x^3 + x - 1$$
$$f'(x) = (3)(4)x^3 + (2)(3)x^2 + 1 - 0$$
$$= 12x^3 + 6x^2 + 1$$

$$f''(x) = (12)(3)x^2 + (6)(2)x + 0$$
$$= 36x^2 + 12x$$

Problem 2. If $y = \dfrac{4}{3}x^3 - \dfrac{2}{x^2} + \dfrac{1}{3x} - \sqrt{x}$ find $\dfrac{d^2y}{dx^2}$ and $\dfrac{d^3y}{dx^3}$.

$$y = \frac{4}{3}x^3 - \frac{2}{x^2} + \frac{1}{3x} - \sqrt{x}$$

$$= \frac{4}{3}x^3 - 2x^{-2} + \frac{1}{3}x^{-1} - x^{\frac{1}{2}}$$

$$\frac{dy}{dx} = [\tfrac{4}{3}](3)\,x^2 - (2)(-2)x^{-3} + \tfrac{1}{3}(-1)x^{-2} - [\tfrac{1}{2}]\,x^{-\frac{1}{2}}$$

$$= 4x^2 + 4x^{-3} - \tfrac{1}{3}x^{-2} - \tfrac{1}{2}x^{-\frac{1}{2}}$$

$$\frac{d^2y}{dx^2} = (4)(2)x + (4)(-3)x^{-4} - [\tfrac{1}{3}](-2)x^{-3} - [\tfrac{1}{2}][-\tfrac{1}{2}]x^{-\frac{3}{2}}$$

$$= 8x - 12x^{-4} + \tfrac{2}{3}x^{-3} + \tfrac{1}{4}x^{-\frac{3}{2}}$$

i.e. $\dfrac{d^2y}{dx^2} = 8x - \dfrac{12}{x^4} + \dfrac{2}{3x^3} + \dfrac{1}{4\sqrt{x^3}}$

$$\frac{d^3y}{dx^3} = 8 - (12)(-4)\,x^{-5} + [\tfrac{2}{3}](-3)x^{-4} + [\tfrac{1}{4}][-\tfrac{3}{2}]\,x^{-\frac{5}{2}}$$

$$= 8 + 48x^{-5} - 2x^{-4} - \tfrac{3}{8}x^{-\frac{5}{2}}$$

i.e. $\dfrac{d^3y}{dx^3} = 8 + \dfrac{48}{x^5} - \dfrac{2}{x^4} - \dfrac{3}{8\sqrt{x^5}}$

Problem 3. Evaluate $f'(t)$ and $f''(t)$, correct to 3 decimal places when $t = \dfrac{1}{2}$ given $f(t) = 3 \ln \cos 2t$.

$$f(t) = 3 \ln \cos 2t$$

$$f'(t) = 3\left(\frac{1}{\cos 2t}\right)(-2\sin 2t)$$

$$= -6 \tan 2t$$

When $t = \frac{1}{2}, f'(t) = -6 \tan 1 = -6 (1.5574) = -9.344$

$$f''(t) = -6 (\sec^2 2t)2$$
$$= -12 \sec^2 2t$$

When $t = \frac{1}{2}, f''(t) = -12 (3.4255) = -41.106$

Problem 4. If $y = Ae^{2x} + Be^{-3x}$ prove that $\dfrac{d^2y}{dx^2} + \dfrac{dy}{dx} - 6y = 0$.

$$y = Ae^{2x} + Be^{-3x}$$

$$\frac{dy}{dx} = 2Ae^{2x} - 3Be^{-3x}$$

$$\frac{d^2y}{dx^2} = 4Ae^{2x} + 9Be^{-3x}$$

$$6y = 6(Ae^{2x} + Be^{-3x}) = 6Ae^{2x} + 6Be^{-3x}$$

Substituting into $\dfrac{d^2y}{dx^2} + \dfrac{dy}{dx} - 6y$ gives:

$$(4Ae^{2x} + 9Be^{-3x}) + (2Ae^{2x} - 3Be^{-3x}) - (6Ae^{2x} + 6Be^{-3x})$$
$$= 4Ae^{2x} + 9Be^{-3x} + 2Ae^{2x} - 3Be^{-3x} - 6Ae^{2x} - 6Be^{-3x} = 0$$

Thus $\dfrac{d^2y}{dx^2} + \dfrac{dy}{dx} - 6y = 0$

(Note that an equation of the form $\dfrac{d^2y}{dx^2} + \dfrac{dy}{dx} - 6y = 0$ is known as a 'differential equation' and such equations are discussed in Chapter 17.)

Further problems on successive differentiation may be found in the following section (5), Problems 129–151, page 242.

5 Further problems

Differentiation of common functions

Find the differential coefficients with respect to x of the functions in Problems 1–6.

1. (a) x^4 (b) x^6 (c) x^9 (d) $x^{3.2}$ (e) $x^{4.7}$
   (a) $[4x^3]$ (b) $[6x^5]$ (c) $[9x^8]$ (d) $[3.2x^{2.2}]$ (e) $[4.7x^{3.7}]$

2. (a) $3x^3$ (b) $4x^7$ (c) $2x^{10}$ (d) $4.6x^{1.5}$ (e) $6x^{5.4}$
   (a) $[9x^2]$ (b) $[28x^6]$ (c) $[20x^9]$ (d) $[6.9x^{0.5}]$
   (e) $[32.4x^{4.4}]$

3. (a) x^{-2} (b) x^{-3} (c) x^{-5} (d) $\dfrac{1}{x}$ (e) $-\dfrac{1}{x^3}$ (f) $\dfrac{1}{x^{10}}$

   (a) $[-2x^{-3}]$ (b) $[-3x^{-4}]$ (c) $[-5x^{-6}]$ (d) $\left[-\dfrac{1}{x^2}\right]$

   (e) $\left[\dfrac{3}{x^4}\right]$ (f) $\left[-\dfrac{10}{x^{11}}\right]$

4. (a) $4x^{-1}$ (b) $-5x^{-4}$ (c) $3x^{-7}$ (d) $-\dfrac{6}{x^2}$ (e) $\dfrac{4}{3x^5}$ (f) $\dfrac{2}{5x^{1.4}}$

   (a) $[-4x^{-2}]$ (b) $[20x^{-5}]$ (c) $[-21x^{-8}]$ (d) $\left[\dfrac{12}{x^3}\right]$

   (e) $\left[-\dfrac{20}{3x^6}\right]$ (f) $\left[\dfrac{-2.8}{5x^{2.4}}\right]$

5. (a) $x^{\frac{7}{2}}$ (b) $x^{\frac{3}{4}}$ (c) $x^{-\frac{3}{2}}$ (d) $\dfrac{1}{x^{\frac{1}{2}}}$ (e) $-\dfrac{1}{x^{\frac{5}{3}}}$ (f) $\dfrac{2}{3x^{\frac{7}{4}}}$

   (a) $[\frac{7}{2}x^{\frac{5}{2}}]$ (b) $[\frac{3}{4}x^{-\frac{1}{4}}]$ (c) $[-\frac{3}{2}x^{-\frac{5}{2}}]$ (d) $\left[\dfrac{-1}{2x^{\frac{3}{2}}}\right]$ (e) $\left[\dfrac{4}{3x^{\frac{7}{3}}}\right]$

   (f) $\left[\dfrac{-7}{6x^{\frac{11}{4}}}\right]$

6. (a) $\dfrac{\sqrt{x}}{2}$ (b) $\sqrt{x^3}$ (c) $\sqrt[3]{x^2}$ (d) $4\sqrt{x^5}$ (e) $\dfrac{3}{5\sqrt{x^7}}$ (f) $\dfrac{-1}{2\sqrt[4]{x^9}}$

   (a) $\left[\dfrac{1}{4\sqrt{x}}\right]$ (b) $\left[\dfrac{3}{2}\sqrt{x}\right]$ (c) $\left[\dfrac{2}{3\sqrt[3]{x}}\right]$ (d) $[10\sqrt{x^3}]$

   (e) $\left[\dfrac{-21}{10\sqrt{x^9}}\right]$ (f) $\left[\dfrac{9}{8\sqrt[4]{x^{13}}}\right]$

Differentiate the functions in Problems 7–26 with respect to the variable:

7. (a) $4u^3$ (b) $\frac{3}{2}t^4$ (a) $[12u^2]$ (b) $[6t^3]$

8. (a) $5v^2$ (b) $1.4z^5$ (a) $[10v]$ (b) $[7z^4]$

9. (a) $\dfrac{4}{a}$ (b) $\dfrac{3}{2S^2}$ (a) $\left[-\dfrac{4}{a^2}\right]$ (b) $\left[-\dfrac{3}{S^3}\right]$

10. (a) $\dfrac{7}{4y^3}$ (b) $3m^{-4}$ (a) $\left[-\dfrac{21}{4y^4}\right]$ (b) $\left[-12m^{-5}\right]$

11. (a) $\sqrt{b}$ (b) $5\sqrt{c^3}$ (a) $\left[\dfrac{1}{2\sqrt{b}}\right]$ (b) $\left[\dfrac{15}{2}\sqrt{c}\right]$

12. (a) $\dfrac{1}{\sqrt{e}}$ (b) $g^{\frac{5}{3}}$ (a) $\left[-\dfrac{1}{2\sqrt{e^3}}\right]$ (b) $[\frac{5}{3}g^{\frac{2}{3}}]$

13. (a) $4\sqrt[3]{k^2}$ (b) $\dfrac{3}{5\sqrt[4]{x^5}}$ (a) $\left[\dfrac{8}{3\sqrt[3]{k}}\right]$ (b) $\left[\dfrac{-3}{4\sqrt[4]{x^9}}\right]$

14. $5x^2 - \dfrac{1}{\sqrt{x^7}}$ $\left[10x + \dfrac{7}{2\sqrt{x^9}}\right]$

15. $3\left(2u - u^{-\frac{1}{2}} + \dfrac{4}{5u}\right)$ $\left[3\left(2 + \dfrac{u^{-\frac{3}{2}}}{2} - \dfrac{4}{5u^2}\right)\right]$

16. $\dfrac{1}{x}\left(3x^3 - \dfrac{2}{x} + \dfrac{\sqrt{x}}{5} + 1\right)$ $\left[6x + \dfrac{4}{x^3} - \dfrac{1}{10\sqrt{x^3}} - \dfrac{1}{x^2}\right]$

17. $\dfrac{3x^2 - 2\sqrt{x} - 5\sqrt[4]{x^3}}{x^2}$ $\left[\dfrac{3}{\sqrt{x^5}} + \dfrac{25}{4\sqrt[4]{x^9}}\right]$

18. $(t + 1)^2$ $[2(t + 1)]$

19. $(3\theta - 1)^2$ $[6(3\theta - 1)]$

20. $(f - 1)^4$ $[4(f^3 - 3f^2 + 3f - 1)$ or $4(f - 1)^3]$

21. (a) $5 \sin \theta$ (b) $4 \cos x$ (a) $[5 \cos \theta]$ (b) $[-4 \sin x]$

22. (a) $3(\sin t + 2 \cos t)$ (b) $7 \sin x - 2 \cos x$
    (a) $[3(\cos t - 2 \sin t)]$ (b) $[7 \cos x + 2 \sin x]$

23. (a) e^{3x} (b) e^{-4y} (a) $[3e^{3x}]$ (b) $[-4e^{-4y}]$

24. (a) $6e^{2x}$ (b) $\dfrac{4}{e^{7t}}$ (a) $[12e^{2x}]$ (b) $\left[\dfrac{-28}{e^{7t}} \right]$

25. (a) $3(e^{8y} - e^{3y})$ (b) $-2(3e^{9x} - 4e^{-2x})$
    (a) $[3(8e^{8y} - 3e^{3y})]$ (b) $[-2(27e^{9x} + 8e^{-2x})]$

26. (a) $\ln 5b$ (b) $4 \ln 3g$ (a) $\left[\dfrac{1}{b} \right]$ (b) $\left[\dfrac{4}{g} \right]$

27. Find the gradient of the curve $y = 4x^3 - 3x^2 + 2x - 4$ at the points $(0, -4)$ and $(1, -1)$. $[2, 8]$

28. What are the coordinates of the point on the graph of $y = 5x^2 - 2x + 1$ where the gradient is zero. $[(\frac{1}{5}, \frac{4}{5})]$

29. Find the point on the curve $f(\theta) = 4\sqrt[3]{\theta^4} + 2$ where the gradient is $10\frac{2}{3}$. $[(8, 66)]$

30. If $f(x) = \dfrac{5x^2}{2} - 6x + 3$ find the coordinates at the point at which the gradient is: (a) 4; and (b) -6.   (a) $[(2, 1)]$ (b) $[(0, 3)]$

Differentiation of products and quotients

Differentiate the products in Problems 31−45 with respect to the variable and express your answers in their simplest form:

31. $3x^3 \sin x$ $[3x^2(x \cos x + 3 \sin x)]$

32. $\sqrt{t^3} \cos t$ $[\sqrt{t}(\frac{3}{2} \cos t - t \sin t)]$

33. $(3x^2 - 4x + 2)(2x^3 + x - 1)$ $[(30x^4 - 32x^3 + 21x^2 - 14x + 6)]$

34. $2 \sin \theta \cos \theta$ $[2(\cos^2 \theta - \sin^2 \theta)]$

35. $5e^{2a} \sin a$ $[5e^{2a}(\cos a + 2 \sin a)]$

36. $e^{7y} \cos y$ $[e^{7y}(7 \cos y - \sin y)]$

37. $b^3 \ln 2b$ $[b^2(1 + 3 \ln 2b)]$

38. $3\sqrt{x}e^{4x}$ $\left[3e^{4x}\left(\dfrac{8x + 1}{2\sqrt{x}} \right) \right]$

39. $e^t \ln t$ $\left[e^t\left(\dfrac{1}{t} + \ln t \right) \right]$

40. $e^{2d}(4d^2 - 3d + 1)$ $[e^{2d}(8d^2 + 2d - 1)]$

41. $3\sqrt{f^5} \ln 5f$ $[3\sqrt{f^3}(1 + \frac{5}{2} \ln 5f)]$

42. $2 \sin g \ln g$ $\left[2\left(\dfrac{1}{g} \sin g + \ln g \cos g \right) \right]$

43. $6e^{5m} \sin m$ $[6e^{5m}(\cos m + 5 \sin m)]$

44. $\sqrt{x}(1 + \sin x)$ $\left[\dfrac{2x \cos x + \sin x + 1}{2\sqrt{x}} \right]$

45. $e^v \ln v \sin v$ $\qquad \left[e^v \left\{ (\sin v + \cos v) \ln v + \dfrac{\sin v}{v} \right\} \right]$

Differentiate the quotients in Problems 46—62 with respect to the variable and express your answers in their simplest form:

46. $\dfrac{4x}{x^2 - 1}$ $\qquad \left[\dfrac{-4(x^2 + 1)}{(x^2 - 1)^2} \right]$

47. $\dfrac{2t - 1}{3t^2 + 5t}$ $\qquad \left[\dfrac{5 + 6t - 6t^2}{(3t^2 + 5t)^2} \right]$

48. $\dfrac{2x^2 - 6x + 2}{3x^2 + 2x - 1}$ $\qquad \left[\dfrac{2(11x^2 - 8x + 1)}{(3x^2 + 2x - 1)^2} \right]$

49. $\dfrac{3e^{2\theta}}{4\theta^2 - 3}$ $\qquad \left[\dfrac{6e^{2\theta}(4\theta^2 - 4\theta - 3)}{(4\theta^2 - 3)^2} \right]$

50. $\dfrac{3u^4 + 2u^2 - 1}{4e^{5u}}$ $\qquad \left[\dfrac{-15u^4 + 12u^3 - 10u^2 + 4u + 5}{4e^{5u}} \right]$

51. $\dfrac{4 \sin c}{5c^2 + 2c}$ $\qquad \left[\dfrac{4(5c^2 + 2c) \cos c - 4(10c + 2) \sin c}{(5c^2 + 2c)^2} \right]$

52. $\dfrac{4\sqrt[3]{f^7}}{3 \sin f}$ $\qquad \left[\dfrac{4(\sqrt[3]{f^4})(7 \sin f - 3 f \cos f)}{9 \sin^2 f} \right]$

53. $\dfrac{6 \cos h}{h^3 + 4}$ $\qquad \left[\dfrac{-6 \{ (h^3 + 4) \sin h + 3h^2 \cos h \}}{(h^3 + 4)^2} \right]$

54. $\dfrac{\sqrt{k^3}}{\cos k}$ $\qquad \left[\dfrac{\sqrt{k}(\frac{3}{2} \cos k + k \sin k)}{\cos^2 k} \right]$

55. $\dfrac{4e^{6x}}{\sin x}$ $\qquad \left[\dfrac{4e^{6x}(6 \sin x - \cos x)}{\sin^2 x} \right]$

56. $\dfrac{3 \ln \frac{5}{2}n}{n^2 + 2n}$ $\qquad \left[\dfrac{3(n + 2) - 6(n + 1) \ln \frac{5n}{2}}{(n^2 + 2n)^2} \right]$

57. $\dfrac{3\sqrt{x} + x}{\frac{7}{2} \ln 4x}$ $\qquad \left[\dfrac{\left(\frac{3}{2\sqrt{x}} + 1 \right) \ln 4x - \left(\frac{3}{\sqrt{x}} + 1 \right)}{\frac{7}{2}(\ln 4x)^2} \right]$

58. $\dfrac{\ln 6y}{6 \sin y}$ $\qquad \left[\dfrac{\frac{1}{y} \sin y - \ln 6y \cos y}{6 \sin^2 y} \right]$

59. $\dfrac{x^2 \ln 4x}{3 \sin x}$ $\qquad \left[\dfrac{x \ln 4x(2 \sin x - x \cos x) + x \sin x}{3 \sin^2 x} \right]$

60. $\dfrac{2\sqrt{t}}{\ln 3t \cos t}$ $\qquad \left[\dfrac{(\ln 3t \cos t + 2t \ln 3t \sin t - 2 \cos t)}{\sqrt{t}(\ln 3t \cos t)^2} \right]$

61. $\dfrac{x^2 \sec x}{e^{2x}}$ $\qquad \left[\dfrac{x \sec x}{e^{2x}} (x \tan x + 2 - 2x) \right]$

62. $\dfrac{k}{e^k \operatorname{cosec} k}$ $\qquad \left[\dfrac{1 + k(\cot k - 1)}{e^k \operatorname{cosec} k} \right]$

63. Find the slope of the curve $y = xe^{-2x}$ at the point $\left(\dfrac{1}{2}, \dfrac{1}{2e} \right)$. $\qquad$ [0]

64. Calculate the gradient of the curve $f(x) = \dfrac{3x^4 - 2\sqrt{x^3} + 2}{5x^2 + 1}$ at the points $(0, 2)$ and $(1, \frac{1}{2})$. $[0, \frac{2}{3}]$

Differentiation by substitution

Find the differential coefficients of the functions in Problems 65–128 with respect to the variable and express your answers in their simplest form.

65. $\sin 4x$ $[4 \cos 4x]$

66. $3 \tan 4x$ $[12 \sec^2 4x]$

67. $\cos 3t$ $[-3 \sin 3t]$

68. $5 \sec 2\theta$ $[10 \sec 2\theta \tan 2\theta]$

69. $4 \operatorname{cosec} 5\mu$ $[-20 \operatorname{cosec} 5\mu \cot 5\mu]$

70. $6 \cot 3\alpha$ $[-18 \operatorname{cosec}^2 3\alpha]$

71. $4 \cos (2x - 5)$ $[-8 \sin(2x - 5)]$

72. $\operatorname{cosec} (5t-1)$ $[-5 \operatorname{cosec} (5t - 1) \cot (5t - 1)]$

73. $(t^3 - 2t + 3)^4$ $[4(t^3 - 2t + 3)^3 (3t^2 - 2)]$

74. $\sqrt{(2v^3 - v)}$ $\left[\dfrac{6v^2 - 1}{2\sqrt{(2v^3 - v)}} \right]$

75. $\sin (3x - 2)$ $[3 \cos (3x - 2)]$

76. $3 \tan (5y - 1)$ $[15 \sec^2 (5y - 1)]$

77. $4 \cos (6x + 5)$ $[-24 \sin (6x + 5)]$

78. $(1 - 2u^2)^7$ $[-28u(1 - 2u^2)^6]$

79. $\dfrac{1}{2n^2 - 3n + 1}$ $\left[\dfrac{3 - 4n}{(2n^2 - 3n + 1)^2} \right]$

80. $\sin^2 t$ $[2 \sin t \cos t]$

81. $3 \cos^2 x$ $[-6 \cos x \sin x]$

82. $\dfrac{1}{(2g - 1)^6}$ $\left[\dfrac{-12}{(2g - 1)^7} \right]$

83. $3 \operatorname{cosec}^2 x$ $[-6 \operatorname{cosec}^2 x \cot x]$

84. $6 \cos^3 t$ $[-18 \cos^2 t \sin t]$

85. $\frac{3}{2} \cot (6x - 2)$ $[-9 \operatorname{cosec}^2 (6x - 2)]$

86. $\sqrt{(4x^3 + 2x^2 - 5x)}$ $\left[\dfrac{12x^2 + 4x - 5}{2\sqrt{(4x^3 + 2x^2 - 5x)}} \right]$

87. $2 \sin^4 b$ $[8 \sin^3 b \cos b]$

88. $\dfrac{3}{(x^2 + 6x - 1)^5}$ $\left[\dfrac{-30(x + 3)}{(x^2 + 6x - 1)^6} \right]$

89. $(x^2 - x + 1)^{12}$ $[12(x^2 - x + 1)^{11} (2x - 1)]$

90. $e^{4q + 3}$ $[4e^{4q + 3}]$

91. $5 e^{x-5}$ $[5 e^{x-5}]$

92. $\ln (3p - 1)$ $\left[\dfrac{3}{3p - 1} \right]$

93. $15 \ln \left(\dfrac{x}{3} + 5 \right)$ $\left[\dfrac{15}{x + 15} \right]$

94. $3 \sec 5g$ $[15 \sec 5g \tan 5g]$

95. $4 \operatorname{cosec}(2k - 1)$ $[-8 \operatorname{cosec}(2k - 1) \cot(2k - 1)]$

96. $7\beta \tan 4\beta$ $[7(4\beta \sec^2 4\beta + \tan 4\beta)]$

97. $\sqrt{x} \sec \dfrac{x}{3}$ $\left[\dfrac{\sqrt{x}}{3} \sec \dfrac{x}{3} \tan \dfrac{x}{3} + \dfrac{1}{2\sqrt{x}} \sec \dfrac{x}{3} \right]$

98. $2 e^{5l} \operatorname{cosec} 3l$ $[2 e^{5l} \operatorname{cosec} 3l(5 - 3 \cot 3l)]$

99. $\ln 5v \cot v$ $\left[\dfrac{\cot v}{v} - \operatorname{cosec}^2 v \ln 5v \right]$

100. $(3S^4 - 2S^2 + 1) \tan \dfrac{2S}{5}$

$\left[\dfrac{2}{5}(3S^4 - 2S^2 + 1) \sec^2 \dfrac{2S}{5} + 4S(3S^2 - 1) \tan \dfrac{2S}{5} \right]$

101. $\dfrac{\sec 2t}{(t - 1)}$ $\left[\dfrac{\sec 2t}{(t - 1)^2} \Big\{ 2(t - 1) \tan 2t - 1 \Big\} \right]$

102. $(x^2 + 1) \sin(2x^2 - 3)$ $[2x\{2(x^2 + 1) \cos(2x^2 - 3) + \sin(2x^2 - 3)\}]$

103. $(2x - 1)^9 \cos 4x$ $[-2(2x - 1)^8\{2(2x - 1)\sin 4x - 9\cos 4x\}]$

104. $\dfrac{2t}{\tan 3t}$ $\left[\dfrac{2(\tan 3t - 3t \sec^2 3t)}{\tan^2 3t} \right]$

105. $\dfrac{1}{\operatorname{cosec}(4v + 1)}$ $[4 \cos(4v + 1)]$

106. $\dfrac{\sin(6x - 5)}{\sqrt{(x^2 - 1)}}$ $\left[\dfrac{6(x^2 - 1) \cos(6x - 5) - x \sin(6x - 5)}{\sqrt{(x^2 - 1)^3}} \right]$

107. $\dfrac{2\sqrt{u}}{3 \operatorname{cosec} 4u}$ $\left[\dfrac{1 + 8u \cot 4u}{3\sqrt{u} \operatorname{cosec} 4u} \right]$

108. $\dfrac{3 \cot x}{\ln 2x}$ $\left[\dfrac{-(3 \operatorname{cosec}^2 x \ln 2x + \dfrac{3}{x} \cot x)}{(\ln 2x)^2} \right]$

109. $\dfrac{5 \tan 3b}{\sqrt{b}}$ $\left[\dfrac{5}{2\sqrt{b^3}}(6b \sec^2 3b - \tan 3b) \right]$

110. $\dfrac{(3\theta^2 - 2)}{4 \sec 2\theta}$ $\left[\dfrac{3\theta - (3\theta^2 - 2) \tan 2\theta}{2 \sec 2\theta} \right]$

111. $\dfrac{3 \sec^2 a}{(2a^2 + 3a - 1)^3}$ $\left[\dfrac{3 \sec^2 a[2(2a^2 + 3a - 1) \tan a - 3(4a + 3)]}{(2a^2 + 3a - 1)^4} \right]$

112. $\dfrac{3e^{7x-1}}{(x - 1)^9}$ $\left[\dfrac{3e^{7x-1}(7x - 16)}{(x - 1)^{10}} \right]$

113. $\dfrac{\sqrt{(3c^2 + 4c - 1)}}{2 \ln 5c}$ $\left[\dfrac{2c(3c + 2) \ln 5c - 2(3c^2 + 4c - 1)}{4c\sqrt{(3c^2 + 4c - 1)}(\ln 5c)^2} \right]$

114. $3 \cos(2x^2 + 1)$ $[-12x \sin(2x^2 + 1)]$

115. $5 \sec(5x^3 - 2x^2 + 2)$

$[5x(15x - 4) \sec(5x^3 - 2x^2 + 2) \tan(5x^3 - 2x^2 + 2)]$

116. $\sin^2(2d - 1)$ $[4 \sin(2d - 1) \cos(2d - 1)]$

117. $3 \tan \sqrt{(4x - 2)}$ $\left[\dfrac{6 \sec^2 \sqrt{(4x - 2)}}{\sqrt{(4x - 2)}} \right]$

118. $3 \cot^3 (5t^2 - 6)$ $[-90t \cot^2 (5t^2 - 6) \operatorname{cosec}^2 (5t^2 - 6)]$

119. $\sin^4 \sqrt{(3f^3 - 5)}$ $\left[\dfrac{18f^2 \sin^3 \sqrt{(3f^3 - 5)} \cos \sqrt{(3f^3 - 5)}}{\sqrt{(3f^3 - 5)}} \right]$

120. $e^{\sec g}$ $[\sec g \tan g \, e^{\sec g}]$

121. $3e^{\operatorname{cosec} (2x-1)}$ $[-6 \operatorname{cosec} (2x - 1) \cot (2x - 1) \, e^{\operatorname{cosec} (2x-1)}]$

122. $3\sqrt[3]{\{\sin (4k - 2)\}^5}$ $[20\sqrt[3]{\{\sin (4k - 2)\}^2} \cos (4k - 2)]$

123. $(3x^3 + 2x)^2 \sin \sqrt{(x^2 - 1)}$

$$\left[(3x^3 + 2x) \left\{ \frac{x(3x^3 + 2x)}{\sqrt{(x^2 - 1)}} \cos \sqrt{(x^2 - 1)} + 2(9x^2 + 2) \sin \sqrt{(x^2 - 1)} \right\} \right]$$

124. $(x + 3)^9 \cos^4 (x^2 + 2)$

$$[(x + 3)^8 \cos^3 (x^2 + 2) \{ 9 \cos (x^2 + 2) - 8x(x + 3) \sin (x^2 + 2) \}]$$

125. $\dfrac{3 \cot^2 3m}{(2m - 1)^5}$ $\left[\dfrac{-6 \cot 3m}{(2m - 1)^6} \left\{ 3(2m - 1) \operatorname{cosec}^2 3m + 5 \cot 3m \right\} \right]$

126. $\dfrac{\sqrt{(3x^2 - 2)}}{\operatorname{cosec}^2 (3x^2 - 2)}$ $\left[\dfrac{3x \{ 1 + 4(3x^2 - 2) \cot (3x^2 - 2) \}}{\sqrt{(3x^2 - 2)} \operatorname{cosec}^2 (3x^2 - 2)} \right]$

127. $\ln \sqrt{(\operatorname{cosec} t)}$ $[-\tfrac{1}{2} \cot t]$

128. $\dfrac{3e^{3x^2 + 2x + 1}}{\ln (\cos x)}$ $\left[\dfrac{3e^{3x^2 + 2x + 1}}{[\ln (\cos x)]^2} \left\{ (6x + 2) \ln (\cos x) + \tan x \right\} \right]$

Successive differentiation

129. If $y = 5x^3 - 6x^2 + 2x - 6$ find $\dfrac{d^2y}{dx^2}$. $[30x - 12]$

130. Find $f''(x)$ given $f(x) = \dfrac{5}{x} + \sqrt{x} - \dfrac{5}{\sqrt{x^5}} + 8$. $\left[\dfrac{10}{x^3} - \dfrac{1}{4\sqrt{x^3}} - \dfrac{175}{4\sqrt{x^9}} \right]$

131. Given $f(\theta) = 3 \sin 4\theta - 2 \cos 3\theta$ find $f'(\theta), f''(\theta)$ and $f'''(\theta)$.
$[f'(\theta) = 6(2 \cos 4\theta + \sin 3\theta); f''(\theta) = 6(3 \cos 3\theta - 8 \sin 4\theta);$
$f'''(\theta) = -6(32 \cos 4\theta + 9 \sin 3\theta)]$

132. If $m = (6p + 1)\left(\dfrac{1}{p} - 3 \right)$ find $\dfrac{d^2m}{dp^2}$ and $\dfrac{d^3m}{dp^3}$. $\left[\dfrac{2}{p^3} ; \dfrac{-6}{p^4} \right]$

In Problems 133–143 find the second differential coefficient with respect to the variable.

133. $3 \ln 5g$ $\left[-\dfrac{3}{g^2} \right]$

134. $(x - 2)^5$ $[20(x - 2)^3]$

135. $3 \sin t - \cos 2t$ $[4 \cos 2t - 3 \sin t]$

136. $3 \tan 2y + 4 \cot 3y$ $[24(\sec^2 2y \tan 2y + 3 \operatorname{cosec}^2 3y \cot 3y)]$

137. $(3m^2 - 2)^6$ $[36(3m^2 - 2)^4 (33m^2 - 2)]$

138. $\dfrac{1}{(2r - 1)^7}$ $\left[\dfrac{224}{(2r - 1)^9} \right]$

139. $3 \cos^2 \theta$ $[6(\sin^2 \theta - \cos^2 \theta)]$

140. $\tfrac{1}{2} \cot (3x - 1)$ $[9 \operatorname{cosec}^2 (3x - 1) \cot (3x - 1)]$

141. $4 \sin^5 n$ $[20 \sin^3 n(4 \cos^2 n - \sin^2 n)]$

142. $3x^2 \sin 2x$ $[6(1 - 2x^2) \sin 2x + 24x \cos 2x]$

143. $\dfrac{\sin t}{2t^2}$ $\left[\dfrac{1}{2t^4} \left\{ (6 - t^2) \sin t - 4t \cos t \right\} \right]$

144. $x = 3t^2 - 2\sqrt{t} + \dfrac{1}{t} - 6$. Evaluate $\dfrac{d^2x}{dt^2}$ when $t = 1$. $[8\frac{1}{2}]$

145. Evaluate $f''(\theta)$ when $\theta = 0$ given $f(\theta) = 5 \sec 2\theta$. $[20]$

146. If $y = \cos \alpha - \sin \alpha$ evaluate α when $\dfrac{d^2y}{d\alpha^2}$ is zero. $\left[\dfrac{\pi}{4} \right]$

147. If $y = Ae^x - Be^{-x}$ prove that: $\dfrac{e^x}{2} \left\{ \dfrac{d^2y}{dx^2} + \dfrac{dy}{dx} \right\} - e^x y = B$.

148. Show that $\dfrac{d^2b}{dS^2} + 6 \dfrac{db}{dS} + 25b = 0$ when $b = e^{-3S} \sin 4S$.

149. Show that $x = 2t\, e^{-2t}$ satisfies the equation: $\dfrac{d^2x}{dt^2} + 4 \dfrac{dx}{dt} + 4x = 0$.

150. If $y = 3x^3 + 2x - 4$ prove that: $\dfrac{d^3y}{dx^3} + \dfrac{2}{9} \dfrac{d^2y}{dx^2} + x \dfrac{dy}{dx} - 3y = 30$.

151. Show that the differential equation $\dfrac{d^2y}{dx^2} - 8 \dfrac{dy}{dx} + 41y = 0$ is satisfied when $y = 2e^{4x} \cos 5x$.

Chapter 13

Applications of differentiation

1   Velocity and acceleration

Let a car move a distance x metres in a time t seconds along a straight road. If the velocity v of the car is constant then

$$v = \frac{x}{t} \text{ m s}^{-1}$$

i.e. the gradient of the distance/time graph shown in Fig. 1 (a) is constant.

If, however, the velocity of the car is not constant then the distance/time graph will not be a straight line. It may be as shown in Fig. 1 (b).

The average velocity over a small time δt and distance δx is given by the gradient of the chord CD, i.e. the average velocity over time $\delta t = \dfrac{\delta x}{\delta t}$.

As $\delta t \to 0$, the chord CD becomes a tangent, such that at point C the velocity v is given by:

$$v = \frac{dx}{dt}$$

Hence the velocity of the car at any instant t is given by the gradient of the distance/time graph. If an expression for the distance x is known in terms of time t then the velocity is obtained by differentiating the expression.

The acceleration a of the car is defined as the rate of change of velocity.

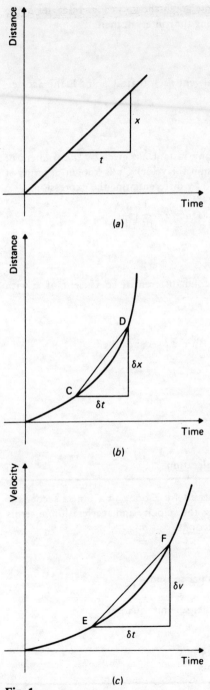

Fig. 1

With reference to the velocity/time graph shown in Fig. 1 (c), let δv be the change in v and δt the corresponding time interval, then:

average acceleration $a = \dfrac{\delta v}{\delta t}$

As $\delta t \to 0$, the chord EF becomes a tangent such that at point E the acceleration is given by:

$a = \dfrac{dv}{dt}$

Hence the acceleration of the car at any instant t is given by the gradient of the velocity/time graph. If an expression for velocity v is known in terms of time t then the acceleration is obtained by differentiating the expression.

Acceleration, $a = \dfrac{dv}{dt}$; but $v = \dfrac{dx}{dt}$. Hence $a = \dfrac{d}{dt}\left(\dfrac{dx}{dt}\right)$

which is written as: $a = \dfrac{d^2 x}{dt^2}$

Thus acceleration is given by the second differential coefficient of x with respect to t.

Summary

If a body moves a distance x metres in a time t seconds then:

distance $x = f(t)$

velocity $v = f'(t)$ or $\dfrac{dx}{dt}$

and acceleration $a = f''(t)$ or $\dfrac{d^2 x}{dt^2}$

Worked problems on velocity and acceleration

Problem 1. The distance x metres moved by a body in a time t seconds is given by $x = 2t^3 + 3t^2 - 6t + 2$. Express the velocity and acceleration in terms of t and find their values when $t = 4$ seconds.

Distance $x = 2t^3 + 3t^2 - 6t + 2$ metres

Velocity $v = \dfrac{dx}{dt} = 6t^2 + 6t - 6$ metres per second

Acceleration $a = \dfrac{d^2 x}{dt^2} = 12t + 6$ metres per second squared

After 4 seconds, $v = 6(4)^2 + 6(4) - 6$

$= 96 + 24 - 6 = 114$ m s^{-1}

$a = 12(4) + 6 = 54$ m s^{-2}

Problem 2. If the distance s metres travelled by a car in time t seconds after the brakes are applied is given by $s = 15t - \frac{5}{3}t^2$: (a) what is the speed (in km h^{-1}) at the instant the brakes are applied, and (b) how far does the car travel before it stops?

(a) Distance $s = 15t - \frac{5}{3}t^2$

Velocity $v = \dfrac{ds}{dt} = 15 - \frac{10}{3}t$

At the instant the brakes are applied, $t = 0$.

Hence velocity = 15 m s^{-1}

$$15 \text{ m s}^{-1} = \frac{15}{1\,000}\,(60 \times 60) \text{ km h}^{-1} = 54 \text{ km h}^{-1}$$

(b) When the car finally stops, the velocity is zero,

i.e. $v = 15 - \frac{10}{3}t = 0$

i.e. $15 = \frac{10}{3}t$ or $t = 4.5$ seconds

Hence the distance travelled before the car stops is given by:

$s = 15t - \frac{5}{3}t^2$

$\quad = 15(4.5) - \frac{5}{3}(4.5)^2$

$\quad = 33.75$ m

Problem 3. The distance x metres moved by a body in t seconds is given by:

$\quad x = 3t^3 - \frac{11}{2}t^2 + 2t + 5$

Find:

(a) its velocity after t seconds;

(b) its velocity at the start and after 4 seconds;

(c) the value of t when the body comes to rest;

(d) its acceleration after t seconds;

(e) its acceleration after 2 seconds;

(f) the value of t when the acceleration is 16 m s^{-2}; and

(g) the average velocity over the third second.

(a) Distance $x = 3t^3 - \frac{11}{2}t^2 + 2t + 5$

Velocity $v = \dfrac{dx}{dt} = 9t^2 - 11t + 2$

(b) Velocity at the start means the velocity when $t = 0$,

i.e. $v_0 = 9(0)^2 - 11(0) + 2 = 2$ m s^{-1}

Velocity after 4 seconds, $v_4 = 9(4)^2 - 11(4) + 2 = 102$ m s^{-1}

(c) When the body comes to rest, $v = 0$

i.e. $9t^2 - 11t + 2 = 0$

$(9t - 2)(t - 1) = 0$

$t = \frac{2}{9}$ s or $t = 1$ s

(d) **Acceleration** $a = \dfrac{d^2x}{dt^2} = (18t - 11)$

(e) Acceleration after 2 seconds, $a_2 = 18(2) - 11 = 25$ m s^{-2}

(f) When the acceleration is 16 m s^{-2} then

$18t - 11 = 16$

$18t = 16 + 11 = 27$

$t = \frac{27}{18} = 1\frac{1}{2}$ seconds

(g) Distance travelled in the third second = (distance travelled after 3 s) − (distance travelled after 2 s)

$= [3(3)^3 - \frac{11}{2}(3)^2 + 2(3) + 5] - [3(2)^3 - \frac{11}{2}(2)^2 + 2(2) + 5]$

$= 42\frac{1}{2} - 11$

$= 31\frac{1}{2} \text{ m}$

Average velocity over the third second $= \dfrac{\text{distance travelled}}{\text{time interval}}$

$$= \frac{31\frac{1}{2} \text{ m}}{1 \text{ s}}$$

$$= 31\frac{1}{2} \text{ m s}^{-1}$$

(Note that should a negative value occur for velocity it merely means that the body is moving in the direction opposite to that with which it started. Also if a negative value occurs for acceleration it indicates a deceleration (or a retardation).)

Further problems on velocity and acceleration may be found in Section 4, Problems 1−15, page 264.

2   Maximum and minimum values

Consider the curve shown in Fig. 2.

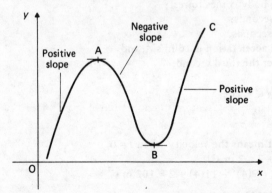

Fig. 2

The slope of the curve (i.e. $\dfrac{dy}{dx}$) between points O and A is positive. The slope of the curve between points A and B is negative and the slope between points B and C is again positive.

At point A the slope is zero and as x increases, the slope of the curve changes from positive just before A to negative just after. Such a point is called a **maximum value**.

At point B the slope is also zero and, as x increases, the slope of the curve changes from negative just before B to positive just after. Such a point is called a **minimum value**.

Points such as A and B are given the general name of **turning-points**.

Maximum and minimum values can be confusing inasmuch as they suggest that they are the largest and smallest values of a curve. However, by their definition this is not so. A maximum value occurs at the 'crest of a wave' and the minimum value at the 'bottom of a valley'. In Fig. 2 the point C has a larger y-ordinate value than A and point O has a smaller y ordinate than B. Points A and B are turning-points and are given the special names of maximum and minimum values respectively.

Summary

1. At a maximum point the slope $\frac{dy}{dx} = 0$ and changes from positive just before the maximum point to negative just after.

2. At a minimum point the slope $\frac{dy}{dx} = 0$ and changes from negative just before the minimum point to positive just after.

Consider the function $y = x^3 - x^2 - 5x + 6$.

The turning-points (i.e. the maximum and minimum values) may be determined without going through the tedious process of drawing up a table of values and plotting the graph.

If $\quad y = x^3 - x^2 - 5x + 6$

then $\frac{dy}{dx} = 3x^2 - 2x - 5$

Now at a maximum or minimum value $\frac{dy}{dx} = 0$.

Hence $3x^2 - 2x - 5 = 0$ for a maximum or minimum value
$\quad (3x - 5)(x + 1) = 0$

i.e. *Either* $\quad 3x - 5 = 0$ giving $x = \frac{5}{3}$

or $\quad\quad x + 1 = 0$ giving $x = -1$

For each value of the independent variable x there is a corresponding value of the dependent variable y.

When $x = \frac{5}{3}$, $y = [\frac{5}{3}]^3 - [\frac{5}{3}]^2 - 5[\frac{5}{3}] + 6 = -\frac{13}{27}$

When $x = -1$, $y = (-1)^3 - (-1)^2 - 5(-1) + 6 = 9$

Hence turning-points occur at $(\frac{5}{3}, -\frac{13}{27})$ and $(-1, 9)$.

The next step is to determine which of the points is a maximum and which is a minimum. There are two methods whereby this may be achieved.

Method 1

Consider firstly the point $(\frac{5}{3}, -\frac{13}{27})$.

$$\frac{dy}{dx} = 3x^2 - 2x - 5 = (3x - 5)(x + 1)$$

If x is slightly less than $\frac{5}{3}$ then $(3x - 5)$ becomes negative, $(x + 1)$ remains positive, making $\frac{dy}{dx} = (-) \times (+) = $ negative

If x is slightly greater than $\frac{5}{3}$ then $(3x - 5)$ becomes positive, $(x + 1)$ remains positive, making $\frac{dy}{dx} = (+) \times (+) = $ positive

Hence the slope is negative just before $(\frac{5}{3}, -\frac{13}{27})$ and positive just after. This is thus a **minimum** value.

Consider now the point $(-1, 9)$.

$$\frac{dy}{dx} = (3x - 5)(x + 1)$$

If x is slightly less than -1 (for example -1.1) then $(3x - 5)$ remains negative, $(x + 1)$ becomes negative, making $\frac{dy}{dx} = (-) \times (-) = $ positive

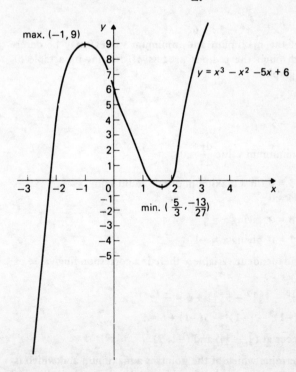

Fig. 3 Graph of $y = x^3 - x^2 - 5x + 6$

If x is slightly greater than -1 (for example -0.9) then $(3x - 5)$ remains negative, $(x + 1)$ becomes positive, making $\frac{dy}{dx} = (-) \times (+) = $ negative

Hence the slope is positive just before $(-1, 9)$ and negative just after. This is thus a **maximum value**.

Figure 3 shows a graph of $y = x^3 - x^2 - 5x + 6$ with the maximum value at $(-1, 9)$ and the minimum at $(\frac{5}{3}, -\frac{13}{27})$.

Method 2

When passing through a maximum value, $\frac{dy}{dx}$ changes from positive, through zero, to negative. By convention, moving from a positive value to a negative value is moving in a negative direction. Hence the rate of change of $\frac{dy}{dx}$ is negative.

i.e. $\frac{d}{dx}\left(\frac{dy}{dx}\right) = \frac{d^2y}{dx^2}$ **is negative at a maximum value.**

Similarly, when passing through a minimum value, $\frac{dy}{dx}$ changes from negative, through zero, to positive. By convention, moving from a negative value to a positive value is moving in a positive direction. Hence the rate of change of $\frac{dy}{dx}$ is positive.

i.e. $\frac{d^2y}{dx^2}$ **is positive at a minimum value.**

Thus, in the above example, to distinguish between the points $(\frac{5}{3}, -\frac{13}{27})$ and $(-1, 9)$ the second differential is required.

Since $\frac{dy}{dx} = 3x^2 - 2x - 5$

then $\frac{d^2y}{dx^2} = 6x - 2$

When $x = \frac{5}{3}$, $\frac{d^2y}{dx^2} = 6[\frac{5}{3}] - 2 = +8$ which is **positive**.

Hence $(\frac{5}{3}, -\frac{13}{27})$ is a **minimum point.**

When $x = -1$, $\frac{d^2y}{dx^2} = 6(-1) - 2 = -8$ which is **negative**.

Hence $(-1, 9)$ is a **maximum point.**

The actual numerical value of the second differential is insignificant for maximum and minimum values — the sign is the important factor. There are thus two methods of distinguishing between maximum and minimum values. Normally, the second method, that of determining the sign of the second differential, is preferred but sometimes the first method, that of examining the sign of the slope just before and just after the turning-point, is necessary because the second differential coefficient is too difficult to obtain.

It is possible to have a turning-point, the slope on either side of which is the same. This point is given the special name of a **point of inflexion**. At a point of inflexion $\frac{d^2y}{dx^2}$ is zero.

Maximum and minimum points and points of inflexion are given the general term of **stationary points**. Examples of each are shown in Fig. 4.

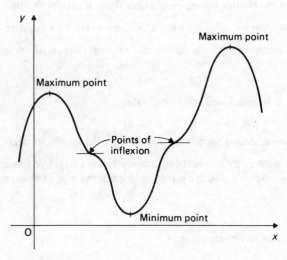

Fig. 4

Procedure for finding and distinguishing between stationary points

(i)   If $y = f(x)$, find $\frac{dy}{dx}$.

(ii) Let $\frac{dy}{dx} = 0$ and solve for the value(s) of x.

(iii) Substitute the value(s) of x into the original equation, $y = f(x)$, to obtain the y-ordinate value(s). Hence the coordinates of the stationary points are established.

(iv) Find $\frac{d^2y}{dx^2}$.

      or

      Determine the sign of the slope of the curve just before and just after the stationary point(s).

(v)   Substitute values of x into $\frac{d^2y}{dx^2}$. If the result is:

(a)   positive — the point is a minimum value;
(b)   negative — the point is a maximum value;
(c)   zero — the point is a point of inflexion.
or
If the sign change for the slope of the curve is:
(a)   positive to negative — the point is a maximum value;
(b)   negative to positive — the point is a minimum value;
(c)   positive to positive; or
(d)   negative to negative — the point is a point of inflexion.

Worked problems on maximum and minimum values

Problem 1. Find the coordinates of the maximum and minimum values of the graph of $y = \frac{2x^3}{3} - 5x^2 + 12x - 7$ and distinguish between them.

From the above procedure:

(i) $y = \frac{2x^3}{3} - 5x^2 + 12x - 7$

$\frac{dy}{dx} = 2x^2 - 10x + 12$

(ii) $\frac{dy}{dx} = 0$ at a turning-point.
Therefore $2x^2 - 10x + 12 = 0$
$2(x^2 - 5x + 6) = 0$
$2(x - 2)(x - 3) = 0$
Hence $x = 2$ or $x = 3$

(iii) When $x = 2$, $y = \frac{2}{3}(2)^3 - 5(2)^2 + 12(2) - 7 = 2\frac{1}{3}$
When $x = 3$, $y = \frac{2}{3}(3)^3 - 5(3)^2 + 12(3) - 7 = 2$
The coordinates of the turning-points are thus $(2, 2\frac{1}{3})$ and $(3, 2)$.

(iv) $\frac{dy}{dx} = 2x^2 - 10x + 12$

$\frac{d^2y}{dx^2} = 4x - 10$

(v)   When $x = 2$, $\frac{d^2y}{dx^2} = -2$, which is negative, giving a maximum value

When $x = 3$, $\frac{d^2y}{dx^2} = +2$, which is positive, giving a minimum value

Hence **the point $(2, 2\frac{1}{3})$ is a maximum value and the point $(3, 2)$ a minimum value.**

Note that with a quadratic equation there will be one turning-point. With a cubic equation (i.e. one containing a highest term of power 3) there may be two turning-points (i.e. one less than the highest power), and so on.

Problem 2. Locate the turning points on the following curves and distinguish between maximum and minimum values: (a) $x(5 - x)$; (b) $2t - e^t$; (c) $2(\theta - \ln \theta)$.

(a) Let $y = x(5 - x) = 5x - x^2$

$\dfrac{dy}{dx} = 5 - 2x = 0$ for a maximum or minimum value.

i.e. $x = 2\frac{1}{2}$

When $x = 2\frac{1}{2}$, $y = 2\frac{1}{2}(5 - 2\frac{1}{2}) = 6\frac{1}{4}$

Hence a turning-point occurs at $(2\frac{1}{2}, 6\frac{1}{4})$

$\dfrac{d^2y}{dx^2} = -2$, which is negative, giving a maximum value.

Hence $(2\frac{1}{2}, 6\frac{1}{4})$ **is a maximum point.**

(b) Let $y = 2t - e^t$

$\dfrac{dy}{dt} = 2 - e^t = 0$ for a maximum or minimum value.

i.e. $\quad 2 = e^t$

$\ln 2 = t$

$t = 0.693\ 1$

When $t = 0.693\ 1$, $y = 2(0.693\ 1) - 2 = -0.613\ 8$

Hence a turning-point occurs at $(0.693\ 1, -0.613\ 8)$ ·

$\dfrac{d^2y}{dt^2} = -e^t$

When $t = 0.693\ 1$, $\dfrac{d^2y}{dt^2} = -2$, which is negative, giving a maximum value.

Hence $(0.693\ 1, -0.613\ 8)$ **is a maximum point.**

(c) Let $y = 2(\theta - \ln \theta) = 2\theta - 2 \ln \theta$

$\dfrac{dy}{d\theta} = 2 - \dfrac{2}{\theta} = 0$ for a maximum or minimum value.

i.e. $\theta = 1$

When $\theta = 1$, $y = 2 - 2 \ln 1 = 2$

Hence a turning-point occurs at $(1, 2)$

$\dfrac{d^2y}{d\theta^2} = +\dfrac{2}{\theta^2}$

When $\theta = 1$, $\dfrac{d^2y}{d\theta^2} = +2$, which is positive, giving a minimum value.

Hence $(1, 2)$ **is a minimum point.**

Problem 3. Find the maximum and minimum values of the function

$$f(p) = \dfrac{(p - 1)(p - 6)}{(p - 10)}$$

$$f(p) = \dfrac{(p - 1)(p - 6)}{(p - 10)} = \dfrac{p^2 - 7p + 6}{(p - 10)} \text{ (i.e. a quotient)}$$

$$f'(p) = \frac{(p - 10)(2p - 7) - (p^2 - 7p + 6)(1)}{(p - 10)^2}$$

$$= \frac{(2p^2 - 27p + 70) - (p^2 - 7p + 6)}{(p - 10)^2}$$

$$= \frac{p^2 - 20p + 64}{(p - 10)^2}$$

$$= \frac{(p - 4)(p - 16)}{(p - 10)^2} = 0 \text{ for a maximum or minimum value.}$$

Therefore $(p - 4)(p - 16) = 0$

i.e. $p = 4$ or $p = 16$.

When $p = 4$, $f(p) = \frac{(3)(-2)}{(-6)} = 1$

When $p = 16$, $f(p) = \frac{(15)(10)}{(6)} = 25$

Hence there are turning-points at $(4, 1)$ and $(16, 25)$.

To use the second-derivative approach in this case would result in a complicated and long expression. Thus the slope is investigated just before and just after the turning-point.

It will be easier to use the factorised version of $f'(p)$.

i.e. $f'(p) = \frac{(p - 4)(p - 16)}{(p - 10)^2}$

Consider the point $(4, 1)$:

When p is just less than 4, $f'(p) = \frac{(-)(-)}{(+)}$, i.e. positive.

When p is just greater than 4, $f'(p) = \frac{(+)(-)}{(+)}$, i.e. negative.

Since the slope changes from positive to negative the point $(4, 1)$ is a maximum.

Consider the point $(16, 25)$:

When p is just less than 16, $f'(p) = \frac{(+)(-)}{(+)}$, i.e. negative.

When p is just greater than 16, $f'(p) = \frac{(+)(+)}{(+)}$, i.e. positive.

Since the slope changes from negative to positive the point $(16, 25)$ is a minimum.

Since, in the question, the maximum and minimum values are asked for (and not the coordinates of the turning-points) the answers are: **maximum value = 1; minimum value = 25.**

Problem 4. Find the maximum and minimum values of $y = 1.25 \cos 2\theta + \sin \theta$ for values of θ between 0 and $\dfrac{\pi}{2}$ inclusive, given $\sin 2\theta = 2 \sin \theta \cos \theta$.

$$y = 1.25 \cos 2\theta + \sin \theta$$

$$\frac{dy}{d\theta} = -2.50 \sin 2\theta + \cos \theta = 0 \text{ for a maximum or minimum value.}$$

But $\sin 2\theta = 2 \sin \theta \cos \theta$

Therefore $\quad -2.50(2 \sin \theta \cos \theta) + \cos \theta = 0$

$$-5.0 \sin \theta \cos \theta + \cos \theta = 0$$

$$\cos \theta(-5.0 \sin \theta + 1) = 0$$

Hence $\cos \theta = 0$, i.e. $\theta = 90°$ or $270°$

or $-5.0 \sin \theta + 1 = 0$, i.e. $\sin \theta = \frac{1}{5}$

$\quad \theta = 11° \, 32'$ or $168° \, 28'$

Thus within the range $\theta = 0$ to $\theta = \dfrac{\pi}{2}$ inclusive, turning-points occur at $11° \, 32'$ and $90°$.

$$\frac{d^2 y}{d\theta^2} = -5.0 \cos 2\theta - \sin \theta$$

When $\theta = 11° \, 32'$, $\dfrac{d^2 y}{d\theta^2} = -4.80$, i.e. it is negative, giving a maximum value.

When $\theta = 90°$, $\dfrac{d^2 y}{d\theta^2} = 4$, i.e. it is positive, giving a minimum value.

$y_{max} = 1.25 \cos 2(11° \, 32') + \sin (11° \, 32') = \mathbf{1.35}$

$y_{min} = 1.25 \cos 2(90°) + \sin (90°) = \mathbf{-0.25}$

Further problems on maximum and minimum values may be found in Section 4, Problems 16–41, page 265.

3 Practical problems involving maximum and minimum values

There are many practical problems on maximum and minimum values in engineering and science which can be solved using the method(s) shown in Section 2. Often the quantity whose maximum or minimum value is required appears at first to be a function of more than one variable. It is thus necessary to eliminate all but one of the variables, and this is often the only difficult part of its solution. Once the quantity has been expressed in terms of a single variable, the procedure is identical to that used in Section 2.

Worked problems on practical problems involving maximum and minimum values

Problem 1. A rectangular area is formed using a piece of wire 36 cm long.

Find the length and breadth of the rectangle if it is to enclose the maximum possible area.

Let the dimensions of the rectangle be x and y.
Perimeter of rectangle = $2x + 2y = 36$
  i.e. $x + y = 18$ ...(1)

Since it is the maximum area that is requured a formula for the area A must be obtained in terms of one variable only.
  Area $A = xy$
  From equation (1) $y = 18 - x$
  Hence $A = x(18 - x) = 18x - x^2$

Now that an expression for the area has been obtained in terms of one variable it can be differentiated with respect to that variable.

$\dfrac{dA}{dx} = 18 - 2x = 0$ for a maximum or minimum value.

  i.e. $x = 9$

$\dfrac{d^2A}{dx^2} = -2$, which is negative, giving a maximum value.

$y = 18 - x = 18 - 9 = 9$

Hence **the length and breadth of the rectangle of maximum area are both 9 cm**, i.e. a square gives the maximum possible area for a given perimeter length. When the perimeter of a rectangle is 36 cm the maximum area possible is 81 cm^2.

Problem 2. Find the area of the largest piece of rectangular ground that can be enclosed by 1 km of fencing if part of an existing straight wall is used as one side.

There are a large number of possible rectangular areas which can be produced from 1 000 m of fencing. Three such possibilities are shown in Fig. 5(a) where AB represents the existing wall. All three rectangles have different areas. There must be one particular condition which gives a maximum area.

Let the dimensions of any rectangle be x and y as shown in Fig. 5 (b).
  Then $2x + y = 1\ 000$ ...(1)
  Area of rectangle, $A = xy$ ...(2)

Since it is the **maximum area** that is required, a formula for the area A must be obtained in terms of one variable only.

From equation (1) $y = 1\ 000 - 2x$
  Hence $A = x(1\ 000 - 2x) = 1\ 000x - 2x^2$

                 $\dfrac{dA}{dx} = 1\ 000 - 4x = 0$ for a maximum or minimum value

  i.e. $x = 250$

$$\frac{d^2A}{dx^2} = -4,$$ which is negative, giving a maximum value.

When $x = 250$, $y = 1\,000 - 2(250) = 500$

Hence the maximum possible area = xy m^2 = $(250)(500)$ m^2 = $125\,000$ m^2.

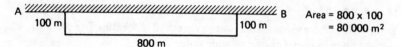

100 m   100 m

800 m

Area = 800 x 100
= 80 000 m^2

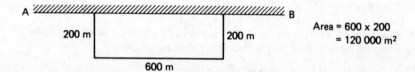

200 m   200 m

600 m

Area = 600 x 200
= 120 000 m^2

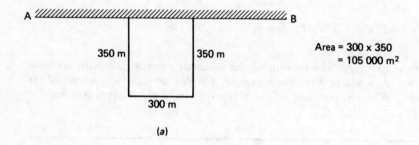

350 m   350 m

300 m

Area = 300 x 350
= 105 000 m^2

(a)

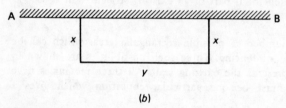

x x

y

(b)

Fig. 5

Problem 3. A lidless, rectangular box with square ends is to be made from a thin sheet of metal. What is the least area of the metal for which the volume is $4\frac{1}{2}$ m^3?

Let the dimensions of the box be x metres by x metres by y metres.

Volume of box = $x^2y = 4\frac{1}{2}$ . . . (1)

Surface area A of box consists of: two ends = $2x^2$

two sides = $2xy$

base = xy

$$A = 2x^2 + 2xy + xy = 2x^2 + 3xy \qquad \qquad \ldots (2)$$

Since it is the **least (i.e. minimum in this case) area** that is required, a formula for the area A must be obtained in terms of one variable only.

From equation (1), $y = \dfrac{4\frac{1}{2}}{x^2} = \dfrac{9}{2x^2}$

Substituting $y = \dfrac{9}{2x^2}$ in equation (2) gives:

$$A = 2x^2 + 3x\left(\frac{9}{2x^2}\right) = 2x^2 + \frac{27}{2x}$$

$$\frac{\mathrm{d}A}{\mathrm{d}x} = 4x - \frac{27}{2x^2} = 0 \text{ for a maximum or minimum value}$$

$$4x = \frac{27}{2x^2}$$

$$x^3 = \tfrac{27}{8}, \text{ i.e. } x = \tfrac{3}{2}$$

$$\frac{\mathrm{d}^2 A}{\mathrm{d}x^2} = 4 + \frac{27}{x^3}$$

When $x = \tfrac{3}{2}$, $\dfrac{\mathrm{d}^2 A}{\mathrm{d}x^2} = 4 + \dfrac{27}{(\frac{3}{2})^3} = +12$, which is positive, giving a minimum (or least) value.

When $x = \tfrac{3}{2}$, $y = \dfrac{9}{2x^2} = \dfrac{9}{2(\frac{3}{2})^2} = 2$

Therefore area $A = 2x^2 + 3xy = 2[\tfrac{3}{2}]^2 + 3[\tfrac{3}{2}](2) = 13\frac{1}{2}$

Hence **the least possible area of metal required to form a rectangular box with square ends of volume $4\frac{1}{2}$ m^3 is $13\frac{1}{2}$ m^2.**

Problem 4. Find the base radius and height of the cylinder of maximum volume which can be cut from a sphere of radius 10.0 cm.

A cylinder of radius r and height h is shown in Fig. 6 enclosed in a sphere of radius $R = 10.0$ cm.

Volume of cylinder, $V = \pi r^2 h$ $\qquad \qquad \ldots (1)$

Using the theorem of Pythagoras on the triangle ABC of Fig. 6 gives:

$$r^2 + \left[\frac{h}{2}\right]^2 = R^2$$

i.e. $r^2 + \dfrac{h^2}{4} = 100$ $\qquad \qquad \ldots (2)$

Since it is the **maximum volume** that is required, a formula for the volume V must be obtained in terms of one variable only.

From equation (2), $r^2 = 100 - \dfrac{h^2}{4}$

Substituting $r^2 = 100 - \dfrac{h^2}{4}$ in equation (1) gives:

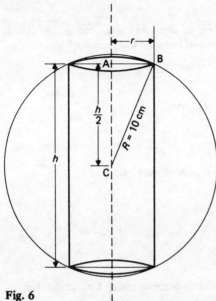

Fig. 6

$$V = \pi \left[100 - \frac{h^2}{4}\right] h = 100\pi h - \frac{\pi h^3}{4}$$

$$\frac{dV}{dh} = 100\pi - \frac{3\pi}{4} h^2 = 0 \text{ for a maximum or minimum value.}$$

$$100\pi = \frac{3\pi}{4} h^2$$

$$h^2 = \frac{400}{3}$$

$$h = 11.55 \text{ cm } (h = -11.55 \text{ cm is neglected for obvious reasons})$$

$$\frac{d^2 V}{dh^2} = -\tfrac{3}{2} \pi h$$

When $h = 11.55$, $\frac{d^2 V}{dh^2} = -\tfrac{3}{2} \pi (11.55) = -54.43$ which is negative, giving a

maximum value.

From equation (2) $r^2 = 100 - \frac{h^2}{4}$

$$r = \sqrt{\left(100 - \frac{h^2}{4}\right)} = 8.164 \text{ cm}$$

Hence the cylinder having the largest volume that can be cut from a sphere of radius 10.0 cm is one in which the base radius is 8.164 cm and the height is 11.55 cm.

Problem 5. A piece of wire 4.0 m long is cut into two parts one of which is bent into a square and the other bent into a circle. Find the radius of the circle if the sum of their areas is a minimum.

Let the square be of side x m and the circle of radius r m.
The sum of the perimeters of the square and circle is given by:

$$4x + 2\pi r = 4$$
$$\text{or} \quad 2x + \pi r = 2 \qquad \qquad \ldots (1)$$

Total area A of the two shapes, $A = x^2 + \pi r^2$ $\qquad \qquad \ldots (2)$

Since it is the **minimum area** that is required a formula for the area A must be obtained in terms of one variable only.

From equation (1), $x = \dfrac{2 - \pi r}{2}$

Substituting $x = \dfrac{2 - \pi r}{2}$ in equation (2) gives:

$$A = \left(\frac{2 - \pi r}{2} \right)^2 + \pi r^2 = \frac{4 - 4\pi r + \pi^2 r^2}{4} + \pi r^2$$

i.e. $A = 1 - \pi r + \dfrac{\pi^2 r^2}{4} + \pi r^2$

$$\frac{dA}{dr} = -\pi + \frac{\pi^2 r}{2} + 2\pi r = 0 \text{ for a maximum or minimum value.}$$

i.e. $\pi = r \left[\dfrac{\pi^2}{2} + 2\pi \right]$

$$r = \frac{\pi}{\left(\dfrac{\pi^2}{2} + 2\pi \right)} = \frac{1}{\left(\dfrac{\pi}{2} + 2 \right)} = 0.280 \text{ m}$$

$\dfrac{d^2 A}{dr^2} = \dfrac{\pi^2}{2} + 2\pi = 11.22$, which is positive, giving a minimum value.

Hence for the sum of the areas of the square and circle to be a minimum the radius of the circle must be 28.0 cm.

Problem 6. Find the base radius of a cylinder of maximum volume which can be cut from a cone of height 12 cm and base radius 9 cm.

A cylinder of base radius r cm and height h cm is shown enclosed in a cone of height 12 cm and base radius 9 cm in Fig. 7.

Volume of the cylinder, $V = \pi r^2 h$ $\qquad \qquad \ldots (1)$
By similar triangles: $\dfrac{12 - h}{r} = \dfrac{12}{9}$ $\qquad \qquad \ldots (2)$

Since it is the **maximum volume** that is required a formula for the volume V must be obtained in terms of one variable only.

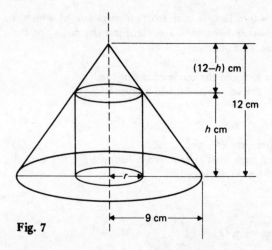

Fig. 7

From equation (2), $9(12 - h) = 12r$

$$108 - 9h = 12r$$

$$h = \frac{108 - 12r}{9}$$

Substituting for h in equation (1) gives:

$$V = \pi r^2 \left[\frac{108 - 12r}{9} \right] = 12\pi r^2 - \frac{4\pi r^3}{3}$$

$\dfrac{\mathrm{d}V}{\mathrm{d}r} = 24\pi r - 4\pi r^2 = 0$ for a maximum or minimum value.

i.e. $4\pi r(6 - r) = 0$

Therefore $r = 0$ or $r = 6$.

$$\frac{\mathrm{d}^2 V}{\mathrm{d}r^2} = 24\pi - 8\pi r$$

When $r = 0$, $\dfrac{\mathrm{d}^2 V}{\mathrm{d}r^2}$ is positive, giving a minimum value (which we would expect).

When $r = 6$, $\dfrac{\mathrm{d}^2 V}{\mathrm{d}r^2} = 24\pi - 48\pi = -24\pi$, which is negative, giving a maximum value.

Hence a cylinder of maximum volume having a base radius of 6 cm can be cut from a cone of height 12 cm and base radius 9 cm.

Problem 7. A rectangular sheet of metal which measures 24.0 cm by 16.0 cm has squares removed from each of the four corners so that an open box may be formed. Find the maximum possible volume for the box.

The squares which are to be removed are shown shaded and having side x cm in Fig. 8.

To form a box the metal has to be bent upwards along the broken lines.

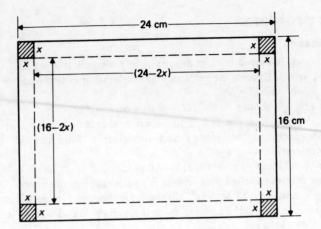

Fig. 8

The dimensions of the box will be: length = $(24.0 - 2x)$ cm
breadth = $(16.0 - 2x)$ cm
height = x cm

If volume of box is V cm^3, $V = (24.0 - 2x)(16.0 - 2x)(x)$
$$= 384x - 80x^2 + 4x^3$$

$$\frac{dV}{dx} = 384 - 160x + 12x^2 = 0 \text{ for a maximum or minimum value.}$$

i.e. $4(3x^2 - 40x + 96) = 0$

$$x = \frac{40 \pm \sqrt{[(-40)^2 - 4(3)(96)]}}{6}$$

$x = 10.194$ cm or $x = 3.139$ cm

Since the breadth = $(16.0 - 2x)$ cm, $x = 10.194$ cm is an impossible solution to this problem and is thus neglected.

Hence $x = 3.139$ cm

$$\frac{d^2V}{dx^2} = -160 + 24x$$

When $x = 3.139$ cm, $\frac{d^2V}{dx^2} = -160 + 24(3.139) = -84.66$ which is negative,

giving a maximum value.

The dimensions of the box are: length = $24.0 - 2(3.139) = 17.72$ cm
breadth = $16.0 - 2(3.139) = 9.722$ cm
height = 3.139 cm

Maximum volume = $(17.72)(9.722)(3.139) = 540.8$ cm^3.

Further problems on practical maximum and minimum problems may be found in the following section (4), Problems 42—69, page 266. There are also some further typical practical differentiation examples, Problems 70—81, page 269.

4   Further problems

Velocity and acceleration

1. The distance x metres moved by a body in a time t seconds is given by $x = 4t^3 + 3t^2 + 5t + 2$. Express the velocity and acceleration in terms of t and find their values when $t = 3$ s.
   $[v = 12t^2 - 6t + 5; v_3 = 95 \text{ m s}^{-1}; a = 24t - 6; a_3 = 66 \text{ m s}^{-2}]$

2. A body obeys the equation $x = 3t - 20t^2$ where x is in metres and t is in seconds. Find expressions for velocity and acceleration. Find also its velocity and acceleration when $t = 1$ s.
   $[v = 3 - 40t; v_1 = -37 \text{ m s}^{-1}; a = -40; a_1 = -40 \text{ m s}^{-2}]$

3. If the distance x metres travelled by a vehicle in t seconds after the brakes are applied is given by: $x = 22.5t - \frac{5}{8}t^2$, then what is the speed in km h^{-1} when the brakes are applied? How far does the vehicle travel before it stops? [81 km h^{-1}; 151.9 m]

4. An object moves in a straight line so that after t seconds its distance x metres from a fixed point on the line is given by $x = \frac{2}{3}t^3 - 5t^2 + 8t - 6$. Obtain an expression for the velocity and acceleration of the object after t seconds and hence calculate the values of t when the object is at rest.
   $[v = 2t^2 - 10t + 8; a = 4t - 10; t = 1 \text{ s or } 4 \text{ s}]$

In Problems 5–9, x denotes the distance in metres of a body moving in a straight line, from a fixed point on the line and t denotes the time in seconds measured from a certain instant. Find the velocity and acceleration of the body when t has the given values. Find also the values of t when the body is momentarily at rest.

5. $x = \frac{4}{3}t^3 - 4t^2 + 3t - 2$; $t = 2$.   [3 m s^{-1}; 8 m s^{-2}; $t = \frac{1}{2}$ or $1\frac{1}{2}$ s]

6. $x = 3 \cos 2t$; $t = \frac{\pi}{4}$.   [-6 m s^{-1}; 0; $t = 0, \dfrac{\pi}{2}, \pi, \dfrac{3\pi}{2}$, etc.]

7. $x = t^4 - \frac{1}{2}t^2 + 1$; $t = 1$.   [3 m s^{-1}; 11 m s^{-2}; $t = 0$ or $\pm\frac{1}{2}$ s]

8. $x = 4t + 2 \cos 2t$; $t = 0$.   [4 m s^{-1}; -8 m s^{-2}; $t = \dfrac{\pi}{4}, \dfrac{5\pi}{4}, \dfrac{9\pi}{4}, \dfrac{13\pi}{4}$, etc.]

9. $x = \dfrac{t^4}{4} - \frac{5}{3}t^3 + 3t^2 + 5$; $t = 2$.   [0; -2 m s^{-2}; $t = 0, 2$ or 3 s]

10. The distance s metres moved by a point in t seconds is given by $s = 5t^3 + 4t^2 - 3t + 2$. Find:
    (a) expressions for velocity and acceleration in terms of t;
    (b) the velocity and acceleration after 3 seconds; and
    (c) the average velocity over the fourth second.
    (a) $[v = (15t^2 + 8t - 3) \text{ m s}^{-1}; a = (30t + 8) \text{ m s}^{-2}]$
    (b) [156 m s^{-1}; 98 m s^{-2}]   (c) [210 m s^{-1}]

11. The distance x metres moved by a body in t seconds is given by $x = \frac{16}{3}t^3 - 32t^2 + 39t - 16$. Find:
    (a) the velocity and acceleration at the start;
    (b) the velocity and acceleration at $t = 3$ seconds;
    (c) the values of t when the body is at rest;

   (d) the value of t when the acceleration is 16 m s^{-2}; and

   (e) the distance travelled in the second second.

   (a) [39 m s^{-1}; -64 m s^{-2}]   (b) [-9 m s^{-1}; 32 m s^{-2}]   (c) [$t = \frac{3}{4}$ or $3\frac{1}{4}$ s]

   (d) [$2\frac{1}{2}$ s]   (e) [$-19\frac{2}{3}$ m (i.e. in the opposite direction to that in which the body initially moved)]

12. The displacement y centimetres of the slide valve of an engine is given by the expression $y = 2.6 \cos 5\pi t + 3.8 \sin 5\pi t$. Find an expression for the velocity v of the valve and evaluate the velocity (in metres per second) when $t = 20$ ms.   [$v = 5\pi(3.8 \cos 5\pi t - 2.6 \sin 5\pi t)$; 0.442 m s^{-1}]

13. At any time t seconds the distance x metres of a particle moving in a straight line from a fixed point is given by: $x = 5t + \ln(1 - 2t)$. Find:

   (a) expressions for the velocity and acceleration in terms of t;

   (b) the initial velocity and acceleration;

   (c) the velocity and acceleration after 2 s; and

   (d) the time when the velocity is zero.

   (a) $\left[\left(5 - \dfrac{2}{(1 - 2t)} \right) \text{m s}^{-1}; \left(\dfrac{-4}{(1 - 2t)^2} \right) \text{m s}^{-2} \right]$

   (b) [3 m s^{-1}; -4 m s^{-2}]   (c) [$5\frac{2}{3}$ m s^{-1}; $-\frac{4}{9}$ m s^{-2}]   (d) [$\frac{3}{10}$ s]

14. If the equation $\theta = 12\pi + 27t - 3t^2$ gives the angle in radians through which a wheel turns in t seconds, find how many seconds the wheel takes to come to rest. Calculate the angle turned through in the last second of movement.   [$4\frac{1}{2}$ s; 3 radians]

15. A missile fired from ground level rises s metres in t seconds, and $s = 75t - 12.5t^2$. Determine:

   (a) the initial velocity of the missile;

   (b) the time when the height of the missile is a maximum;

   (c) the maximum height reached; and

   (d) the velocity with which the missile strikes the ground.

   (a) [75 m s^{-1}]   (b) [3 s]   (c) [112.5 m]   (d) [75 ms^{-1}]

Maximum and minimum values

In Problems 16–20 find the turning-points and distinguish between them by examining the sign of the slope on either side.

16. $y = 2x^2 - 4x$ [min. (1, -2)]

17. $y = 3t^2 - 2t + 6$ [min. $(\frac{1}{3}, 5\frac{2}{3})$]

18. $x = \theta^3 - 3\theta + 3$ [max. (-1, 5); min. (1, 1)]

19. $y = 3x^3 + 6x^2 + 3x - 2$ [max. (-1, -2); min. ($-\frac{1}{3}$, $-2\frac{4}{9}$)]

20. $y = 7t^3 - 4t^2 - 5t + 6$ [max. ($-\frac{1}{3}$, $6\frac{26}{27}$); min. ($\frac{5}{7}$, $2\frac{46}{49}$)]

Locate the turning-points on the curves in Problems 21–39 and determine whether they are maximum or minimum points.

21. $y = x(7 - x)$ [max. $(3\frac{1}{2}, 12\frac{1}{4})$]

22. $y = 4x^2 - 2x + 3$ [min. $(\frac{1}{4}, 2\frac{3}{4})$]

23. $y = 2x^3 + 7x^2 + 4x - 3$ [max. (-2, 1); min. ($-\frac{1}{3}$, $-3\frac{17}{27}$)]

24. $2pq = 18p^2 + 8$ [max. ($-\frac{2}{3}$, -12); min. ($\frac{2}{3}$, 12)]

25. $y = 3t + e^{-t}$ [min. ($-1.098\,6$, -0.2958)]

26. $x = 3 \ln \theta - 4\theta$ [max. (0.75, -3.863)]

27. $S = 5t^3 - \frac{3}{2}t^2 - 12t + 6$ [max. $(-\frac{4}{5}, 12\frac{2}{25})$; min. $(1, -2\frac{1}{2})$]

28. $y = 4x - 2 \ln x$ [min. $(0.5, 3.386)$]

29. $y = 3x - e^x$ [max. $(1.098\ 6, 0.295\ 8)$]

30. $p = \dfrac{(q - 1)(q - 3)}{q}$ [max. $(-1.732, -7.464)$; min. $(1.732, -0.535\ 9)$]

31. $y = \dfrac{(x - 2)(x - 5)}{(x - 6)}$ [max. $(4, 1)$; min. $(8, 9)$]

32. $y = 3 \sin \theta - 4 \cos \theta$ in the range θ to 2π.
    [max. 5 at $143° 8'$; min. -5 at $323° 8'$]

33. $y = 4 \cos 2\theta + 3 \sin \theta$ in the range 0 to $\dfrac{\pi}{2}$ inclusive, given that

    $\sin 2\theta = 2 \sin \theta \cos \theta$.   [max. 4.281 2 at $10° 48'$; min. -1 at $90°$]

34. $V = l^2 (l - 1)$ [max. $(0, 0)$; min. $(\frac{2}{3}, \frac{-4}{27})$]

35. $y = 8x + \dfrac{1}{2x^2}$ [min. $(\frac{1}{2}, 6)$]

36. $x = t^3 + \dfrac{t^2}{2} - 2t + 4$ [max. $-1, 5\frac{1}{2}$); min. $(\frac{2}{3}, 3\frac{5}{27})$]

37. $y = \dfrac{3x}{(x - 1)(x - 4)}$ [max. $(2, -3)$; min. $(-2, -\frac{1}{3})$]

38. $y = (x - 1)^3 + 3x(x - 2)$ [max. $(-1, 1)$; min. $(1, -3)$]

39. $y = \frac{1}{2} \ln (\sin x) - \sin x$ in the range 0 to $\dfrac{\pi}{4}$ [max. $-0.846\ 6$ at $30°$]

40. (a) If $p + q = 7$, find the maximum value of $3pq + q^2$.
    (b) If $3a - 2b = 5$, find the least value of $2a^2b$.
    (a) $[55\frac{1}{8}]$ (b) $[-2\frac{14}{243}$ or $-2.057\ 6]$

41. The sum of a number and its reciprocal is to be a minimum. Find the number.   [1]

Practical maximum and minimum problems

42. Find the maximum area of a rectangular piece of ground that can be enclosed by 200 m of fencing.   [2 500 m^2]

43. A rectangular area is formed using a piece of wire of length 26 cm. Find the dimensions of the rectangle if it is to enclose the maximum possible area.   [$6\frac{1}{2}$ cm by $6\frac{1}{2}$ cm]

44. A shell is projected upwards with a speed of 12 m s^{-1} and the distance vertically s metres is given by $s = 12t - 3t^2$, where t is the time in seconds. Find the maximum height reached.   [12 m]

45. A length of 42 cm of thin wire is bent into a rectangular shape with one side repeated. Find the largest area that can be enclosed.   [73.5 cm^2]

46. Find the area of the largest piece of rectangular ground that can be enclosed by 800 m of fencing if part of an existing wall is used on one side.
    [80 000 m^2]

47. The bending moment M of a beam of length l at a distance a from one end is given by $M = \dfrac{Wa}{2} (l - a)$, where W is the load per unit length. Find

the maximum bending moment. $\left[\dfrac{Wl^2}{8}\right]$

48. A lidless box with square ends is to be made from a thin sheet of metal. What is the least area of the metal for which the volume of the box is 6.64 m^3? $\quad [17.50 \text{ m}^2]$

49. Find the height and the radius of a cylinder of volume 150 cm^3 which has the least surface area. $\quad [5.759 \text{ cm}; 2.879 \text{ cm}]$

50. Find the height of a right circular cylinder of greatest volume which can be cut from a sphere of radius R. $\quad \left[\dfrac{2R}{\sqrt{3}}\right]$

51. The power P developed in a resistor R by a battery of e.m.f. E and internal resistance r is given by $P = \dfrac{E^2 R}{(R + r)^2}$.

    Differentiate P with respect to R and show that the power is a maximum when $R = r$.

52. A piece of wire 5.0 m long is cut into two parts, one of which is bent into a square and the other into a circle. Find the diameter of the circle if the sum of their areas is a minimum. $\quad [0.700 \text{ m}]$

53. Find the height of a cylinder of maximum volume which can be cut from a cone of height 15 cm and base radius 7.5 cm. $\quad [5 \text{ cm}]$

54. An alternating current is given by $i = 100 \sin(50\pi t + 0.32)$ amperes, where t is the time in seconds. Determine the maximum value of the current and the time when this maximum first occurs.
    [100 amperes when $t = 7.96$ ms].

55. A frame for a box kite with a square cross-section is made of 16 pieces of wood as shown in Fig. 9. Find the maximum volume of the frame if a total length of 12 m of wood is used.
    $[\frac{4}{9} \text{ m}^3]$

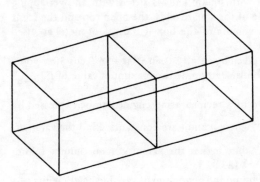

Fig. 9

56. A rectangular box with a lid which covers the top and front has a volume of 150 cm^3 and the length of the base is to be $1\frac{1}{2}$ times the height. Find the dimensions of the box so that the surface area shall be a minimum.
    [3.816 cm by 5.724 cm by 6.867 cm]

57. The force F required to move a body along a rough horizontal plane is given by $F = \dfrac{\mu W}{\cos \theta + \mu \sin \theta}$ where μ is the coefficient of friction and θ the angle to the direction of F. If F varies with θ show that F is a minimum when $\tan \theta = \mu$.

58. A closed cylindrical container has a surface area of 300 cm^2. Find its dimensions for maximum volume.
   [radius = 3.989 cm; height = 7.981 cm]

59. A rectangular block of metal, with a square cross-section, has a total surface area of 240 cm^2. Find the maximum volume of the block of metal.   [253.0 cm^3]

60. The displacement s metres in a damped harmonic oscillation is given by $s = 4e^{-2t} \sin 2t$, where t is the time in milliseconds. Find the values of t to give maximum displacements. $\left[\dfrac{\pi}{8}, \dfrac{5\pi}{8}, \dfrac{9\pi}{8}, \text{and so on} \right]$

61. A square sheet of metal of side 25.0 cm has squares cut from each corner, so that an open box may be formed. Find the surface area and the volume of the box if the volume is to be a maximum.
   [555.6 cm^2; 1 157 cm^3]

62. A right circular cylinder of maximum volume is to be cut from a sphere of radius 14.0 cm. Determine the base diameter and the height of the cylinder.   [22.86 cm; 16.17 cm]

63. The speed v of a signal transmitted through a cable is given by $v = kx^2 \ln \dfrac{1}{x}$, where x is the ratio of the inner to the outer diameters of the core and k is a constant. Find the value of x for maximum speed of the transmitted signal. $[x = e^{-\frac{1}{2}} = 0.606\ 5]$

64. An open rectangular box with square ends is fitted with an overlapping lid which covers the whole of the square ends, the open top and the front face. Find the maximum volume of the box if 8.0 m^2 of metal are used altogether.   [0.871 m^3]

65. An electrical voltage E is given by: $E = 12.0 \sin 50\pi t + 36.0 \cos 50\pi t$ volts, where t is the time in seconds. Determine the maximum value of E.
   [37.95 volts]

66. The velocity v of a piston of a reciprocating engine can be expressed by $v = 2\pi nr \left(\dfrac{\sin 2\theta}{16} + \sin \theta \right)$, where n and r are constants. Find the value of θ between $0°$ and $360°$ that makes the velocity a maximum. (Note: $\cos 2\theta = 2\cos^2 \theta - 1$.) $[83°\ 2']$

67. The periodic time T of a compound pendulum of variable height is given by $T = 2\pi \sqrt{\left[\dfrac{b^2 + k^2}{gb} \right]}$, where k and g are constants. Find the minimum value of T. $\left[T_{\min} = 2\pi \sqrt{\left(\dfrac{2k}{g} \right)} \text{ when } b = k \right]$

68. The heat capacity (C) of carbon monoxide varies with absolute tempera-

ture (T) as shown: $C = 26.53 + 7.70 \times 10^{-3}T - 1.17 \times 10^{-6}T^2$. Determine the maximum value of C and the temperature at which it occurs.
[$C = 39.20$, $T = 3.291 \times 10^3$]

69. The electromotive force (E) of the Clark cell is given by
$E = 1.4 - 0.001\ 2\ (T - 288) - 0.000\ 007\ (T - 288)^2$ volts. Determine the maximum value of E.   [1.451 4 volts]

Practical differentiation

70. The length l metres of a certain rod at temperature $t°C$ is given by $l = 1 + 0.000\ 02t + 0.000\ 000\ 2t^2$. Find the rate at which l increases with respect to t $\left(\text{i.e.}\ \dfrac{dl}{dt}\right)$ when the temperature is: (a) 100°C; and (b) 300°C.
(a) [0.000 06 m °C^{-1}]   (b) [0.000 14 m °C^{-1}]

71. An alternating voltage v volts is given by $v = 125 \sin 80\ t$, where t is the time in seconds. Calculate the rate of change of voltage $\left(\text{i.e.}\ \dfrac{dv}{dt}\right)$ when $t = 20$ ms.   [−292 volts per second]

72. In a first-order reaction the concentration c after time t is governed by the relation $c = ae^{-kt}$, where a is the initial concentration and k is the rate constant. Show that the value of $\dfrac{dc}{dt}$ is given by $-kc$.

73. A displacement s metres is given by $s = \frac{1}{3}t^3 - 4\ t^2 + 15\ t$, where t is the time in seconds. At what times is the velocity v $\left(\text{i.e.}\ \dfrac{ds}{dt}\right)$ zero? Determine the acceleration $\left(\text{i.e.}\ \dfrac{dv}{dt}\right)$ when $t = 6$ seconds.   [$t = 3$ s or 5 s; 4 m s^{-2}]

74. The luminous intensity, I candelas, of a lamp at different voltages V is given by $I = 4 \times 10^{-4}\ V^2$. Find the voltage at which the light is increasing at a rate of 0.2 candelas per volt, $\left(\text{i.e. when}\ \dfrac{dI}{dV} = 0.2\right)$ [250 V]

75. The relationship between pressure p and volume v is given by $pv^n = k$, where n and k are constants. Prove that $v^{n+1}\ \dfrac{dp}{dv} + kn = 0$.

76. An alternating current i amperes is given by $i = 70 \sin 2\pi f\ t$, where f is the frequency in hertz and t the time in seconds. Find the rate of change of current $\left(\text{i.e.}\ \dfrac{di}{dt}\right)$ when $t = 20$ ms, given that the frequency is 50 hertz.
[$7\ 000\pi$ A s^{-1}]

77. Newton's law of cooling is given by $\theta = \theta_0 e^{-kt}$, where the excess of temperature at zero time is θ_0 °C and at time t seconds is θ °C. Determine the rate of change of temperature $\left(\text{i.e.}\ \dfrac{d\theta}{dt}\right)$, given that $\theta_0 = 15°C$, $k = -0.017$ and $t = 60$ seconds.   [0.707 °C s^{-1}]

78. A coil has a self inductance L of 2 henries and a resistance R of 100 ohms. A d.c. supply voltage E of 100 volts is applied to the coil. The

instantaneous current i amperes is given by $i = \dfrac{E}{R}\left(1 - e^{-\frac{Rt}{L}}\right)$. Find: (a)
the rate at which the current increases at the moment of switching on
$\left(\text{i.e. } \dfrac{di}{dt} \text{ when } t = 0\right)$; and (b) the rate after 10 ms.   (a) $[50 \text{ A s}^{-1}]$
(b) $[30.3 \text{ A s}^{-1}]$

79. A fully charged capacitor C of 0.1 microfarads has a potential difference
V of 150 volts between its plates. The capacitor is then discharged
through a resistor R of 1 megohm. If the potential difference v across the
plate at any time t seconds after closing the circuit is given by $v = Ve^{-\frac{t}{RC}}$
calculate:

(a) the initial rate of loss of voltage $\left(\text{i.e. } \dfrac{dv}{dt} \text{ at } t = 0\right)$;

(b) the rate after 0.1 seconds.

(a) $[1\,500 \text{ V s}^{-1}]$ (b) $[552 \text{ V s}^{-1}]$

80. The pressure p of the atmosphere at height b above ground level is given
by $p = p_0\, e^{-\frac{b}{c}}$, where p_0 is the pressure at ground level and c is a
constant.

Determine the rate of change of pressure with height $\left(\text{i.e. } \dfrac{dp}{db}\right)$ when p_0

is 1.013×10^5 pascals and c is 6.062×10^4 at $1\,500$ metres.
$[-1.630 \text{ Pa/m}]$

81. The displacement s cm of the end of a stiff spring at time t seconds is
given by $s = ae^{-kt} \sin 2\pi f\, t$. Find the velocity $v\, \left(\text{i.e. } \dfrac{ds}{dt}\right)$ and acceleration
$a\, \left(\text{i.e. } \dfrac{d^2 s}{dt^2}\right)$ of the end of the spring after 3 seconds if $a = 4$, $k = 0.8$ and
$f = 2$. $[4.56 \text{ cm s}^{-1}, -7.30 \text{ cm s}^{-2}]$

Chapter 14

Methods of integration

1 Introduction to integration

The process of integration reverses the process of differentiation. In differentiation, if $f(x) = x^2$ then $f'(x) = 2x$. Since integration reverses the process of moving from $f(x)$ to $f'(x)$, it follows that the integral of $2x$ is x^2, i.e. it is the process of moving from $f'(x)$ to $f(x)$. Similarly, if $y = x^3$ then $\dfrac{dy}{dx} = 3x^2$. Reversing this process shows that the integral of $3x^2$ is x^3.

Integration is also a process of summation or adding parts together and an elongated 'S', shown as $\int$, is used to replace the words 'the integral of'.

Thus $\int 2x = x^2$ and $\int 3x^2 = x^3$.

In differentiation, the differential coefficient $\dfrac{dy}{dx}$ or $\dfrac{d}{dx}[f(x)]$ indicates that a function of x is being differentiated with respect to x, the dx indicating this. In integration, the variable of integration is shown by adding d (the variable) after the function to be integrated. Thus $\int 2x\, dx$ means 'the integral of $2x$ with respect to x' and $\int 3u^2\, du$ means 'the integral of $3u^2$ with respect to u'. It follows that $\int y\, dx$ means 'the integral of y with respect to x' and since only functions of x can be integrated with respect to x, y must be expressed as a function of x before the process of integration can be performed.

The arbitrary constant of integration

The differential coefficient of x^2 is $2x$, hence $\int 2x \, dx = x^2$. Also, the differential coefficient of $x^2 + 3$ is $2x$, hence $\int 2x \, dx = x^2 + 3$. Since the differential coefficient of any constant is zero, it follows that the differential coefficient of $x^2 + c$, where c is any constant, is $2x$. To allow for the possible presence of this constant, whenever the process of integration is performed the constant should be added to the result. Hence $\int 2x \, dx = x^2 + c$.

c is called the arbitrary constant of integration and it is important to include it in all work involving the process of determining integrals. Its omission will result in obtaining incorrect solutions in later work, such as in the solution of differential equations (see chapter 17).

2   The general solution of integrals of the form x^n

$$\int x^n \, dx = \frac{x^{n+1}}{n+1} + c$$

In order to integrate x^n it is necessary to:

(a) increase the power of x by 1, i.e. the power of x^n is raised by 1 to x^{n+1};
(b) divide by the new power of x, i.e. x^{n+1} is divided by $n + 1$; and
(c) add the arbitrary constant of integration, c.

Thus to integrate x^4, the power of x is increased by 1 to x^{n+1} or x^{4+1}, i.e. x^5 and the term is divided by $(n + 1)$ or $(4 + 1)$, i.e. 5.

So the integral of x^4 is $\dfrac{x^5}{5} + c$.

In the general solution of $\int x^n \, dx$ given above, n may be a positive or negative integer or fraction, or zero, with just one exception, that being $n = -1$.

It was shown in differentiation that $\dfrac{d}{dx} (\ln x) = \dfrac{1}{x}$

Thus $\displaystyle\int \frac{1}{x} \, dx \ (= \int x^{-1} \, dx) = \ln x + c$

More generally, $\dfrac{d}{dx} (\ln ax) = \dfrac{d}{dx} (\ln x + \ln a)$

$$= \frac{1}{x} + 0$$

Therefore, $\displaystyle\int \frac{1}{x} \, dx = \ln ax + c$

Rules of integration

Three of the basic rules of integration are:

(i) The integral of a constant k is $kx + c$. For example,

$\int 5\ dx = \int 5x^0\ dx$ since $x^0 = 1$.

Applying the standard integral $\int x^n\ dx = \dfrac{x^{n+1}}{n+1} + c$ gives:

$\int 5\ dx = \dfrac{5x^{0+1}}{0+1} + c = 5x + c$

(ii) As in differentiation, constants associated with variables are carried forward, i.e. they are not involved in the integration. For example,

$\int 3x^4\ dx = 3 \int x^4\ dx = 3 \left(\dfrac{x^5}{5} \right) + c$

$\qquad\qquad = \dfrac{3}{5} x^5 + c$

(iii) As in differentiation, the rules of algebra apply where functions of a variable are added or subtracted. For example,

$\int (x^2 + x^5)\ dx = \int x^2\ dx + \int x^5\ dx = \dfrac{x^3}{3} + \dfrac{x^6}{6} + c$

and $\int (2x^3 + 4)\ dx = 2 \int x^3\ dx + \int 4\ dx = 2 \left(\dfrac{x^4}{4} \right) + 4x + c$

$\qquad\qquad\qquad\qquad\qquad\qquad = \dfrac{x^4}{2} + 4x + c$

It should be noted that only one constant c is included since any sum of arbitrary constants gives another arbitrary constant.

Combining rule (ii) with the standard integral for x^n gives:

$\int ax^n\ dx = \dfrac{ax^{n+1}}{n+1} + c$

where a and n are constants and n is **not** equal to -1.

Integrals written in this form are called 'indefinite integrals', since their precise value cannot be found (i.e. c cannot be calculated) unless additional information is provided. (In differentiation there are special rules for multiplication and division of functions. However, there are no such special rules for multiplication and division in integration.)

3 Definite integrals

Limits can be applied to integrals and such integrals are then called 'definite integrals'. The increase in the value of the integral $(x^2 - 3)$ as x increases from 1 to 2 can be written as:

$[\int (x^2 - 3)\ dx]_1^2$

However, this is invariably abbreviated by showing the value of the upper limit at the top of the integral sign and the value of the lower limit at the bottom, i.e.

$$\left[\int (x^2 - 3)\ dx\right]_1^2 = \int_1^2 (x^2 - 3)\ dx$$

The integral is evaluated as for an indefinite integral and then placed in the square brackets of the limit operator.

$$\text{Thus} \int_1^2 (x^2 - 3)\ dx = \left[\frac{x^3}{3} - 3x + c\right]_1^2$$

$$= \left[\frac{(2)^3}{3} - 3(2) + c\right] - \left[\frac{(1)^3}{3} - 3(1) + c\right]$$

$$= (\tfrac{8}{3} - 6 + c) - (\tfrac{1}{3} - 3 + c)$$

$$= 2\tfrac{2}{3} - 6 - \tfrac{1}{3} + 3 = -\tfrac{2}{3}$$

The arbitrary constant of integration, c, always cancels out when limits are applied to an integral and it is not usually shown when evaluating a definite integral.

4 Integrals of sin *ax*, cos *ax*, sec² *ax* and *eᵃˣ*

Since integration is the reverse process to that of differentiation the following standard integrals may be deduced.

(a) $\dfrac{d}{dx} (\sin x) = \cos x$

Hence $\int \cos x\ dx = \sin x + c$

More generally: $\dfrac{d}{dx} (\sin ax) = a \cos ax$

Hence $\int a \cos ax\ dx = \sin ax + c$

$$\int \cos ax\ dx = \frac{1}{a} \sin ax + c$$

(b) $\dfrac{d}{dx} (\cos x) = -\sin x$

Hence $\int -\sin x\ dx = \cos x + c$

$\int \sin x\ dx = -\cos x + c$

More generally: $\dfrac{d}{dx} (\cos ax) = -a \sin ax$

Hence $\int -a \sin ax\ dx = \cos ax + c$

$$\int \sin ax\ dx = -\frac{1}{a} \cos ax + c$$

(c) $\dfrac{d}{dx} (\tan x) = \sec^2 x$

Hence $\int \sec^2 x\, dx = \tan x + c$

More generally: $\dfrac{d}{dx}(\tan ax) = a \sec^2 ax$

Hence $\int a \sec^2 ax\, dx = \tan ax + c$

$$\int \sec^2 ax\, dx = \frac{1}{a}\tan ax + c$$

(d) $\dfrac{d}{dx}(e^x) = e^x$

Hence $\int e^x\, dx = e^x + c$

More generally: $\dfrac{d}{dx}(e^{ax}) = ae^{ax}$

Hence $\int ae^{ax}\, dx = e^{ax} + c$

$$\int e^{ax}\, dx = \frac{1}{a}e^{ax} + c$$

Summary of standard integrals

1. $\int ax^n\, dx \quad = \dfrac{ax^{n+1}}{n+1} + c$ (except where $n = -1$)

2. $\int \cos ax\, dx = \dfrac{1}{a}\sin ax + c$

3. $\int \sin ax\, dx \quad = -\dfrac{1}{a}\cos ax + c$

4. $\int \sec^2 ax\, dx = \dfrac{1}{a}\tan ax + c$

5. $\int e^{ax}\, dx \quad = \dfrac{1}{a}e^{ax} + c$

6. $\int \dfrac{1}{x}\, dx \quad = \ln x + c$

Worked problems on standard integrals

Problem 1. Integrate the following with respect to the variable: (a) x^7; (b) $5.2y^{1.6}$; (c) $\dfrac{2}{p^3}$.

(a) $\int x^7\, dx = \dfrac{x^{7+1}}{7+1} + c = \dfrac{x^8}{8} + c$

(b) $\int 5.2y^{1.6}\, dy = \dfrac{5.2y^{1.6+1}}{1.6+1} + c = \dfrac{5.2y^{2.6}}{2.6} + c = 2.0y^{2.6} + c$

(c) $\int \dfrac{2}{p^3} \, dp = \int 2p^{-3} \, dp = \dfrac{2p^{-3+1}}{-3+1} + c$

$$= \dfrac{2p^{-2}}{-2} + c = \dfrac{-1}{p^2} + c$$

If the final answer of an integration is differentiated then the original must result (otherwise an error has occurred). For example, in (a) above:

$$\dfrac{d}{dx}\left(\dfrac{x^8}{8} + c \right) = \dfrac{8x^7}{8} = x^7 \text{ (i.e. the original integral)}$$

It will be assumed that in all future integral problems such a check will be made.

Problem 2. Integrate with respect to the variable:

(a) $\left(2x^5 - 4\sqrt{x} + \dfrac{5}{x^4} - \dfrac{2}{\sqrt{x^3}} + 6\right)$;

(b) $\left(\dfrac{4p^5 - 3 + p}{p^3} \right)$

(a) $\int \left(2x^5 - 4\sqrt{x} + \dfrac{5}{x^4} - \dfrac{2}{\sqrt{x^3}} + 6 \right) dx = \int \left(2x^5 - 4x^{\frac{1}{2}} + 5x^{-4} - 2x^{-\frac{3}{2}} + 6\right) dx$

$$= \dfrac{2x^{5+1}}{(5+1)} - \dfrac{4x^{\frac{1}{2}+1}}{(\frac{1}{2}+1)} + \dfrac{5x^{-4+1}}{(-4+1)} - \dfrac{2x^{-\frac{3}{2}+1}}{(-\frac{3}{2}+1)} + 6x + c$$

$$= \dfrac{2x^6}{6} - \dfrac{4x^{\frac{3}{2}}}{\frac{3}{2}} + \dfrac{5x^{-3}}{-3} - \dfrac{2x^{-\frac{1}{2}}}{-\frac{1}{2}} + 6x + c$$

$$= \dfrac{x^6}{3} - \dfrac{8\sqrt{x^3}}{3} - \dfrac{5}{3x^3} + \dfrac{4}{\sqrt{x}} + 6x + c$$

(b) $\int \left(\dfrac{4p^5 - 3 + p}{p^3} \right) dp = \int \left(\dfrac{4p^5}{p^3} - \dfrac{3}{p^3} + \dfrac{p}{p^3} \right) dp$

$$= \int (4p^2 - 3p^{-3} + p^{-2}) \, dp$$

$$= \dfrac{4p^3}{3} - \dfrac{3p^{-2}}{-2} + \dfrac{p^{-1}}{-1} + c$$

$$= \dfrac{4}{3}p^3 + \dfrac{3}{2p^2} - \dfrac{1}{p} + c$$

Problem 3. Given $y = \int \left(r + \dfrac{1}{r} \right)^2 dr$, find the value of the arbitrary constant of integration if $y = \dfrac{1}{3}$ when $r = 1$.

$$y = \int \left(r + \dfrac{1}{r} \right)^2 dr = \int \left(r^2 + 2 + \dfrac{1}{r^2} \right) dr$$

$$= \dfrac{r^3}{3} + 2r - \dfrac{1}{r} + c$$

$y = \frac{1}{3}$ when $r = 1$. Hence $\frac{1}{3} = \frac{(1)^3}{3} + 2(1) - \frac{1}{(1)} + c$

$$\frac{1}{3} = \frac{1}{3} + 2 - 1 + c$$
$$c = -1$$

Hence the arbitrary constant of integration is -1.

Problem 4. Integrate with respect to the variable:
(a) $4 \cos 3\theta$; (b) $7 \sin 2x$; (c) $3 \sec^2 5t$.

(a) $\int 4 \cos 3\theta \, d\theta = 4(\frac{1}{3} \sin 3\theta) + c = \frac{4}{3} \sin 3\theta + c$

(b) $\int 7 \sin 2x \, dx = 7(-\frac{1}{2} \cos 2x) + c = -\frac{7}{2} \cos 2x + c$

(c) $\int 3 \sec^2 5t \, dt = 3(\frac{1}{5} \tan 5t) + c = \frac{3}{5} \tan 5t + c$

Problem 5. Find: (a) $\int 6e^{4x} \, dx$; (b) $\int \frac{3}{e^{2t}} \, dt$; (c) $\int \frac{3}{2u} \, du$.

(a) $\int 6e^{4x} \, dx = 6\left(\frac{e^{4x}}{4}\right) + c = \frac{3}{2} e^{4x} + c$

(b) $\int \frac{3}{e^{2t}} \, dt = \int 3e^{-2t} \, dt = 3\left(\frac{e^{-2t}}{-2}\right) + c = \frac{-3}{2} e^{-2t} + c = \frac{-3}{2e^{2t}} + c$

(c) $\int \frac{3}{2u} \, du = \frac{3}{2} \int \frac{1}{u} \, du = \frac{3}{2} \ln u + c$

Problem 6. Evaluate: (a) $\int_1^3 (4x - 3)^2 \, dx$; (b) $\int_0^4 \left(5\sqrt{b} - \frac{1}{\sqrt{b}}\right) db$.

(a) $\int_1^3 (4x - 3)^2 \, dx = \int_1^3 (16x^2 - 24x + 9) \, dx$

$$= \left[\frac{16}{3} x^3 - 24\frac{x^2}{2} + 9x + c\right]_1^3$$

$$= \left[\frac{16}{3}(3)^3 - 12(3)^2 + 9(3) + c\right] - \left[\frac{16}{3}(1)^3 - 12(1)^2 + 9(1) + c\right]$$

$$= (144 - 108 + 27 + c) - (5\tfrac{1}{3} - 12 + 9 + c)$$
$$= (63 + c) - (2\tfrac{1}{3} + c)$$
$$= 60\tfrac{2}{3}$$

The arbitrary constant of integration, c, cancels out, thus showing it to be an unnecessary inclusion when evaluating definite integrals.

(b) $\int_0^4 \left(5\sqrt{b} - \frac{1}{\sqrt{b}}\right) db = \int_0^4 (5b^{\frac{1}{2}} - b^{-\frac{1}{2}}) \, db$

$$= \left[\frac{5b^{\frac{3}{2}}}{\frac{3}{2}} - \frac{b^{\frac{1}{2}}}{\frac{1}{2}}\right]_0^4 = \left[\frac{10}{3}\sqrt{b^3} - 2\sqrt{b}\right]_0^4$$

$$= \left(\frac{10}{3} \sqrt{4^3} - 2\sqrt{4} \right) - \left(\frac{10}{3} \sqrt{0^3} - 2\sqrt{0} \right)$$

$$= \frac{10}{3}(8) - 2(2) - 0 = \frac{80}{3} - 4 = 22\frac{2}{3}$$

(taking positive values of square roots only).

Problem 7. Evaluate: (a) $\int_0^{\frac{\pi}{2}} 4 \sin 2x \, dx$; (b) $\int_0^1 3 \cos 3t \, dt$;

(c) $\int_{\frac{\pi}{6}}^{\frac{\pi}{3}} (2 \sin \theta - 3 \cos 2\theta + 4 \sec^2 \theta) \, d\theta$.

(a) $\int_0^{\frac{\pi}{2}} 4 \sin 2x \, dx = \left[-\frac{4}{2} \cos 2x \right]_0^{\frac{\pi}{2}}$

$$= \left(-2 \cos 2 \left(\frac{\pi}{2} \right) \right) - \left(-2 \cos 2(0) \right)$$

$$= (-2 \cos \pi) - (-2 \cos 0)$$
$$= (-2(-1)) - (-2(1))$$
$$= 2 + 2 = 4$$

(b) $\int_0^1 3 \cos 3t \, dt = [\frac{3}{3} \sin 3t]_0^1 = [\sin 3t]_0^1 = (\sin 3 - \sin 0)$

The limits in trigonometric functions are expressed in radians.

Thus 'sin 3' means 'the sine of 3 radians or $3 \left(\frac{180}{\pi} \right)^\circ$', i.e. 171.89°.

Hence $\sin 3 - \sin 0 = \sin 171.89° - \sin 0°$
$$= 0.141\ 1 - 0 = 0.1411$$

Thus $\int_0^1 3 \cos 3t \, dt = 0.141\ 1$

(c) $\int_{\frac{\pi}{6}}^{\frac{\pi}{3}} (2 \sin \theta - 3 \cos 2\theta + 4 \sec^2 \theta) \, d\theta = \left[-2 \cos \theta - \frac{3}{2} \sin 2\theta + 4 \tan \theta \right]_{\frac{\pi}{6}}^{\frac{\pi}{3}}$

$$= \left(-2 \cos \frac{\pi}{3} - \frac{3}{2} \sin \frac{2\pi}{3} + 4 \tan \frac{\pi}{3} \right) - \left(-2 \cos \frac{\pi}{6} - \frac{3}{2} \sin \frac{2\pi}{6} + 4 \tan \frac{\pi}{6} \right)$$

or $(-2 \cos 60° - \frac{3}{2} \sin 120° + 4 \tan 60°) - (-2 \cos 30° - \frac{3}{2} \sin 60° + 4 \tan 30°)$

$$= (-1 - 1.2990 + 6.9282) - (-1.7321 - 1.2990 + 2.3094)$$

$$= 5.3509$$

Problem 8. Evaluate: (a) $\int_1^2 3e^{4x} \, dx$; (b) $\int_3^4 \frac{5}{x} \, dx$.

(a) $\int_{1}^{2} 3e^{4x} \, dx = [\frac{3}{4} e^{4x}]_{1}^{2} = \frac{3}{4} e^{8} - \frac{3}{4} e^{4} = \frac{3}{4} e^{4} (e^{4} - 1) = \mathbf{2\ 195}$

(b) $\int_{3}^{4} \frac{5}{x} \, dx = 5 [\ln x]_{3}^{4} = 5 [\ln 4 - \ln 3]$

$= 5 \ln \frac{4}{3} = \mathbf{1.438\ 4}$

Further problems on standard integrals may be found in Section 6, Problems 1–65, page 283.

5 Integration by substitution

Functions which require integrating are not usually in the standard integral form previously met. However, by using suitable substitutions some functions can be changed into a form which can be readily integrated. The substitution usually made is to let u be equal to $f(x)$, such that $f(u) \, du$ is a standard integral.

A most important point in the use of substitution is that once a substitution has been made the original variable must be removed completely, because a variable can only be integrated with respect to itself, i.e. we cannot integrate, for example, a function of t with respect to x.

A concept that $\dfrac{du}{dx}$ is a single entity (measuring the differential coefficient of u with respect to x) has been established in the work done on differentiation. Frequently in work on integration and differential equations, $\dfrac{du}{dx}$ is split. Provided that when this is done, the original differential coefficient can be re-formed by applying the rules of algebra, then it is in order to do it. For example, if $\dfrac{dy}{dx} = x$ then it is in order to write $dy = x \, dx$ since dividing both sides by dx re-forms the original differential coefficient. This principle is shown in the following worked problems.

Worked problems on integration by substitution

Problem 1. Find: $\int \cos (5x + 2) \, dx$.

Let $u = 5x + 2$

then $\dfrac{du}{dx} = 5$, i.e. $dx = \dfrac{du}{5}$

$\int \cos (5x + 2) \, dx = \int \cos u \, \dfrac{du}{5} = \frac{1}{5} \int \cos u \, du$

$= \frac{1}{5} (\sin u) + c$

Since the original integral is given in terms of x, the result should be stated in terms of x.

$u = 5x + 2$

Hence $\int \cos (5x + 2) \, dx = \frac{1}{5} \sin (5x + 2) + c$

Problem 2. Find: $\int (4t - 3)^7 \, dt$.

Let $u = 4t - 3$

then $\dfrac{du}{dt} = 4$, i.e. $dt = \dfrac{du}{4}$

$$\int (4t - 3)^7 \, dt = \int u^7 \frac{du}{4} = \tfrac{1}{4} \int u^7 \, du$$

$$= \tfrac{1}{4} \left(\frac{u^8}{8} \right) + c$$

$$= \frac{u^8}{32} + c$$

Since $u = (4t - 3)$,

$\int (4t - 3)^7 \, dt = \tfrac{1}{32} (4t - 3)^8 + c$

Problem 3. Integrate $\dfrac{1}{7x + 2}$ with respect to x.

Let $u = 7x + 2$

then $\dfrac{du}{dx} = 7$, i.e. $dx = \dfrac{du}{7}$

$$\int \frac{1}{7x + 2} \, dx = \int \frac{1}{u} \frac{du}{7}$$

$$= \tfrac{1}{7} \ln u + c$$

Since $u = (7x + 2)$,

$$\int \frac{1}{7x + 2} \, dx = \tfrac{1}{7} \ln (7x + 2) + c$$

From Problems 1–3 above it may be seen that:

If 'x' in a standard integral is replaced by $(ax + b)$ where a and b are constants,
then $(ax + b)$ is written for x in the result and the result is multiplied by $\dfrac{1}{a}$.

For example, $\int (ax + b) \, dx = \dfrac{1}{2a} (ax + b)^2 + c$ and, more generally,

$\int (ax + b)^n \, dx = \dfrac{1}{a(n + 1)} (ax + b)^{n+1} + c$ (except when $n = -1$).

Problem 4. Integrate the following with respect to x, using the general rule
(i.e. without making a substitution): (a) $3 \sin (2x - 1)$; (b) $2e^{8x+3}$; (c) $\dfrac{5}{9x - 2}$

(a) $\int 3 \sin (2x - 1) \, dx = 3(\tfrac{1}{2}) \, [- \cos (2x - 1)] + C$

$\qquad\qquad\qquad\qquad = -\tfrac{3}{2} \cos (2x - 1) + c$

(b) $\int 2e^{8x+3} \, dx = 2(e^{8x+3})(\tfrac{1}{8}) + c = \tfrac{1}{4} e^{8x+3} + c$

(c) $\int \dfrac{5}{9x - 2} \, dx = 5 \left[\ln (9x - 2) \right] \frac{1}{9} + c = \frac{5}{9} \ln (9x - 2) + c$

Problem 5. Find $\frac{3}{2} \int (x^2 + 2)^6 \, 2x \, dx$.

Let $u = x^2 + 2$

then $\dfrac{du}{dx} = 2x$, i.e. $dx = \dfrac{du}{2x}$

Hence $\frac{3}{2} \displaystyle\int (x^2 + 2)^6 \, 2x \, dx = \frac{3}{2} \int u^6 \, 2x \, \dfrac{du}{2x} = \frac{3}{2} \int u^6 \, du$

The original variable, x, has been removed completely and the integral is now only in terms of u.

$\frac{3}{2} \int u^6 \, du = \frac{3}{2} \left(\dfrac{u^7}{7} \right) + c$

Since $u = x^2 + 2$,

$\int 3x(x^2 + 2)^6 \, dx = \frac{3}{14} (x^2 + 2)^7 + c$

Problem 6. Find $\int \sin \theta \cos \theta \, d\theta$.

Let $u = \sin \theta$

then $\dfrac{du}{d\theta} = \cos \theta$, i.e. $d\theta = \dfrac{du}{\cos \theta}$

Hence $\int \sin \theta \cos \theta \, d\theta = \displaystyle\int u \cos \theta \, \dfrac{du}{\cos \theta} = \int u \, du = \dfrac{u^2}{2} + c$

Since $u = \sin \theta$,

$\int \sin \theta \cos \theta \, d\theta = \frac{1}{2} \sin^2 \theta + c$

Another solution to this integral is possible.

Let $u = \cos \theta$

then $\dfrac{du}{d\theta} = - \sin \theta$, i.e. $d\theta = \dfrac{-du}{\sin \theta}$

Hence $\int \sin \theta \cos \theta \, d\theta = \displaystyle\int \sin \theta \, (u) \left(\dfrac{-du}{\sin \theta} \right) = - \int u \, du = - \dfrac{u^2}{2} + c$

Since $u = \cos \theta$,

$\int \sin \theta \cos \theta \, d\theta = -\frac{1}{2} \cos^2 \theta + c$

From Problems 5 and 6 above it may be seen that:

Integrals of the form $k \int [f(x)]^n \, f'(x) \, dx$ (where k is a constant) can be integrated by substituting u for $f(x)$.

Problem 7. Find: $\frac{1}{2} \displaystyle\int \dfrac{(4x + 6)}{\sqrt{(2x^2 + 6x - 1)}} \, dx$

Let $u = 2x^2 + 6x - 1$

then $\dfrac{du}{dx} = 4x + 6$, i.e. $dx = \dfrac{du}{4x + 6}$

Hence $\dfrac{1}{2} \displaystyle\int \dfrac{(4x + 6)}{\sqrt{(2x^2 + 6x - 1)}}\ dx = \dfrac{1}{2} \int \dfrac{(4x + 6)}{\sqrt{u}}\ \dfrac{du}{(4x + 6)} = \dfrac{1}{2} \int \dfrac{du}{\sqrt{u}}$

$$= \dfrac{1}{2} \int u^{-\frac{1}{2}}\ du = \dfrac{1}{2} \left(\dfrac{u^{\frac{1}{2}}}{\frac{1}{2}} \right) + c = u^{\frac{1}{2}} + c$$

Since $u = 2x^2 + 6x - 1$,

$$\dfrac{1}{2} \int \dfrac{(4x + 6)}{\sqrt{(2x^2 + 6x - 1)}}\ dx = \sqrt{(2x^2 + 6x - 1)} + c$$

Problem 8. Find: $\int \tan \theta\ d\theta$.

$$\int \tan \theta\ d\theta = \int \dfrac{\sin \theta}{\cos \theta}\ d\theta$$

Let $u = \cos \theta$

then $\dfrac{du}{d\theta} = -\sin \theta$, i.e. $d\theta = \dfrac{-du}{\sin \theta}$

Hence $\displaystyle\int \dfrac{\sin \theta}{\cos \theta}\ d\theta = \int \dfrac{\sin \theta}{u} \left(\dfrac{-du}{\sin \theta} \right) = -\int \dfrac{1}{u}\ du = -\ln u + c = \ln u^{-1} + c$

Since $u = \cos \theta$,

$\int \tan \theta\ d\theta = \ln (\cos \theta)^{-1} + c$

$= \ln (\sec \theta) + c$

From Problems 7 and 8 above it may be seen that:

Integrals of the form $k \displaystyle\int \dfrac{f'(x)}{[f(x)]^n}\ dx$ (where k and n are constants) can be integrated by substituting u for $f(x)$.

Problem 9. Evaluate the following:

(a) $\displaystyle\int_0^1 3 \sec^2 (4\theta - 1)\ d\theta$

(b) $\displaystyle\int_0^4 5x\sqrt{(2x^2 + 4)}\ dx$, taking positive values of roots only

(c) $\displaystyle\int_1^3 \dfrac{e^t}{3 + e^t}\ dt$

(a) $\displaystyle\int_0^1 3 \sec^2 (4\theta - 1)\ d\theta = [\tfrac{3}{4} \tan (4\theta - 1)]_0^1 = \tfrac{3}{4} [\tan 3 - \tan(-1)]$

$= \tfrac{3}{4} [\tan 171.89° - \tan (-57.30°)]$

$= \tfrac{3}{4} [(-0.142\ 5) - (-1.557\ 7)]$

$= \tfrac{3}{4} (1.4152) = \mathbf{1.061\ 4}$

(b) $\displaystyle\int_0^4 5x\sqrt{(2x^2 + 4)}\ dx = \int_0^4 5x(2x^2 + 4)^{\frac{1}{2}}\ dx$

Let $u = 2x^2 + 4$

then $\dfrac{du}{dx} = 4x$, i.e. $dx = \dfrac{du}{4x}$

$\int 5x(2x^2 + 4)^{\frac{1}{2}}\ dx = \int 5x(u^{\frac{1}{2}})\dfrac{du}{4x} = \tfrac{5}{4}\int u^{\frac{1}{2}}\ du$

$$= \tfrac{5}{4}\left(\dfrac{u^{\frac{3}{2}}}{\frac{3}{2}}\right) + c = \tfrac{5}{6}(\sqrt{u^3}) + c$$

Since $u = 2x^2 + 4$,

$$\int_0^4 5x\sqrt{(2x^2 + 4)}\ dx = [\tfrac{5}{6}\sqrt{(2x^2 + 4)^3}\,]_0^4$$

$$= \tfrac{5}{6}\left\{\sqrt{[(2(4)^2 + 4)]^3} - \sqrt{(4)^3}\right\}$$
$$= \tfrac{5}{6}(216 - 8), \text{ taking positive values of roots only}$$
$$= 173\tfrac{1}{3}$$

(c) $\displaystyle\int_1^3 \dfrac{e^t}{3 + e^t}\ dt$

Let $u = 3 + e^t$

then $\dfrac{du}{dt} = e^t$, i.e. $dt = \dfrac{du}{e^t}$

Hence $\int \dfrac{e^t}{3 + e^t}\ dt = \int \dfrac{e^t}{u}\dfrac{du}{e^t} = \int \dfrac{du}{u} = \ln u + c$

Since $u = 3 + e^t$,

$$\int_1^3 \dfrac{e^t}{3 + e^t}\ dt = [\ln(3 + e^t)]_1^3$$

$$= [\ln(3 + e^3) - \ln(3 + e^1)]$$

$$= \ln\left[\dfrac{3 + e^3}{3 + e^1}\right] = \ln\left[\dfrac{23.086}{5.718\,3}\right]$$

$$= 1.395\,6$$

Further problems on integration by substitution may be found in the following Section (6), Problems 66–125, page 287.

6   Further problems

Standard integrals

In Problems 1–35 integrate with respect to the variable.

1. x^5 $\left[\dfrac{x^6}{6} + c\right]$

2. $2p^3 \quad \left[\dfrac{p^4}{2} + c\right]$

3. $3k^6 \quad [\tfrac{3}{7}k^7 + c]$

4. $4u^{2.3} \quad \left[\dfrac{4}{3.3}u^{3.3} + c\right]$

5. $x^{-2.1} \quad \left[\dfrac{-x^{-1.1}}{1.1} + c\right]$

6. $\dfrac{2}{x^2} \quad \left[\dfrac{-2}{x} + c\right]$

7. $\dfrac{3}{p} \quad [3\ln p + c]$

8. $\sqrt{y} \quad [\tfrac{2}{3}\sqrt{y^3} + c]$

9. $2\sqrt{S^3} \quad [\tfrac{4}{5}\sqrt{S^5} + c]$

10. $\dfrac{1}{3\sqrt{t}} \quad [\tfrac{2}{3}\sqrt{t} + c]$

11. $\dfrac{4}{\sqrt[3]{k^2}} \quad [12\sqrt[3]{k} + c]$

12. $3a^3 - \tfrac{2}{3}\sqrt{a} \quad \left[\dfrac{3a^4}{4} - \tfrac{4}{9}\sqrt{a^3} + c\right]$

13. $\dfrac{-4}{v^{1.4}} \quad \left[\dfrac{10}{v^{0.4}} + c\right]$

14. $\dfrac{x}{3}(2x + \sqrt{x}) \quad \left[\dfrac{2x^3}{9} + \dfrac{2}{15}\sqrt{x^5} + c\right]$

15. $\dfrac{r^3 + 2r - 1}{r^2} \quad \left[\dfrac{r^2}{2} + 2\ln r + \dfrac{1}{r} + c\right]$

16. $(x + 2)^2 \quad \left[\dfrac{x^3}{3} + 2x^2 + 4x + c\right]$

17. $(1 + \sqrt{w})^2 \quad \left[w + \tfrac{4}{3}\sqrt{w^3} + \dfrac{w^2}{2} + c\right]$

18. $\sin 2\theta \quad [-\tfrac{1}{2}\cos 2\theta + c]$

19. $\cos 4\alpha \quad [\tfrac{1}{4}\sin 4\alpha + c]$

20. $2\sin 3t \quad [-\tfrac{2}{3}\cos 3t + c]$

21. $-4\cos 5x \quad [-\tfrac{4}{5}\sin 5x + c]$

22. $\sec^2 6\beta \quad [\tfrac{1}{6}\tan 6\beta + c]$

23. $-3\sec^2 t \quad [-3\tan t + c]$

24. $4(\cos 2\theta - 3\sin \theta) \quad [2(\sin 2\theta + 6\cos \theta) + c]$

25. $e^{3x} \quad \left[\dfrac{e^{3x}}{3} + c\right]$

26. $2e^{-4t} \quad [-\tfrac{1}{2}e^{-4t} + c]$

27. $\dfrac{6}{e^t} \quad \left[-\dfrac{6}{e^t} + c\right]$

28. $3(e^x - e^{-x}) \quad [3(e^x + e^{-x}) + c]$

29. $3(e^t - 1)^2 \quad \left[3\left(\dfrac{e^{2t}}{2} - 2e^t + t\right) + c\right]$

30. $\dfrac{4}{e^{2x}} + e^x$ $\qquad \left[\dfrac{-2}{e^{2x}} + e^x + c \right]$

31. $\dfrac{1}{4t}$ $\qquad [\frac{1}{4} \ln t + c]$

32. $\dfrac{3}{5t} + \sqrt{t^5}$ $\qquad [\frac{3}{5} \ln t + \frac{2}{7}\sqrt{t^7} + c]$

33. $\left(\dfrac{1}{x} + x \right)^2$ $\qquad \left[-\dfrac{1}{x} + 2x + \dfrac{x^3}{3} + c \right]$

34. $3 \sin 50\pi t + 4 \cos 50\pi t$ $\qquad \left[\dfrac{1}{50\pi} (4 \sin 50\pi t - 3 \cos 50\pi t) + c \right]$

35. $(e^{2x} - 1)(e^{-2x} + 1)$ $\qquad [\frac{1}{2}(e^{2x} + e^{-2x}) + c]$

In Problems 36–65 evaluate the definite integrals. (Where roots are involved in the solution, take positive values only when evaluating.)

36. $\displaystyle\int_1^3 2 \, dt$ $\qquad [4]$

37. $\displaystyle\int_3^5 4x \, dx$ $\qquad [32]$

38. $\displaystyle\int_{-4}^2 -3u^2 \, du$ $\qquad [-72]$

39. $\displaystyle\int_{-1}^1 \frac{3}{4} f^2 \, df$ $\qquad [\frac{1}{2}]$

40. $\displaystyle\int_1^4 x^{-1.5} \, dx$ $\qquad [1]$

41. $\displaystyle\int_1^9 \frac{dx}{\sqrt{x}}$ $\qquad [4]$

42. $\displaystyle\int_2^5 \frac{4}{x} \, dx$ $\qquad [3.665]$

43. $\displaystyle\int_0^2 (x^2 + 2x - 1) \, dx$ $\qquad [4\frac{2}{3}]$

44. $\displaystyle\int_1^4 \left(\sqrt{r} - \frac{1}{\sqrt{r}} \right) dr$ $\qquad [2\frac{2}{3}]$

45. $\displaystyle\int_1^4 (3x^3 - 4x^2 + x - 2) \, dx$ $\qquad [108\frac{3}{4}]$

46. $\displaystyle\int_1^3 (m - 2)(m - 1) \, dm$ $\qquad [\frac{2}{3}]$

47. $\displaystyle\int_1^2 \left(\frac{1}{x^2} + \frac{1}{x} + \frac{1}{2} \right) dx$ $\qquad [1.693]$

48. $\int_{-2}^{2} (3x - 1)\, dx$ $[-4]$

49. $\int_{1}^{3} \left(\frac{2}{t^2} - 3t^2 + 4 \right) dt$ $[-16\frac{2}{3}]$

50. $\int_{0}^{\frac{\pi}{2}} \sin \theta\, d\theta$ $[1]$

51. $\int_{0}^{\frac{\pi}{3}} 3 \sin 2x\, dx$ $[2\frac{1}{4}]$

52. $\int_{0}^{\frac{\pi}{6}} 4 \sin 3\theta\, d\theta$ $[1\frac{1}{3}]$

53. $\int_{\frac{\pi}{6}}^{\frac{\pi}{3}} 2 \cos t\, dt$ $[0.732\ 1]$

54. $\int_{0}^{1} 5 \sin 2\theta\, d\theta$ $[3.540\ 4]$

55. $\frac{1}{2}\int_{1}^{2} \cos 3\alpha\, d\alpha$ $[-0.070\ 1]$

56. $\int_{0.1}^{0.6} (\frac{1}{4} \sin 3\beta + \frac{1}{2} \cos 2\beta)\, d\beta$ $[0.281\ 9]$

57. $\int_{-\frac{\pi}{2}}^{\frac{\pi}{2}} 3 \cos \theta\, d\theta$ $[6]$

58. $\int_{0}^{\frac{\pi}{4}} 3 \sec^2 \theta\, d\theta$ $[3]$

59. $\int_{-1}^{1} 3 \sec^2 2t\, dt$ $[-6.555]$

60. $\int_{1}^{2} \frac{e^{3x}}{5}\, dx$ $[25.56]$

61. $\int_{0.4}^{0.7} 3e^{2t}\, dt$ $[2.744]$

62. $\int_{0}^{1} \frac{2}{e^{3t}}\, dt$ $[0.633\ 5]$

63. $\int_{1}^{4} \left(\frac{t + 2}{\sqrt{t}} \right) dt$ $[8\frac{2}{3}]$

64. $\int_{1}^{3} \frac{(3x + 2)(x - 4)}{x}\, dx$ $[-16.789]$

65. $\int_{0}^{1} 2\sqrt{x}(x + 2)^2\, dx$ $[9.105]$

Integration by substitution

In Problems 65–105 integrate with respect to the appropriate variable.

66. $\sin(3x + 2)$ $[-\frac{1}{3}\cos(3x + 2) + c]$

67. $2\cos(4t + 1)$ $[\frac{1}{2}\sin(4t + 1) + c]$

68. $3\sec^2(t + 5)$ $[3\tan(t + 5) + c]$

69. $4\sin(6\theta - 3)$ $[-\frac{2}{3}\cos(6\theta - 3) + c]$

70. $(2x + 1)^5$ $[\frac{1}{12}(2x + 1)^6 + c]$

71. $3(4S - 7)^4$ $[\frac{3}{20}(4S - 7)^5 + c]$

72. $\frac{1}{12}(9x + 5)^8$ $[\frac{1}{972}(9x + 5)^9 + c]$

73. $\dfrac{1}{3a + 1}$ $[\frac{1}{3}\ln(3a + 1) + c]$

74. $\dfrac{5}{5f - 2}$ $[\ln(5f - 2) + c]$

75. $\dfrac{7}{2x + 1}$ $[\frac{7}{2}\ln(2x + 1) + c]$

76. $\dfrac{-1}{6x + 5}$ $[-\frac{1}{6}\ln(6x + 5) + c]$

77. $\dfrac{3}{15y - 2}$ $[\frac{1}{5}\ln(15y - 2) + c]$

78. e^{3x+2} $[\frac{1}{3}e^{3x+2} + c]$

79. $4e^{7t-1}$ $[\frac{4}{7}e^{7t-1} + c]$

80. $2e^{2-3x}$ $[-\frac{2}{3}e^{2-3x} + c]$

81. $4x(2x^2 + 3)^5$ $[\frac{1}{6}(2x^2 + 3)^6 + c]$

82. $5t(t^2 - 1)^7$ $[\frac{5}{16}(t^2 - 1)^8 + c]$

83. $(3x^2 + 4)^8 x$ $[\frac{1}{54}(3x^2 + 4)^9 + c]$

84. $\sin^2\theta \cos\theta$ $[\frac{1}{3}\sin^3\theta + c]$

85. $\sin^3 t \cos t$ $[\frac{1}{4}\sin^4 t + c]$

86. $2\cos^2\beta \sin\beta$ $[-\frac{2}{3}\cos^3\beta + c]$

87. $\sec^2\theta \tan\theta$ $[\frac{1}{2}\tan^2\theta + c]$

88. $3\tan 2x \sec^2 2x$ $[\frac{3}{4}\tan^2 2x + c]$

89. $\frac{6}{5}\sin^5\theta \cos\theta$ $[\frac{1}{5}\sin^6\theta + c]$

90. $6x\sqrt{(3x^2 + 2)}$ $[\frac{2}{3}\sqrt{(3x^2 + 2)^3} + c]$

91. $(4x^2 - 1)\sqrt{(4x^3 - 3x + 1)}$ $[\frac{2}{9}\sqrt{(4x^3 - 3x + 1)^3} + c]$

92. $\dfrac{3\ln t}{t}$ $[\frac{3}{2}(\ln t)^2 + c]$

93. $\dfrac{6x + 2}{(3x^2 + 2x - 1)^5}$ $\left[\dfrac{-1}{4(3x^2 + 2x - 1)^4} + c\right]$

94. $\dfrac{4y - 1}{(4y^2 - 2y + 5)^7}$ $\left[\dfrac{-1}{12(4y^2 - 2y + 5)^6} + c\right]$

95. $\dfrac{2x}{\sqrt{(x^2 + 1)}}$ $[2\sqrt{(x^2 + 1)} + c]$

96. $\dfrac{3a}{\sqrt{(3a^2 + 5)}}$ $[\sqrt{(3a^2 + 5)} + c]$

97. $\dfrac{12x^2 + 1}{\sqrt{(4x^3 + x - 1)}}$ $[2\sqrt{(4x^3 + x - 1)} + c]$

98. $\dfrac{r^2 - 1}{\sqrt{(r^3 - 3r + 2)}}$ $\quad$ $[\frac{2}{3}\sqrt{(r^3 - 3r + 2)} + c]$

99. $\dfrac{3e^t}{\sqrt{(1 + e^t)}}$ $\quad$ $[6\sqrt{(1 + e^t)} + c]$

100. $2x \sin (x^2 + 1)$ $\quad$ $[-\cos (x^2 + 1) + c]$

101. $(4\theta + 1) \sec^2 (4\theta^2 + 2\theta)$ $\quad$ $[\frac{1}{2} \tan (4\theta^2 + 2\theta) + c]$

102. $\frac{1}{3}(4x + 1) \cos (2x^2 + x - 1)$ $\quad$ $[\frac{1}{3} \sin (2x^2 + x - 1) + c]$

103. $4te^{2t^2 - 3}$ $\quad$ $[e^{2t^2 - 3} + c]$

104. $3 \tan \beta$ $\quad$ $[3 \ln (\sec \beta) + c]$

105. $(5x - 2)e^{5x^2 - 4x + 1}$ $\quad$ $[\frac{1}{2} e^{5x^2 - 4x + 1} + c]$

In Problems 106–125 evaluate the definite integrals.

106. $\displaystyle\int_0^1 (3x - 1)^4 \, dx$ $\quad$ $[2\frac{1}{3}]$

107. $\displaystyle\int_0^2 (8x - 3)(4x^2 - 3x)^3 \, dx$ $\quad$ $[2\,500]$

108. $\displaystyle\int_1^3 x\sqrt{(x^2 + 1)} \, dx$ $\quad$ $[9.598]$

109. $\displaystyle\int_0^{\frac{\pi}{4}} \sin \left(4\theta + \dfrac{\pi}{3} \right) d\theta$ $\quad$ $[\frac{1}{4}]$

110. $\displaystyle\int_{\frac{1}{3}}^1 \sec^2 (3x - 1) \, dx$ $\quad$ $[-0.728\,3]$

111. $\displaystyle\int_1^2 3 \cos (5t - 2) \, dt$ $\quad$ $[0.508\,9]$

112. $\displaystyle\int_{\frac{1}{2}}^2 \dfrac{1}{(4s - 1)} \, ds$ $\quad$ $[0.486\,5]$

113. $\displaystyle\int_0^2 (9x^2 - 4)\sqrt{(3x^3 - 4x)} \, dx$ $\quad$ $[42\frac{2}{3}]$

114. $\displaystyle\int_1^3 \dfrac{4 \ln x}{x} \, dx$ $\quad$ $[2.413\,9]$

115. $\displaystyle\int_0^2 \dfrac{t}{\sqrt{(2t^2 + 1)}} \, dt$ $\quad$ $[1]$

116. $\displaystyle\int_1^2 \dfrac{4x - 3}{(2x^2 - 3x - 1)^4} \, dx$ $\quad$ $[-\frac{3}{8}]$

117. $\displaystyle\int_1^2 3\theta \sin (2\theta^2 + 1) \, d\theta$ $\quad$ $[-0.059\,1]$

118. $\displaystyle\int_0^1 2te^{3t^2 - 1} \, dt$ $\quad$ $[2.340\,4]$

119. $\int_0^{\frac{\pi}{2}} 3 \sin^4 \theta \cos \theta \, d\theta$ $\left[\frac{3}{5}\right]$

120. $\int_1^2 \frac{dx}{(2x-1)^3}$ $\left[\frac{2}{9}\right]$

121. $\int_1^2 \frac{2e^{3\theta}}{e^{3\theta}-5} \, d\theta$ $[2.182\,5]$

122. $\int_0^1 2t \sec^2(3t^2) \, dt$ $[-0.047\,5]$

123. $\int_1^2 x \sin(2x^2 - 1) \, dx$ $[-0.053\,4]$

124. $\int_{\frac{\pi}{6}}^{\frac{\pi}{3}} \frac{2}{3} \sin t \cos^3 t \, dt$ $[0.083\,3]$

125. $\int_1^2 \frac{e^{3\theta} - e^{-3\theta}}{2} \, d\theta$ $[63.88]$

Chapter 15

Applications of integration to areas, mean values and root mean square values

1 The area between a curve, the *x* axis and given ordinates

There are several instances in branches of engineering and science where the area under a curve is required to be accurately determined. For example, the areas, between given limits, of:

(a) velocity/time graphs give distances travelled;
(b) force/distance graphs give work done;
(c) acceleration/time graphs give velocities;
(d) voltage/current graphs give power;
(e) pressure/volume graphs give work done;
(f) normal distribution curves give frequencies.

Provided there is a known relationship [e.g. $y = f(x)$] between the variables forming the axes of the above graphs then the areas may be calculated exactly using integral calculus. If a relationship between variables is not known then areas have to be approximately determined using such techniques as the trapezoidal rule, the mid-ordinate rule or Simpson's rule (see Appendix C, page 349).

Let A be the area enclosed between the curve $y = f(x)$, the x axis and the ordinates $x = a$ and $x = b$. Also let A be subdivided into a number of elemental strips each of width δx as shown in Fig. 1.

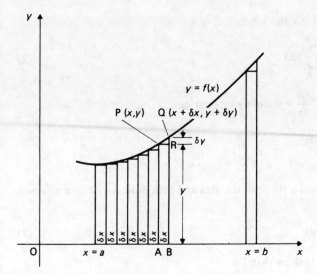

Fig. 1

One such strip is shown as PQRBA, with point P having coordinates (x, y) and point Q having coordinates $(x + \delta x, y + \delta y)$. Let the area PQRBA be δA, which can be seen from Fig. 1 to consist of a rectangle PRBA, of area $y\delta x$, and PQR, which approximates to a triangle of area $\frac{1}{2}\delta x \delta y$,

i.e. $\delta A \simeq y\delta x + \frac{1}{2}\delta x \delta y$

Dividing both sides by δx gives:

$$\frac{\delta A}{\delta x} \simeq y + \frac{1}{2}\delta y$$

As δx is made smaller and smaller, the number of rectangles increases and all such areas as PQR become smaller and smaller. Also δy becomes smaller and in the limit as δx approaches zero, $\dfrac{\delta A}{\delta x}$ becomes the differential coefficient $\dfrac{dA}{dx}$ and δy becomes zero,

i.e. $\displaystyle \lim_{\delta x \to 0} \left(\frac{\delta A}{\delta x} \right) = \frac{dA}{dx} = y + \frac{1}{2}(0) = y$

Hence $\dfrac{dA}{dx} = y$ ... (1)

This shows that when a limiting value is taken, all such areas as PQR become zero. Hence the area beneath the curve is given by the sum of all such rectangles as PRBA,

i.e. Area $= \Sigma y\delta x$.

Between the limits $x = a$ and $x = b$,

$$\text{Area, } A = \frac{\text{limit}}{\delta x \to 0} \sum_{x = a}^{x = b} y \delta x \qquad \qquad \ldots (2)$$

From equation (1), $\frac{dA}{dx} = y$ and by integration:

$$\int \frac{dA}{dx} \, dx = \int y \, dx$$

Hence $A = \int y \, dx$

The ordinates $x = a$ and $x = b$ limit the area and such ordinate values are shown as limits.

$$\text{Thus } A = \int_a^b y \, dx \qquad \qquad \ldots (3)$$

Equations (2) and (3) show that:

$$\text{Area, } A = \frac{\text{limit}}{\delta x \to 0} \sum_{x = a}^{x = b} y \delta x = \int_a^b y \, dx$$

This statement that the limiting value of a sum is equal to the integral between the same limits forms a fundamental theorem of integration. This can be illustrated by considering simple shapes of known areas. For example, Fig. 2 (a) shows a rectangle bounded by the line $y = b$, ordinates $x = a$ and $x = b$ and the x-axis.

Let the rectangle be divided into n equal vertical strips of width δx. The area of strip PQAB is $b\delta x$ and since there are n strips making up the total area the total area $= nb\delta x$. The base length of the rectangle, i.e. $(b - a)$, is made up of n strips, each δx in width, hence $n\delta x = (b - a)$. Therefore the total area $= b(b - a)$.

The total area is also obtained by adding the areas of all such strips as PQAB and is independent of the value of n, that is, n can be infinitely large.

$$\text{Hence total area} = \frac{\text{limit}}{\delta x \to 0} \sum_{x = a}^{x = b} b\delta x = b(b - a) \qquad \qquad \ldots (4)$$

Also the total area is given by $\int_a^b y \, dx = \int_a^b b \, dx$

$$= [bx]_a^b = b(b - a) \qquad \qquad \ldots (5)$$

But this is the area obtained from equation (4).

$$\text{Hence } \lim_{\delta x \to 0} \sum_{x = a}^{x = b} b\delta x = \int_a^b b \, dx$$

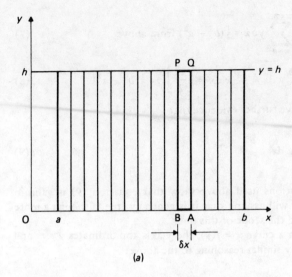

(a)

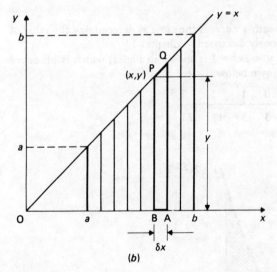

(b)

Fig. 2

Similarly for, say, a trapezium bounded by the line $y = x$, the ordinates $x = a$ and $x = b$ and the x-axis (as shown in Fig. 2(b)), the total area is given by:

(half the sum of the parallel sides)(perpendicular distance between these sides)

i.e. $\frac{1}{2}(a + b)(b - a)$ or $\frac{1}{2}(b^2 - a^2)$ . . . (6)

Also, the total area will be given by the sum of all areas such as PQAB which each have an area of $y\delta x$ provided δx is infinitely small.

i.e. total area = $\displaystyle\lim_{\delta x \to 0} \sum_{x=a}^{x=b} y\delta x = \tfrac{1}{2}(b^2 - a^2)$ from above   . . . (7)

Also, the total area = $\displaystyle\int_a^b y \, dx = \int_a^b x \, dx = \left[\frac{x^2}{2}\right]_a^b = \tfrac{1}{2}(b^2 - a^2)$ . . . (8)

Equations (7) and (8) give further evidence that

$$\lim_{\delta x \to 0} \sum_{x=a}^{x=b} y\delta x = \int_a^b y \, dx \qquad \qquad \text{. . . (9)}$$

The two simple illustrations used above show that equation (9) is valid in these two cases and we will assume that it is generally true, although a more rigorous proof is beyond the scope of this book.

If the area between a curve $x = f(y)$, the y-axis and ordinates $y = m$ and $y = n$ is required, then by similar reasoning to the above:

$$\text{Area} = \int_m^n x \, dy.$$

Thus finding the area beneath a curve is the same as determining the value of a definite integral as previously discussed in Chapter 14.

A part of the curve $y = 2x^2 + 3$ is shown in Fig. 3, which is produced from the table of values shown below.

x	-2	-1	0	1	2	3
$y = 2x^2 + 3$	11	5	3	5	11	21

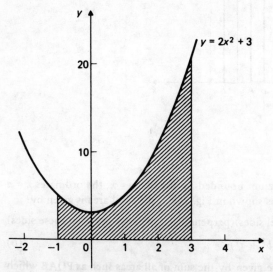

Fig. 3   Graph of $y = 2x^2 + 3$

The area between the curve, the x-axis and the ordinates $x = -1$ and $x = 3$ is shown shaded. This area is given by:

$$\text{Area} = \int_{-1}^{3} y \, dx = \int_{-1}^{3} (2x^2 + 3) \, dx$$

$$= \left[\frac{2x^3}{3} + 3x \right]_{-1}^{3}$$

$$= \left[\frac{2(3)^3}{3} + 3(3) \right] - \left[\frac{2(-1)^3}{3} + 3(-1) \right]$$

$$= 30\tfrac{2}{3} \text{ square units}$$

With the curve $y = 2x^2 + 3$ shown in Fig. 3 all values of y are positive. Hence all the terms in $\Sigma y \delta x$ are positive and $\int_{a}^{b} y \, dx$ is positive. However, if a curve should drop below the x-axis, then y becomes negative, all terms in $\Sigma y \delta x$ become negative and $\int_{a}^{b} y \, dx$ is negative.

In Fig. 4 the total area between the curve $y = f(x)$, the x-axis and the ordinates $x = a$ and $x = b$ is given by

$$\text{area P}\left(\text{i.e. } \int_{a}^{c} f(x)dx\right) + \text{area Q}\left(\text{i.e. } - \int_{c}^{d} f(x)dx\right) + \text{area R}\left(\text{i.e. } \int_{d}^{b} f(x)dx\right).$$

i.e. $\int_{a}^{c} f(x) \, dx - \int_{c}^{d} f(x) \, dx + \int_{d}^{b} f(x) \, dx$

This is **not** the same as the value given by $\int_{a}^{b} f(x) \, dx$.

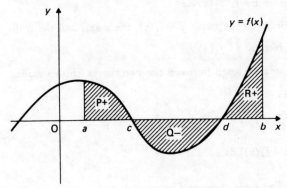

Fig. 4

For this reason, if there is any doubt about the shape of the graph of a function or any possibility of all or part of it lying below the x-axis, a sketch should be made over the required limits to determine if any part of the curve lies below the x-axis.

2 The area between two curves

Let the graphs of the functions $y = f_1(x)$ and $y = f_2(x)$ intersect at points A $(x = a)$ and B $(x = b)$ as shown in Fig. 5.

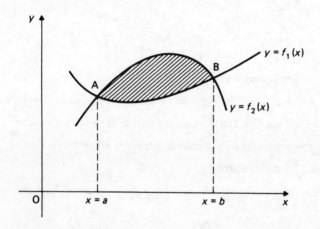

Fig. 5

At the points of intersection $f_1(x) = f_2(x)$.

The area enclosed between the curve $y = f_2(x)$, the x-axis and the ordinates $x = a$ and $x = b$ is given by $\int_a^b f_2(x)\,dx$.

. The area enclosed between the curve $y = f_1(x)$, the x-axis and the ordinates $x = a$ and $x = b$ is given by $\int_a^b f_1(x)\,dx$.

It follows that the area enclosed between the two curves (shown shaded in Fig. 5) is given by:

Shaded area $= \int_a^b f_2(x)\,dx - \int_a^b f_1(x)\,dx$

$$= \int_a^b [f_2(x) - f_1(x)]\,dx$$

Worked problems on finding areas under and between curves

Problem 1. Sketch the curves and find the areas enclosed by the given curves, the x-axis and the given ordinates: (a) $y = \sin 2x$, $x = 0$, $x = \dfrac{\pi}{2}$; (b) $y = 3\cos\dfrac{1}{2}x$, $x = 0$, $x = \dfrac{2\pi}{3}$.

(a) A sketch of $y = \sin 2x$ in the range $x = 0$ to $x = \pi$ is shown in Fig. 6(a).

The area shown shaded is given by:

$$\text{Area} = \int_0^{\frac{\pi}{2}} \sin 2x \, dx$$

$$= \left[-\frac{\cos 2x}{2} \right]_0^{\frac{\pi}{2}} = \left(\frac{-\cos 2(\pi/2)}{2} \right) - \left(\frac{-\cos 0}{2} \right)$$

$$= \left(\frac{-\cos \pi}{2} \right) - \left(\frac{-\cos 0}{2} \right) = (--\tfrac{1}{2}) - (-\tfrac{1}{2})$$

$$= 1 \text{ square unit}$$

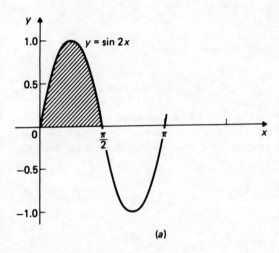

(a)

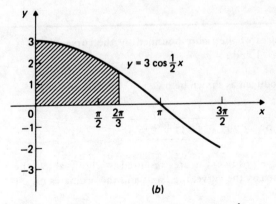

(b)

Fig. 6   Graphs of $y = \sin 2x$ and $y = 3 \cos \frac{1}{2} x$

(b) A sketch of $y = 3 \cos \frac{1}{2}x$ in the range $x = 0$ to $x = \frac{2\pi}{3}$ is shown in Fig. 6(b).

The area shown shaded is given by:

$$\text{Area} = \int_0^{2\pi/3} 3 \cos \tfrac{1}{2}x \, dx$$

$$= \left[6 \sin \tfrac{1}{2}x \right]_0^{2\pi/3} = \left(6 \sin \frac{\pi}{3} \right) - (6 \sin 0)$$

$$= 6 \sin 60° = \textbf{5.196 square units}$$

Problem 2. Find the area enclosed by the curve $y = 2x^2 - x + 3$, the x-axis and the ordinates $x = -1$ and $x = 2$.

A table of values is produced as shown below.

x	−1	0	1	2
y	6	3	4	9

The area between the curve, the x-axis and the ordinates $x = -1$ and $x = 2$ is wholly above the x-axis, since all values of y in the table are positive. Thus the area is positive. In such cases as this it is unnecessary to actually draw the graph.

$$\text{Area} = \int_{-1}^{2} (2x^2 - x + 3) \, dx$$

$$= \left[\frac{2x^3}{3} - \frac{x^2}{2} + 3x \right]_{-1}^{2}$$

$$= (\tfrac{16}{3} - 2 + 6) - (-\tfrac{2}{3} - \tfrac{1}{2} - 3)$$

$$= (9\tfrac{1}{3}) - (-4\tfrac{1}{6}) = \textbf{13}\tfrac{1}{2} \textbf{ square units}$$

Problem 3. Calculate the area of the figure bounded by the curve $y = 2e^{t/2}$, the t-axis and ordinates $t = -1$ and $t = 3$.

A table of values is produced as shown below.

t	−1	0	1	2	3
$y = 2e^{t/2}$	1.213	2.000	3.297	5.437	8.963

Since all the values of y are positive, the area required is wholly above the t-axis. Hence the area enclosed by the curve, the t-axis and the ordinates $t = -1$ and $t = 3$ is given by:

$$\text{Area} = \int_{-1}^{3} 2e^{t/2}\, dt$$

$$= \left[4e^{t/2} \right]_{-1}^{3} = 4[e^{\frac{3}{2}} - e^{-\frac{1}{2}}]$$

$$= 4[4.481\ 7 - 0.606\ 5]$$

$$= 15.50 \text{ square units}$$

Problem 4. Find the area enclosed by the curve $y = x^2 + 3$, the x-axis and the ordinates $x = 0$ and $x = 3$. Sketch the curve within these limits. Find also, using integration, the area enclosed by the curve and the y-axis, between the same limits.

A table of values is produced as shown below.

x	0	1	2	3
y	3	4	7	12

(a) Part of the curve $y = x^2 + 3$ is shown in Fig. 7.

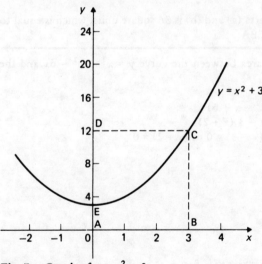

Fig. 7 Graph of $y = x^2 + 3$

The area enclosed by the curve, the x-axis and ordinates $x = 0$ and $x = 3$ (i.e. area ECBA of Fig. 7) is given by:

$$\text{Area} = \int_{0}^{3} (x^2 + 3)\, dx = \left[\frac{x^3}{3} + 3x \right]_{0}^{3}$$

$$= 18 \text{ square units}$$

(b) When $x = 3$, $y = x^2 + 3 = 12$

when $x = 0$, $y = 3$

If $y = x^2 + 3$ then $x^2 = y - 3$ and $x = \sqrt{(y - 3)}$

Hence the area enclosed by the curve $y = x^2 + 3$ (i.e. the curve $x = \sqrt{(y - 3)}$), the y-axis and the ordinates $y = 3$ and $y = 12$ (i.e. area EDC of Fig. 7) is given by:

$$\text{Area} = \int_{y=3}^{y=12} x \, dy = \int_{3}^{12} \sqrt{(y - 3)} \, dy$$

Let $u = y - 3$

then $\dfrac{du}{dy} = 1$, i.e. $dy = du$

Hence $\int (y - 3)^{\frac{1}{2}} \, dy = \int u^{\frac{1}{2}} \, du = \dfrac{2u^{\frac{3}{2}}}{3}$

Since $u = y - 3$ then

$$\text{Area} = \int_{3}^{12} \sqrt{(y - 3)} \, dy = \left[\tfrac{2}{3}(y - 3)^{\frac{3}{2}} \right]_{3}^{12}$$
$$= \tfrac{2}{3}[\sqrt{9^3} - 0]$$
$$= \textbf{18 square units}$$

The sum of the areas in parts (a) and (b) is 36 square units, which is equal to the area of the rectangle DCBA.

Problem 5. Calculate the area between the curve $y = x^3 - x^2 - 6x$ and the x-axis.

$$y = x^3 - x^2 - 6x = x(x^2 - x - 6)$$
$$= x(x - 3)(x + 2)$$

Thus when $y = 0$, $x = 0$ or $(x - 3) = 0$ or $(x + 2) = 0$
i.e. $x = 0$, $x = 3$ or $x = -2$.

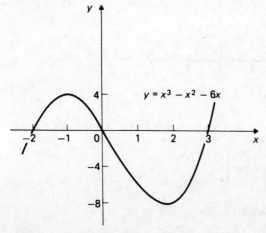

Fig. 8   Graph of $y = x^3 - x^2 - 6x$

Hence the curve cuts the x-axis at $x = 0$, 3 and -2. Since the curve is a continuous function, only one other value need be calculated before a sketch of the curve can be produced. For example, when $x = 1$, $y = -6$, which shows that the portion of the curve between ordinates $x = 0$ and $x = 3$ is negative. Hence the portion of the curve between ordinates $x = 0$ and $x = -2$ must be positive.

A sketch of part of the curve $y = x^3 - x^2 - 6x$ is shown in Fig. 8.

If $y = f(x)$ had not factorised as above, then a table of values could have been produced and the graph sketched in the usual manner.

The sketch shows that the area needs to be calculated in two parts, one part being positive and the other negative, as shown in the second integral below.

The area between the curve and the x-axis is given by:

$$\text{Area} = \int_{-2}^{0} (x^3 - x^2 - 6x) \, \mathrm{d}x - \int_{0}^{3} (x^3 - x^2 - 6x) \, \mathrm{d}x$$

$$= \left[\frac{x^4}{4} - \frac{x^3}{3} - 3x^2 \right]_{-2}^{0} - \left[\frac{x^4}{4} - \frac{x^3}{3} - 3x^2 \right]_{0}^{3}$$

$$= (5\tfrac{1}{3}) - (-15\tfrac{3}{4})$$

$$= 21\tfrac{1}{12} \text{ square units}$$

Problem 6. Find the area enclosed between the curves $y = x^2 + 2$ and $y + x = 14$.

The first step is to find the points of intersection of the two curves. This will enable us to limit the range of values when drawing up a table of values in order to sketch the curves. At the points of intersection the curves are equal (i.e. their coordinates are the same). Since $y = x^2 + 2$ and $y + x = 14$ (i.e. $y = 14 - x$) then $x^2 + 2 = 14 - x$ at the points of intersection.

i.e. $x^2 + x - 12 = 0$

$(x - 3)(x + 4) = 0$

Hence $x = 3$ and $x = -4$ at the points of intersection.

Tables of values may now be produced as shown below.

x	-4	-3	-2	-1	0	1	2	3
$y = x^2 + 2$	18	11	6	3	2	3	6	11

x	-4	0	3
$y = 14 - x$	18	14	11

$y = 14 - x$ is a straight line thus only two points are needed (plus one more to check).

A sketch of the two curves is shown in Fig. 9.

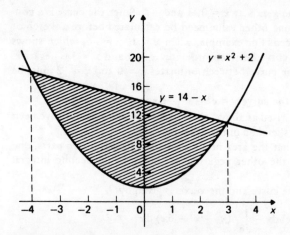

Fig. 9   Graphs of $y = x^2 + 2$ and $y = 14 - x$

The area between the two curves (shown shaded) is given by:

Shaded area $= \displaystyle\int_{-4}^{3} (14 - x)\, dx - \int_{-4}^{3} (x^2 + 2)\, dx$

$$= \left[14x - \frac{x^2}{2} \right]_{-4}^{3} - \left[\frac{x^3}{3} + 2x \right]_{-4}^{3}$$

$$= 101\tfrac{1}{2} - 44\tfrac{1}{3}$$

$$= 57\tfrac{1}{6} \text{ square units}$$

Problem 7. Find the points of intersection of the two curves $x^2 = 2y$ and $\dfrac{y^2}{16} = x$.
Sketch the two curves and calculate the area enclosed by them.

$$x^2 = 2y, \text{ i.e. } y = \frac{x^2}{2} \text{ or } y^2 = \frac{x^4}{4}$$

$$\frac{y^2}{16} = x, \text{ i.e. } y^2 = 16x$$

At the points of intersection, $\dfrac{x^4}{4} = 16x$

$$\text{i.e. } x^4 = 64x$$

Hence $\qquad\qquad x^4 - 64x = 0$

$$x(x^3 - 64) = 0$$

i.e. $\qquad\qquad x = 0 \text{ or } x^3 - 64 = 0$

Hence at the points of intersection $x = 0$ and $x = 4$.

Using $y = \dfrac{x^2}{2}$, when $x = 0$, $y = 0$

$$\text{when } x = 4, \ y = \frac{(4)^2}{2} = 8.$$

[Check, using $y^2 = 16x$. When $x = 0$, $y = 0$
 When $x = 4$, $y^2 = 64$, $y = 8$]

Hence the points of intersection of the two curves $x^2 = 2y$ and $\dfrac{y^2}{16} = x$ are

(0, 0) and (4, 8).

A sketch of the two curves (given the special name of parabolas) is shown in Fig. 10.

The area enclosed by the two curves, i.e. OABC (shown shaded), is given by:

$$\text{Area} = \int_0^4 4\sqrt{x}\,dx - \int_0^4 \frac{x^2}{2}\,dx$$

(Note that for one curve $y = \pm 4\sqrt{x}$. The $-4\sqrt{x}$ is neglected since the shaded area required is above the x-axis, and hence positive.)

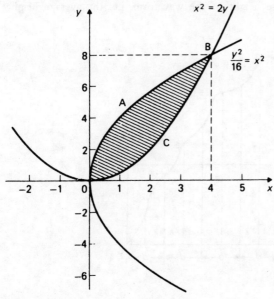

Fig. 10 Graphs of $x^2 = 2y$ and $\dfrac{y^2}{16} = x$

$$\begin{aligned}
\textbf{Area} &= 4\left[\tfrac{2}{3}x^{\frac{3}{2}}\right]_0^4 - \tfrac{1}{2}\left[\frac{x^3}{3}\right]_0^4 \\
&= 21\tfrac{1}{3} - 10\tfrac{2}{3} \\
&= \mathbf{10\tfrac{2}{3}} \textbf{ square units.}
\end{aligned}$$

Further problems on areas under and between curves may be found in Section 5, Problems 1 to 48, page 309.

3 Mean or average values

Figure 11 shows the positive half cycle of a periodic waveform of an alternating quantity. If the negative half cycle is the same shape as the positive half cycle then every positive value is balanced by a corresponding negative value and thus the average value of the complete cycle is zero, i.e. the average or mean value over a complete cycle of a symmetrically alternating quantity is zero. However, over half a cycle it has a non zero value.

Let the area of the waveform in Fig. 11 representing the positive half cycle be divided into, say, 7 strips each of width d, with ordinates at the mid-point of each strip (mid-ordinates) represented by y_1, y_2, y_3 and so on. Let EF be drawn parallel to base OG such that the area under the curve between O and G is equal to the area of rectangle OEFG. Then OE represents the mean or average height of the waveform, i.e. the average height of the y ordinates.

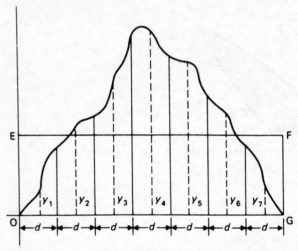

Fig. 11

From the mid-ordinate rule (see Appendix C, page 349):

Area under curve = $d (y_1 + y_2 + y_3 + y_4 + y_5 + y_6 + y_7)$.

Also, area of rectangle OEFG = (OE)(OG)

$$= \text{(average value)} (7d)$$

But area under curve = area of rectangle OEFG.

Thus $d (y_1 + y_2 + y_3 + y_4 + y_5 + y_6 + y_7) = \text{(average value)} (7d)$

Let the average value be denoted by $\bar{y}$ (pronounced y bar).

Then $\bar{y} = \dfrac{d (y_1 + y_2 + y_3 + y_4 + y_5 + y_6 + y_7)}{7d}$

i.e. $\bar{y} = \dfrac{\textbf{area under curve}}{\textbf{length of base}}$

In the example shown in Fig. 11 the mid-ordinate rule is used to find the area under the curve, although other approximate methods such as Simpson's rule or the trapezoidal rule (see Appendix C) could equally well have been used.

An exact method of finding areas under curves is that of integration discussed in Section 1, although this is only possible if (a) there is an equation relating the variables, and (b) the equation can be integrated.

Figure 12 shows part of a curve $y = f(x)$. The mean value, $\bar{y}$, of the curve between the limits $x = a$ and $x = b$ is given by:

$$\bar{y} = \frac{\text{area under curve}}{\text{length of base}} = \frac{\text{area PSRQ}}{b - a}$$

From Section 1, area under the curve $y = f(x)$ between the limits $x = a$ and $x = b$ is given by:

$$\int_a^b f(x)\, dx$$

Hence $\bar{y} = \dfrac{\int_a^b f(x)\, dx}{b - a} = \dfrac{1}{b - a} \int_a^b y\, dx$

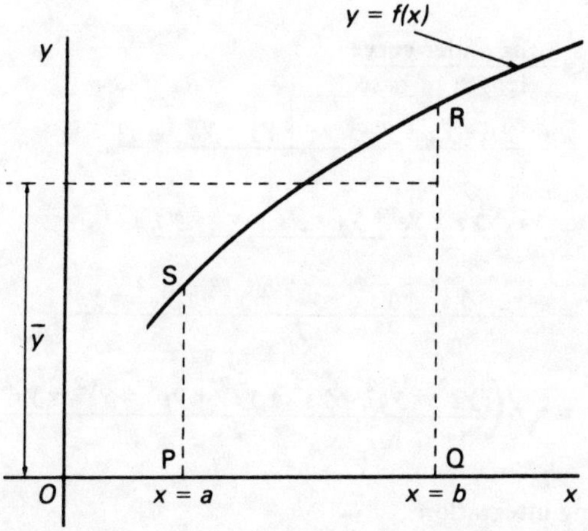

Fig. 12

4 Root mean square values

The root mean square value of a quantity is 'the square root of the average value of the squared values of the quantity' taken over an interval. In many scientific applications — particularly those involving periodic waveforms — mean values, when determined, are found to be zero because there are equal numbers of positive and negative values which cancel each other out. In such cases the root mean square (r.m.s.) values can be valuable e.g.:

(a) the average rate of the heating effect of an electric current (i.e. proportional to current^2),

(b) the standard deviation, used in statistics to estimate the spread or scatter of a set of data (i.e. proportional to distance^2), and

(c) the average linear velocity of a particle in a body which is rotating about an axis (i.e. proportional to velocity^2).

Each of these applications depend upon **square values**, which do not cancel. For example, a direct current I amperes passing through a resistor R ohms for t seconds produces a heating effect given by I^2Rt joules. When an alternating current i amperes is passed through the same resistor R for the same time, the instantaneous value of the heating effect, i.e. i^2Rt, varies. In order to give the same heating effect as the equivalent direct current, i^2 is replaced by the **mean square value**. Then the r.m.s. value of an alternating current is defined as that current which will give the same heating effect as the equivalent direct current, I amperes.

The r.m.s. value obtained without using integration

Referring to Fig. 11.

Average or mean value, $\bar{y}$ $= \dfrac{\text{area under curve}}{\text{length of base}}$

$$= \frac{d(y_1 + y_2 + y_3 + y_4 + y_5 + y_6 + y_7)}{7d}$$

$$= \frac{y_1 + y_2 + y_3 + y_4 + y_5 + y_6 + y_7}{7}$$

Average value of the squares of the function $= \dfrac{y_1{}^2 + y_2{}^2 + y_3{}^2 + y_4{}^2 + y_5{}^2 + y_6{}^2 + y_7{}^2}{7}$

The square root of the average value of the squares of the function, i.e. the r.m.s. value $= \sqrt{\left(\dfrac{y_1{}^2 + y_2{}^2 + y_3{}^2 + y_4{}^2 + y_5{}^2 + y_6{}^2 + y_7{}^2}{7}\right)}$

The r.m.s. value obtained using integration

The average value $\bar{y} = \dfrac{1}{b-a}\displaystyle\int_a^b y\,dx$ (from section 3)

The average value of the square of the function $= \dfrac{1}{b-a}\displaystyle\int_a^b y^2\,dx$

The square root of the average value of the squares of the function, i.e. the r.m.s. value $= \sqrt{\left[\dfrac{1}{b-a}\displaystyle\int_a^b y^2\,dx\right]}$

One of the principle applications of r.m.s. values is in alternating currents and voltages in electrical engineering. Alternating waveforms are frequently of the form $i = I_m \sin \theta$ or $v = V_m \sin \theta$, and, when determining r.m.s. values, integrals of the form $\int (I_m \sin \theta)^2 \, d\theta$ result, i.e. it is necessary to be able to integrate $\sin^2 \theta$ and also $\cos^2 \theta$.

From Appendix B, section 3, equation 12 (page 349):

$$\cos 2A = 1 - 2 \sin^2 A$$

Thus $\quad \sin^2 A = \dfrac{1 - \cos 2A}{2}$

Hence $\displaystyle \int \sin^2 A \, dA = \int \dfrac{1 - \cos 2A}{2} \, dA = \dfrac{1}{2}\left[A - \dfrac{\sin 2A}{2}\right] + c$

From Appendix B, section 3, equation 11 (page 349)

$$\cos 2A = 2 \cos^2 A - 1$$

Thus $\quad \cos^2 A = \dfrac{1 + \cos 2A}{2}$

Hence $\displaystyle \int \cos^2 A \, dA = \int \dfrac{1 + \cos 2A}{2} \, dA = \dfrac{1}{2}\left[A + \dfrac{\sin 2A}{2}\right] + c$

Worked problems on mean and r.m.s. values

Problem 1. Determine (a) the mean value and (b) the r.m.s. value of $y = 3x^2$ between $x = 1$ and $x = 3$, using integration.

(a) Mean value, $\bar{y} = \dfrac{1}{3 - 1} \displaystyle\int_1^3 3x^2 \, dx$

$= \dfrac{1}{2}\left[x^3\right]_1^3 = \dfrac{1}{2}(27 - 1) = 13$

(b) r.m.s. value $= \sqrt{\left[\dfrac{1}{3-1}\displaystyle\int_1^3 (3x^2)^2 \, dx\right]}$

$= \sqrt{\left[\dfrac{1}{2}\displaystyle\int_1^3 9 x^4 \, dx\right]}$

$= \sqrt{\left\{\dfrac{9}{2}\left[\dfrac{x^5}{5}\right]_1^3\right\}}$

$= \sqrt{\left\{\dfrac{9}{10}[243 - 1]\right\}} = \sqrt{\left[\dfrac{9(242)}{10}\right]}$

$= \sqrt{217.8} \qquad = 14.76$

Problem 2. A sinusoidal electrical current is given by $i = 10.0 \sin \theta$ amperes. Determine the mean value of the current over half a cycle using integration.

Average or mean value, $\bar{y} = \dfrac{1}{\pi - 0}\displaystyle\int_0^\pi 10.0 \sin \theta \, d\theta$

$= \dfrac{10.0}{\pi}[-\cos \theta]_0^\pi$

$$= \frac{10.0}{\pi} \left[(-\cos \pi) - (-\cos 0) \right]$$

$$= \frac{10.0}{\pi} \left[(--1) - (-1) \right] = \frac{10.0}{\pi} \ (2)$$

$$= \frac{2}{\pi} \times 10.0 = \textbf{6.366 amperes.}$$

Note that for a sine wave, the mean value $= \frac{2}{\pi} \times$ maximum value.

Problem 3. Using the current given in problem 2, determine the r.m.s. value using integration.

$$\text{r.m.s. value} = \sqrt{\left\{ \frac{1}{\pi} \int_0^\pi (10.0 \sin \theta)^2 \ d\theta \right\}}$$

$$= \sqrt{\left\{ \frac{100.0}{\pi} \int_0^\pi \sin^2 \theta \ d\theta \right\}}$$

From Appendix B, section 3, $\cos 2\theta = 1 - 2 \sin^2 \theta$

from which $\sin^2 \theta = \dfrac{1 - \cos 2\theta}{2}$

Hence r.m.s. value $= \sqrt{\left\{ \frac{100.0}{\pi} \int_0^\pi \frac{1 - \cos 2\theta}{2} \ d\theta \right\}}$

$$= \sqrt{\left\{ \left(\frac{100.0}{\pi} \right) \frac{1}{2} \left[\theta - \frac{\sin 2\theta}{2} \right]_0^\pi \right\}}$$

$$= \sqrt{\left\{ \left(\frac{100.0}{\pi} \right) \frac{1}{2} \left[\left(\pi - \frac{\sin 2\pi}{2} \right) - \left(0 - \frac{\sin 2(0)}{2} \right) \right] \right\}}$$

$$= \sqrt{\left\{ \frac{100.0}{\pi} \left(\frac{\pi}{2} \right) \right\}} = \frac{10.0}{\sqrt{2}} = \textbf{7.071 amperes.}$$

Note that for a sine wave, the r.m.s. value $= \dfrac{1}{\sqrt{2}} . \times$ maximum value.

Problem 4. Find the area bounded by the curve $y = 6x - x^2$ and the x axis for values of x from 0 to 6. Determine also the mean value and the r.m.s. value of y over the same range.

A table of values is drawn up as shown below.

$y = 6x - x^2$

x	0	1	2	3	4	5	6
y	0	5	8	9	8	5	0

Since all the values of y are positive the area required is wholly above the x axis. Hence the area enclosed by the curve, the x axis and the ordinates $x = 0$ and $x = 6$ is given by:

$$\text{Area} = \int_0^6 y \, dx = \int_0^6 (6x - x^2) \, dx$$

$$= \left[\frac{6x^2}{2} - \frac{x^3}{3} \right]_0^6 = (108 - 72) - (0 - 0) = \textbf{36 square units.}$$

Mean or average value $= \dfrac{\text{area under curve}}{\text{length of base}} = \dfrac{36}{6} = 6$

$$\text{r.m.s. value} = \sqrt{\left\{ \frac{1}{6-0} \int_0^6 (6x - x^2)^2 \, dx \right\}}$$

$$= \sqrt{\left\{ \frac{1}{6} \int_0^6 (36x^2 - 12x^3 + x^4) \, dx \right\}}$$

$$= \sqrt{\left\{ \frac{1}{6} \left[\frac{36x^3}{3} - \frac{12x^4}{4} + \frac{x^5}{5} \right]_0^6 \right\}}$$

$$= \sqrt{\left\{ \frac{1}{6} \left[\left(12(6)^3 - 3(6)^4 + \frac{(6)^5}{5} \right) - (0) \right] \right\}}$$

$$= \sqrt{\left\{ \frac{1}{6} (2\,592 - 3\,888 + 1\,555.2) \right\}}$$

$$= \sqrt{\left\{ \frac{1}{6} (259.2) \right\}} = \sqrt{43.2} = \textbf{6.573}$$

Further problems on mean and r.m.s. values may be found in the following section (5), problems 49 to 83, page 312.

5 Further problems

Areas under and between curves.

All answers are in square units.

In problems 1 to 22 find the area enclosed between the given curve, the horizontal axis and the given ordinates. Sketch the curve in the given range for each.

1. $y = 2x; x = 0, x = 5$ [25]
2. $y = x^2 - x + 2; x = -1, x = 2$ $[7\frac{1}{2}]$
3. $y = \dfrac{x}{2}; x = 3, x = 7$ [10]
4. $y = p - 1; p = 1, p = 5$ [8]
5. $F = 8S - 2S^2; S = 0, S = 2$ $[10\frac{2}{3}]$
6. $y = (x - 1)(x - 2); x = 0, x = 3$ $[1\frac{5}{6}]$
7. $y = 8 + 2x - x^2; x = -2, x = 4$ [36]
8. $u = 2(4 - t^2); t = -2, t = 2$ $[21\frac{1}{3}]$
9. $y = x(x - 1)(x + 3); x = -2, x = 1$ $[7\frac{11}{12}]$
10. $x = 4a^3; a = -2, a = 2$ [32]
11. $y = x(x - 1)(x - 3); x = 0, x = 3$ $[3\frac{1}{12}]$

12. $a = t^3 + t^2 - 4t - 4$; $t = -3$, $t = 3$ $[24\frac{1}{3}]$

13. $y = \sin\theta$; $\theta = 0$, $\theta = \dfrac{\pi}{2}$ $[1]$

14. $y = \cos x$; $x = \dfrac{\pi}{4}$, $x = \dfrac{\pi}{2}$ $[0.292\ 9]$

15. $y = 3\sin 2\beta$; $\beta = 0$, $\beta = \dfrac{\pi}{4}$ $[1\frac{1}{2}]$

16. $y = 5\cos 3\alpha$; $\alpha = 0$, $\alpha = \dfrac{\pi}{6}$ $[1\frac{2}{3}]$

17. $y = \sin x - \cos x$; $x = 0$, $x = \dfrac{\pi}{4}$ $[0.414\ 2]$

18. $2y^2 = x$; $x = 0$, $x = 2$ $[2\frac{2}{3}]$
19. $5 = xy$; $x = 2$, $x = 5$ $[4.581]$
20. $y = 2e^{2t}$; $t = 0$, $t = 2$ $[53.60]$
21. $ye^{4x} = 3$; $x = 1$, $x = 3$ $[0.013\ 7]$
22. $y = 2x + e^x$; $x = 0$, $x = 3$ $[28.09]$
23. Find the area between the curve $y = 3x - x^2$ and the x axis. $[4\frac{1}{2}]$
24. Calculate the area enclosed between the curve $y = 12 - x - x^2$ and the x axis using integration. $[57\frac{1}{6}]$

25. Sketch the curve $y = \sec^2 2x$ from $x = 0$ to $x = \dfrac{\pi}{4}$ and calculate the area enclosed between the curve, the x axis and the ordinates $x = 0$ and $x = \dfrac{\pi}{6}$. $[0.866]$

26. Find the area of the template enclosed between the curve $y = \dfrac{1}{x-2}$, the x axis and the ordinates $x = 3$ cm and $x = 5$ cm. $[1.098\ 6\ \text{cm}^2]$
27. Sketch the curves $y = x^2 + 4$ and $y + x = 10$ and find the area enclosed by them. $[20\frac{5}{6}]$
28. Calculate the area enclosed between the curves $y = \sin\theta$ and $y = \cos\theta$ and the θ axis between the limits $\theta = 0$ and $\theta = \dfrac{\pi}{4}$. $[0.414\ 2]$

29. Find the area between the two parabolas $9y^2 = 16x$ and $x^2 = 6y$. $[3\frac{5}{9}]$
30. Calculate the area of the metal plate enclosed between $y = x\,(x-4)$ and the x axis where x is in metres. $[10\frac{2}{3}\ \text{m}^2]$
31. Sketch the curve $x^2 - y = 3x + 10$ and find the area enclosed between it and the x axis. $[57\frac{1}{6}]$
32. Find the area enclosed by the curve $y = 4\,(x^2 - 1)$, the x axis and the ordinates $x = 0$ and $x = 2$. Find also the area enclosed by the curve and the y axis between the same limits. $[8, 21\frac{1}{3}]$
33. Calculate the area between the curve $y = x\,(x^2 - 2x - 3)$ and the x axis using integration. $[11\frac{5}{6}]$

34. Find the area of the figure bounded by the curve $y = 3e^{2x}$, the x axis and the ordinates $x = -2$ and $x = 2$. $[81.87]$
35. Find the area enclosed between the curves $y = x^2 - 3x + 5$ and $y - 1 = 2x$. $[4\frac{1}{2}]$

36. Find the points of intersection of the two curves $\frac{x^2}{2} = \sqrt{2y}$ and $y^2 = 8x$ and calculate the area enclosed by them. [(0,0), (4,5.657); 7.542]

37. Calculate the area bounded by the curve $y = x^2 + x + 4$ and the line $y = 2(x + 5)$. [$20\frac{5}{6}$]

38. Find the area enclosed between the curves $y = x^2$ and $y = 8 - x^2$. [$21\frac{1}{3}$]

39. Calculate the area between the curve $y = 3x^3$ and the line $\frac{y}{12} = x$ in the first quadrant. [12]

40. Find the area bounded by the three straight lines $y = 4(2 - x)$, $y = 4x$ and $3y = 4x$. [2]

41. A vehicle has an acceleration a of $(30 + 2t)$ metres per second after t seconds. If the vehicle starts from rest find its velocity after 10 seconds.

(Velocity $= \int_{t_1}^{t_2} a \, dt$) [400 m s^{-1}]

42. A car has a velocity v of $(3 + 4t)$ metres per second after t seconds. How far does it move in the first 4 seconds? Find the distance travelled in the fifth second.

(Distance travelled $= \int_{t_1}^{t_2} v \, dt$) [44 m; 21 m]

43. A gas expands according to the law $pv = $ constant. When the volume is 2 m^3 the pressure is 200 kPa. Find the work done as the gas expands from 2 m^3 to a volume of 5 m^3.

(Work done $= \int_{v_1}^{v_2} p \, dv$) [367 kJ]

44. The brakes are applied to a train and the velocity v at any time t seconds after applying the brakes is given by $(16 - 2.5t)$ m s^{-1}. Calculate the distance travelled in 8 seconds.

(Distance travelled $= \int_{t_1}^{t_2} v \, dt$) [48 m]

45. The force F newtons acting on a body at a distance x metres from a fixed point is given by $F = 3x + \frac{1}{x^2}$. Find the work done when the body moves from the position where $x = 1$ m to that where $x = 3$ m.

(Work done $= \int_{x_1}^{x_2} F \, dx$) [$12\frac{2}{3}$ newton metres]

46. The velocity v of a body t seconds after a certain instant is $(4t^2 + 3)$ m s^{-1}. Find how far it moves in the interval from $t = 2$ s to $t = 6$ s.

(Distance travelled $= \int_{t_1}^{t_2} v \, dt$) [$289\frac{1}{3}$ m]

47. The heat required to raise the temperature of carbon dioxide from 300 K to 600 K is determined from the area formed when the heat capacity

(C_p) is plotted against the temperature (T) between 300 K and 600 K. If $C_p = 27 + 42 \times 10^{-3} \, T - 14.22 \times 10^{-6} \, T^2$, determine the area by integration.   [12 870]

48. The entropy required to raise hydrogen sulphide from 400 K to 500 K is determined from the area formed when C_p is plotted against the temperature (T) between 400 K and 500 K. Given that $C_p = 37 + 0.008 \, T$, determine the area by integration.   [4060]

Mean and r.m.s. values.

In problems 49 to 55 find the mean values over the ranges stated.

49. $y = 2\sqrt{x}$ from $x = 0$ to $x = 4$. $[2\frac{2}{3}]$

50. $y = t(2 - t)$ from $t = 0$ to $t = 2$. $[\frac{2}{3}]$

51. $y = \sin\theta$ from $\theta = 0$ to $\theta = 2\pi$.   [0]

52. $y = \sin\theta$ from $\theta = 0$ to $\theta = \pi$. $\left[\dfrac{2}{\pi} \text{ or } 0.637\right]$

53. $y = 2\cos 2x$ from $x = 0$ to $x = \dfrac{\pi}{4}$. $\left[\dfrac{4}{\pi} \text{ or } 1.273\right]$

54. $y = 2e^x$ from $x = 1$ to $x = 4$.   [34.59]

55. $y = \dfrac{2}{x}$ from $x = 1$ to $x = 3$.   [1.099]

56. Determine the mean value of the curve $y = t - t^2 + 2$ which lies above the t axis by the mid-ordinate rule and check your result using integration. $[1\frac{1}{2}]$

57. The velocity v of a piston moving with simple harmonic motion at any time t is given by $v = k \sin \omega t$. Find the mean velocity between $t = 0$ and $t = \dfrac{\pi}{\omega}$. $\left[\dfrac{2k}{\pi}\right]$

58. Calculate the mean value of $y = 3x - x^2$ in the range $x = 0$ to $x = 3$ by integration   [1.5]

59. If the speed v m s^{-1} of a car is given by $v = 3t + 5$, where t is the time in seconds, find the mean value of the speed from $t = 2$ s to $t = 5$ s. $[15\frac{1}{2}$ m s$^{-1}]$

60. The number of atoms N remaining in a mass of material during radioactive decay after time t seconds is given by $N = N_o \, e^{-\lambda t}$, where N_o and λ are constants. Determine the mean number of atoms in the mass of material for the time period $t = 0$ to $t = \dfrac{1}{\lambda}$. $[0.632 \, N_o]$

61. A force $9\sqrt{x}$ newtons acts on a body whilst it moves from $x = 0$ to $x = 4$ metres. Find the mean value of the force with respect to distance x. [12 N]

62. The rotor of an electric motor has a tangential velocity v (given by $v = (9 - t^2)$) metres per second after t seconds. Find how far a point on the circumference of the rotor moves in 3 seconds from $t = 0$ and the average velocity during this time.   [18 m, 6 m/s]

63. The vertical height y kilometres of a rocket fired from a launcher varies

with the horizontal distance x kilometres and is given by $y = 6x - x^2$.
Determine the mean height of the rocket from $x = 0$ to $x = 6$ kilometres.
[6 km]

In problems 64 to 71 find the r.m.s. values over the ranges stated.

64. $y = 2x$ from $x = 0$ to $x = 4$.   [4.619]

65. $y = x^2$ from $x = 1$ to $x = 3$.   [4.919]

66. $y = \sin t$ from $t = 0$ to $t = 2\pi$. $\left[\dfrac{1}{\sqrt{2}} \text{ or } 0.707\right]$

67. $y = \sin t$ from $t = 0$ to $t = \pi$. $\left[\dfrac{1}{\sqrt{2}} \text{ or } 0.707\right]$

68. $y = 4 + 2 \cos x$ from $x = 0$ to $x = 2\pi$.   [4.243]

69. $y = \sin 3\theta$ from $\theta = 0$ to $\theta = \dfrac{\pi}{6}$. $\left[\dfrac{1}{\sqrt{2}} \text{ or } 0.707\right]$

70. $y = 1 + \sin t$ from $t = 0$ to $t = 2\pi$.   [1.225]

71. $y = \cos \theta - \sin \theta$ from $\theta = 0$ to $\theta = \dfrac{\pi}{4}$.   [0.603]

72. Determine: (a) the average value; and (b) the r.m.s. value of a sine wave of maximum value 5.0 for:
  (i) a half cycle; and
  (ii) one cycle   (a) (i) [3.18]   (ii) [0]
                    (b) (i) [3.54]   (ii) [3.54]

73. The distances of points, y, from the mean value of a frequency distribution are related to the variate, x, by the equation $y = x + \dfrac{1}{x}$. Determine the standard deviation (i.e. the r.m.s. value), correct to 4 significant figures, for values of x from 1 to 2.   [2.198]

74. Show that the ratio of the r.m.s. value to the mean value of $y = \sin x$ over the period $x = 0$ to $x = \pi$ is given by $\dfrac{\pi}{2\sqrt{2}}$.

75. Draw the graph of $4t - t^2$ for values of t from 0 to 4. Determine the area bounded by the curve and the t axis by integration. Find also the mean and r.m.s. values over the same range.
[Area = $10\frac{2}{3}$ square units; mean value = 2.67; r.m.s. value = 2.92]

76. An alternating voltage is given by $v = 20.0 \cos 50\pi t$ volts. Find: (a) the mean value; and (b) the r.m.s. value over the interval from $t = 0$ to $t = 0.01$ seconds.   [12.73 V; 14.14 V]

77. A voltage, $v = 24 \sin 50\pi t$ volts is applied across an electrical circuit. Find its mean and r.m.s. values over the range $t = 0$ to $t = 10$ ms, each correct to 4 significant figures.   [15.28 V, 16.97 V]

78. A sinusoidal voltage has a maximum value of 150 volts. Calculate its r.m.s. and mean values.   [106.1 V, 95.49 V]

79. In a frequency distribution the average distance from the mean, p, is related to the variable, q, by the equation $p = 3q^2 - 2$. Determine the r.m.s. deviation from the mean for values of q from -2 to $+3$, correct to 3 significant figures.   [8.66]

80. If the dipolar coupling (y) between two parallel magnetic dipoles in a liquid is given by $y = 1 - 3x^2$ determine the average value of y between $x = 1$ and -1.   [0]

81. Determine the average heat capacity $\bar{c}_p$ of magnesium between 300 K and 400 K given that:

$$c_p = 6.2 + 1.3 \times 10^{-3}\ T - 6.8 \times 10^4\ T^{-2}$$

[6.09]

82. If the rate of a chemical reaction (r) is given by:

$$r = 2.5\ (3.2 - x)\ (3 - x),$$

where x is the moles of the product, determine the average rate for x to increase from 0 to 1 mole.   [17.1]

83. Find the average velocity ($\bar{v}$) of a chemical change during the first 5 minutes of reaction when $v = e^{-3t}$, where t is the time in minutes.

$$\left[\frac{1 - e^{-15}}{15}\right]$$

Chapter 16

Numerical integration

1 Introduction

In Chapter 14 it was shown that a number of functions, such as ax^n, $\sin ax$, $\cos ax$, e^{ax} and $\dfrac{1}{x}$, are termed 'standard integrals', and they may be integrated 'on sight'. It was also shown that with some other simple functions, such as $\cos (5x + 2)$, $(4t - 3)^7$ and $\dfrac{1}{7x + 2}$, an algebraic substitution may be used to change the function into a form which can be readily integrated. However, even with more advanced methods of integration, there are many mathematical functions which cannot be integrated by analytical methods and thus approximate methods have then to be used. Also, in some cases, only a set of observed tabulated numerical values of the function to be integrated may be available. Approximate values of definite integrals may be determined by what is termed **numerical integration**. It is shown in Chapters 14 and 15 that determining the value of a definite integral is, in fact, finding the area between a curve, the horizontal axis and the specified ordinates. Three methods of finding approximate areas under curves are the trapezoidal rule, the mid-ordinate rule and Simpson's rule and these rules are used as a basis for numerical integration.

2 The trapezoidal rule

Let a required definite integral be denoted by $\int_a^b y\,dx$ and be represented

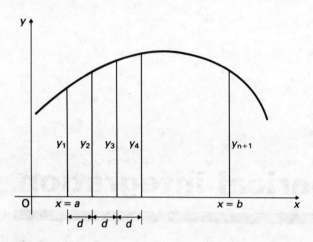

Fig. 1

by the area under the graph of y between the limits $x = a$ and $x = b$, as shown in Fig. 1. Let the range of integration be divided into n equal intervals each of width d, such that $nd = b - a$, i.e., $d = \dfrac{b - a}{n}$.

Let the ordinates be labelled $y_1, y_2, \ldots y_{n+1}$, as shown. An approximation to the area under the curve is obtained by joining the tops of the ordinates by straight lines. Each strip of area is thus a trapezium and since the area of a trapezium is given by:

area of trapezium = $\dfrac{1}{2}$ (sum of the parallel sides) (perpendicular distance between them)

then

$$\int_a^b y\,dx \approx \frac{1}{2}(y_1 + y_2)d + \frac{1}{2}(y_2 + y_3)d + \frac{1}{2}(y_3 + y_4)d + \ldots$$

$$+ \frac{1}{2}(y_n + y_{n+1})d$$

$$\approx d\left[\frac{1}{2}y_1 + y_2 + y_3 + \ldots + y_n + \frac{1}{2}y_{n+1}\right]$$

i.e., $\int_a^b y\,dx \approx \begin{pmatrix}\text{width of}\\\text{interval}\end{pmatrix}\left\{\frac{1}{2}\begin{pmatrix}\text{first + last}\\\text{ordinate}\end{pmatrix} + \text{sum of remaining}\atop\text{ordinates}\right\} \ldots$ (1)

To demonstrate this method of numerical integration let an integral be chosen whose value may be determined exactly using integration.

Evaluating $\int_1^3 \dfrac{1}{\sqrt{x}}\,dx$ by integration gives $\left[\dfrac{x^{-\frac{1}{2}+1}}{-\frac{1}{2}+1} \right]_1^3 = \left[2\sqrt{x} \right]_1^3$

$$= 2(\sqrt{3} - \sqrt{1})$$

$$= 1.464, \text{ correct to 3 decimal places.}$$

The range of integration is the difference between the upper and lower limits, i.e., $3 - 1 = 2$. Using the trapezoidal rule with, say, 4 intervals, gives an interval width, d of $\dfrac{3-1}{4} = \dfrac{1}{2}$, and ordinates situated at 1.0, 1.5, 2.0, 2.5 and 3.0. Corresponding values of $\dfrac{1}{\sqrt{x}}$ are as shown in the table below, each given correct to 4 decimal places.

x	1.0	1.5	2.0	2.5	3.0
$\dfrac{1}{\sqrt{x}}$	1.0000	0.8165	0.7071	0.6325	0.5774

From equation (1):

$$\int_1^3 \frac{1}{\sqrt{x}}\,dx \approx \left(\frac{1}{2}\right)\left[\frac{1}{2}(1.0000 + 0.5774) + 0.8165 + 0.7071 + 0.6325\right]$$

$$= 1.472, \text{ correct to 3 decimal places.}$$

Using the trapezoidal rule with, say, 8 intervals, each of width $\dfrac{3-1}{8}$, i.e., 0.25, gives ordinates situated at 1.00, 1.25, 1.50, 1.75, 2.00, 2.25, 2.50, 2.75 and 3.00. Corresponding values of $\dfrac{1}{\sqrt{x}}$ are as shown in the table below.

x	1.00	1.25	1.50	1.75	2.00	2.25	2.50	2.75	3.00
$\dfrac{1}{\sqrt{x}}$	1.0000	0.8944	0.8165	0.7559	0.7071	0.6667	0.6325	0.6030	0.5774

From equation (1):

$$\int_1^3 \frac{1}{\sqrt{x}}\,dx \approx (0.25)\left[\begin{array}{l}\frac{1}{2}(1.0000 + 0.5774) + 0.8944 + 0.8165 + 0.7559 \\ + 0.7071 + 0.6667 + 0.6325 + 0.6030\end{array}\right]$$

$$= 1.466, \text{ correct to 3 decimal places.}$$

The greater the number of intervals chosen (i.e., the smaller the interval width) the more accurate will be the value of the definite integral. The exact value is found when the number of intervals is infinite, i.e., when the interval width d tends to zero, and this is of course what the process of integration is based upon.

3   The mid-ordinate rule

Let a required definite integral be denoted again by $\int_a^b y\, dx$ and represented by the area under the graph of y between the limits $x = a$ and $x = b$, as shown in Fig. 2.

With this rule each strip of width d is assumed to be replaced by a rectangle of height equal to the ordinates at the middle point of each interval, shown as $y_1, y_2, y_3, \ldots y_n$ in Fig. 2. Thus,

$$\int_a^b y\, dx \approx d\, y_1 + d\, y_2 + d\, y_3 + \ldots + d\, y_n$$

$$\approx d\, (y_1 + y_2 + y_3 + \ldots + y_n)$$

i.e., $\int_a^b y\, dx \approx$ (width of interval) (sum of mid-ordinates)   ...(2)

The more intervals chosen the more accurate will be the value of the definite integral.

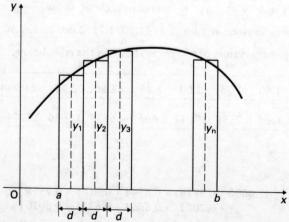

Fig. 2

Applying this rule to evaluating $\int_1^3 \frac{1}{\sqrt{x}}\, dx$ with, say, 4 intervals means that the width interval d is $\frac{3-1}{4}$, i.e., $\frac{1}{2}$ and that ordinates exist at 1.0, 1.5, 2.0, 2.5 and 3.0. Hence mid-ordinates y_1, y_2, y_3 and y_4 occur at 1.25, 1.75, 2.25 and 2.75. Corresponding values of $\frac{1}{\sqrt{x}}$ are shown in the following table:

x	1.25	1.75	2.25	2.75
$\dfrac{1}{\sqrt{x}}$	0.8944	0.7559	0.6667	0.6030

From equation (2):

$$\int_1^3 \frac{1}{\sqrt{x}}\, dx \approx (\tfrac{1}{2})\ [0.8944 + 0.7559 + 0.6667 + 0.6030]$$
$$= \mathbf{1.460}, \quad \text{correct to 3 decimal places.}$$

Using the mid-ordinate rule with, say, 8 intervals, each of width 0.25, gives ordinates at 1.00, 1.25, 1.50, 1.75 . . . and thus mid-ordinates at 1.125, 1.375, 1.625, 1.875, ... Corresponding values of $\frac{1}{\sqrt{x}}$ are shown in the following table.

x	1.125	1.375	1.625	1.875	2.125	2.375	2.625	2.875
$\dfrac{1}{\sqrt{x}}$	0.9428	0.8528	0.7845	0.7303	0.6860	0.6489	0.6172	0.5898

From equation (2):

$$\int_1^3 \frac{1}{\sqrt{x}}\, dx \approx (0.25)\ \begin{bmatrix} 0.9428 + 0.8528 + 0.7845 + 0.7303 + 0.6860 \\ + 0.6489 + 0.6172 + 0.5898 \end{bmatrix}$$
$$= \mathbf{1.463}, \quad \text{correct to 3 decimal places.}$$

As before, the greater the number of values chosen the nearer the result will be to the true one.

4 Simpson's rule

In section 2, it is shown that the approximation made with the trapezoidal rule is to join the tops of two successive ordinates by a straight line, i.e., by using a linear approximation of the form $a + bx$. With Simpson's rule, the approximation made is to join the tops of three successive ordinates by a parabola, i.e., by using a quadratic approximation of the form $a + bx + cx^2$.

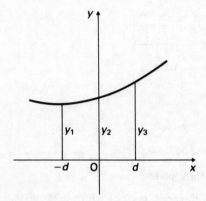

Fig. 3

Figure 3 shows three ordinates, y_1, y_2 and y_3 of a parabola $y = a + bx + cx^2$ at $x = -d$, $x = 0$ and $x = d$ respectively. Thus the width of each of the two intervals is d. The area under the parabola from $x = -d$ to $x = d$ is given by:

$$\int_{-d}^{d} (a + bx + cx^2)\, dx = \left[ax + \frac{bx^2}{2} + \frac{cx^3}{3} \right]_{-d}^{d}$$

$$= (ad + \frac{bd^2}{2} + \frac{cd^3}{3}) - (-ad + \frac{bd^2}{2} - \frac{cd^3}{3})$$

$$= 2\,ad + \frac{2}{3}cd^3 \quad = \frac{1}{3} d\,(6a + 2\,cd^2) \qquad \ldots (3)$$

Since $y = a + bx + cx^2$, at $x = -d$, $y_1 = a - bd + cd^2$,

$$\text{at } x = 0,\ y_2 = a,$$

and at $x = d$, $y_3 = a + bd + cd^2$.

Hence $y_1 + y_3 = 2a + 2cd^2$

and $y_1 + 4y_2 + y_3 = 6a + 2cd^2$ $\qquad \ldots (4)$

Thus the area under the parabola between $x = -d$ and $x = d$ in Fig. 3 is (from equations (3) and (4)):

$$\frac{1}{3} d (y_1 + 4y_2 + y_3).$$

and this result can be seen to be independent of the position of the origin.

Let a definite integral be denoted by $\displaystyle\int_a^b y\ dx$ and represented by the area under the graph of y between the limits $x = a$ and $x = b$, as shown in Fig. 4. The range of integration, $b - a$, is divided into an **even** number of intervals, say, $2n$, each of width d.

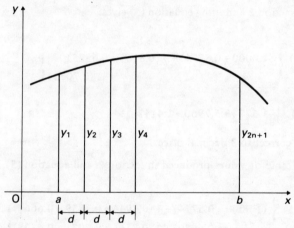

Fig. 4

Since an even number of intervals is specified, an odd number of ordinates, $2n + 1$, exists. Let an approximation to the curve over the first two intervals be a parabola of the form $y = a + bx + cx^2$ which passes through the tops of the three ordinates y_1, y_2 and y_3. Similarly, let an approximation to the curve over the next two intervals be the parabola which passes through the tops of the ordinates y_3, y_4 and y_5, and so on.

Then $\displaystyle\int_a^b y\ dx \approx \frac{1}{3} d (y_1 + 4y_2 + y_3) + \frac{1}{3} d (y_3 + 4y_4 + y_5) + \ldots$

$$+ \frac{1}{3} d (y_{2n-1} + 4y_{2n} + y_{2n+1})$$

$$\approx \frac{1}{3} d \left[(y_1 + y_{2n+1}) + 4 (y_2 + y_4 + \ldots + y_{2n}) + 2(y_3 + y_5 + \ldots + y_{2n-1}) \right]$$

i.e., $\int_a^b y\,\mathrm{d}x \approx \frac{1}{3}\begin{pmatrix}\text{width of}\\\text{interval}\end{pmatrix}\left\{\begin{pmatrix}\text{first + last}\\\text{ordinate}\end{pmatrix} + 4\begin{pmatrix}\text{sum of even}\\\text{ordinates}\end{pmatrix}\right.$

$$\left. + 2\begin{pmatrix}\text{sum of remaining}\\\text{odd ordinates}\end{pmatrix}\right\}$$

$$\dots (5)$$

Again, the more intervals chosen the more accurate will be the value of the definite integral.

Applying this rule to evaluate $\int_1^3 \frac{1}{\sqrt{x}}\,\mathrm{d}x$ with, say, 4 intervals, using the table

of values produced in section 2 and using equation (5) gives:

$$\int_1^3 \frac{1}{\sqrt{x}}\,\mathrm{d}x \approx \frac{1}{3}(0.5)\left\{(1.0000 + 0.5774) + 4(0.8165 + 0.6325) \atop + 2(0.7071)\right\}$$

$$\approx \frac{1}{3}(0.5)\left\{1.5774 + 5.7960 + 1.4142\right\}$$

$$= 1.465, \text{ correct to 3 decimal places.}$$

Using 8 intervals, the table of values produced in section 2, and equation (5) gives:

$$\int_1^3 \frac{1}{\sqrt{x}}\,\mathrm{d}x \approx \frac{1}{3}(0.25)\left\{(1.0000 + 0.5774) + 4(0.8944 + 0.7559 + 0.6667 \atop + 0.6030) + 2(0.8165 + 0.7071 + 0.6325)\right\}$$

$$\approx \frac{1}{3}(0.25)\left\{1.5774 + 11.6800 + 4.3122\right\}$$

$$= 1.464, \text{ correct to 3 decimal places, which is the same value as} \atop \text{obtained by integration.}$$

Simpson's rule is generally regarded as the most accurate of the three approximate methods used in numerical integration.

Worked problems on numerical integration

Problem 1. Evaluate $\int_0^1 \frac{2}{1 + x^2}\,\mathrm{d}x$, using the trapezoidal rule with 8 inter-

vals, giving the answer correct to 3 decimal places.

The range of integration is from 0 to 1 and hence if 8 intervals are chosen then each will be of width $\dfrac{1-0}{8}$ i.e., d = 0.125. Thus ordinates occur at 0, 0.125, 0.250, 0.375 . . . and for each of these values $\dfrac{2}{1+x^2}$ may be evaluated. The results are shown in the following table.

x	0	0.125	0.250	0.375	0.500	0.625	0.750	0.875	1.000
$\dfrac{2}{1+x^2}$	2.0000	1.9692	1.8824	1.7534	1.6000	1.4382	1.2800	1.1327	1.0000

(Note that since 3-decimal place accuracy is required in the final answer, values in the table are taken correct to one decimal place more than this, i.e., correct to 4 decimal places.)

From equation (1), using the trapezoidal rule with 8 intervals:

$$\int_0^1 \frac{2}{1+x^2}\,dx \approx d\left[\frac{1}{2}\begin{pmatrix} \text{first + last} \\ \text{ordinate} \end{pmatrix} + \text{sum of remaining ordinates}\right]$$

$$\approx (0.125)\left[\frac{1}{2}(2.0000+1.0000)+1.9692+1.8824+1.7534 \\ +1.6000+1.4382+1.2800+1.1327\right]$$

$$= \mathbf{1.569}, \text{ correct to 3 decimal places.}$$

Problem 2. Determine the value of $\displaystyle\int_1^5 \ln x\,dx$ using the mid-ordinate rule with (a) 4 intervals, (b) 8 intervals. Give the answers correct to 4 significant figures.

(a) The range of integration is from 1 to 5 and hence if 4 intervals are chosen then each will be of width $\dfrac{5-1}{4}$, i.e., d = 1.

Hence ordinates occur at 1, 2, 3, 4 and 5 and thus mid-ordinates occur at 1.5, 2.5, 3.5 and 4.5. Corresponding values of $\ln x$ are shown in the table below.

x	1.5	2.5	3.5	4.5
$\ln x$	0.40547	0.91629	1.25276	1.50408

From equation (2), using the mid-ordinate rule with 4 intervals:

$$\int_1^5 \ln x \, dx \approx \text{(width of interval) (sum of mid-ordinates)}$$
$$\approx (1)(0.40547 + 0.91629 + 1.25276 + 1.50408)$$
$$= \mathbf{4.079}, \text{ correct to 4 significant figures.}$$

(b) With 8 intervals, width $d = \dfrac{5-1}{8} = 0.5$, ordinates occur at 1.0, 1.5, 2.0, 2.5, ... 5, and thus mid-ordinates occur at 1.25, 1.75, 2.25, ... 4.75

Hence from equation (2):

$$\int_1^5 \ln x \, dx \approx (0.5)\,[\ln 1.25 + \ln 1.75 + \ln 2.25 + \ln 2.75 + \ln 3.25 + \ln 3.75$$
$$+ \ln 4.25 + \ln 4.75]$$
$$= \mathbf{4.055}, \text{ correct to 4 significant figures.}$$

Problem 3. Evaluate $\displaystyle\int_0^{\frac{\pi}{2}} \dfrac{1}{1 + \frac{1}{2}\sin^2 \theta}\, d\theta$, using Simpson's rule with 6 intervals, correct to 3 decimal places.

With 6 intervals chosen, each will have a width of $\dfrac{\frac{\pi}{2} - 0}{6}$, i.e. $\dfrac{\pi}{12}$ rad (or $15°$) and the ordinates occur at $0, \dfrac{\pi}{12}, \dfrac{\pi}{6}, \dfrac{\pi}{4}, \dfrac{\pi}{3}, \dfrac{5\pi}{12}$ and $\dfrac{\pi}{2}$.

Corresponding values of $\dfrac{1}{1 + \frac{1}{2}\sin^2 \theta}$ are evaluated and are shown in the table below.

θ	0	$\frac{\pi}{12}$ (or 15°)	$\frac{\pi}{6}$ (or 30°)	$\frac{\pi}{4}$ (or 45°)	$\frac{\pi}{3}$ (or 60°)	$\frac{5\pi}{12}$ (or 75°)	$\frac{\pi}{2}$ (or 90°)
$\dfrac{1}{1 + \frac{1}{2}\sin^2 \theta}$	1.0000	0.9676	0.8889	0.8000	0.7273	0.6819	0.6667

From equation (5), using Simpson's rule with 6 intervals:

$$\int_0^{\frac{\pi}{2}} \frac{1}{1 + \frac{1}{2}\sin^2 \theta}\, d\theta \approx \frac{1}{3}\begin{pmatrix}\text{width of} \\ \text{intervals}\end{pmatrix}\left\{\begin{pmatrix}\text{first + last} \\ \text{ordinate}\end{pmatrix} + 4\begin{pmatrix}\text{sum of even} \\ \text{ordinates}\end{pmatrix} \right.$$
$$\left. + 2\begin{pmatrix}\text{sum of remaining} \\ \text{odd ordinates}\end{pmatrix}\right\}$$

$$\approx \frac{1}{3}\left(\frac{\pi}{12}\right)\left\{(1.0000+0.6667)+4(0.9676+0.8000 \right.$$
$$\left. +0.6819)+2(0.8889+0.7273)\right\}$$

$$\approx \frac{\pi}{36}\left\{1.6667+9.7980+3.2324\right\}$$

$$\approx 0.4083\pi = \textbf{1.283}, \text{ correct to 3 decimal places.}$$

Problem 4. The velocity v of a car has the following values for corresponding values of time t from $t = 0$ to $t = 8$ s.

v m s^{-1}	0	0.6	1.7	2.8	4.9	7.0	9.2	10.8	12.0
t s	0	1	2	3	4	5	6	7	8

The distance travelled by the car in 8 s is given by $\int_0^8 v\, dt$.

Determine the approximate distance travelled by using (a) the trapezoidal rule, and (b) Simpson's rule, using 8 intervals in each case.

Since 8 intervals are chosen, each has a width of 1 s.

(a) From equation (1), using the trapezoidal rule with 8 intervals:

$$\int_0^8 v\, dt \approx (1)\left[\frac{1}{2}(0+12.0)+0.6+1.7+2.8+4.9+7.0+9.2+10.8\right]$$

$$= \textbf{43 m}$$

(b) From equation (5), using Simpson's rule with 8 intervals:

$$\int_0^8 v\, dt \approx \frac{1}{3}(1)\left\{(0+12.0)+4(0.6+2.8+7.0+10.8)+2(1.7+4.9+9.2)\right\}$$

$$\approx \frac{1}{3}(1)[12.0+84.8+31.6]$$

$$= \textbf{42.8 m}$$

Problem 5. Evaluate $\int_0^{1.2} e^{-\frac{x^2}{2}}\, dx$ using (a) the trapezoidal rule, (b) the

mid-ordinate rule and (c) Simpson's rule. Use 6 intervals in each case and give answers correct to 3 significant figures.

Since 6 intervals are chosen then each is of width $\frac{1.2-0}{6}$, i.e., 0.2

Hence ordinates occur at 0, 0.2, 0.4, 0.6, 0.8, 1.0 and 1.2

Corresponding values of $e^{-\frac{x^2}{2}}$ are evaluated and shown in the following table.

x	0	0.2	0.4	0.6	0.8	1.0	1.2
$e^{-\frac{x^2}{2}}$	1.0000	0.9802	0.9231	0.8353	0.7261	0.6065	0.4868

(a) From equation (1), using the trapezoidal rule with 6 intervals:

$$\int_0^{1.2} e^{-\frac{x^2}{2}} \, dx \approx (0.2) \left[\frac{1}{2}(1.0000 + 0.4868) + 0.9802 + 0.9231 \right.$$
$$\left. + 0.8353 + 0.7261 + 0.6065 \right]$$

$$= \mathbf{0.963}, \text{ correct to 3 significant figures.}$$

(b) Mid-ordinates occur at 0.1, 0.3, 0.5, 0.7, 0.9 and 1.1 and corresponding

values of $e^{-\frac{x^2}{2}}$ are evaluated and shown in the following table.

x	0.1	0.3	0.5	0.7	0.9	1.1
$e^{-\frac{x^2}{2}}$	0.9950	0.9560	0.8825	0.7827	0.6670	0.5461

From equation (2), using the mid-ordinate rule with 6 intervals:

$$\int_0^{1.2} e^{-\frac{x^2}{2}} \, dx \approx (0.2)(0.9950 + 0.9560 + 0.8825 + 0.7827 + 0.6670$$
$$+ 0.5461)$$

$$= \mathbf{0.966}, \text{ correct to 3 significant figures.}$$

(c) From equation (5), using Simpson's rule with 6 intervals and the table of values in part (a) above:

$$\int_0^{1.2} e^{-\frac{x^2}{2}} \, dx \approx \frac{1}{3}(0.2) \left\{ (1.0000 + 0.4868) + 4(0.9802 + 0.8353 \right.$$
$$\left. + 0.6065) + 2(0.9231 + 0.7261) \right\}$$

$$\approx \frac{1}{3}(0.2)[1.4868 + 9.6880 + 3.2984]$$

$$= \mathbf{0.965}, \text{ correct to 3 significant figures.}$$

Problem 6. Evaluate, correct to 3 decimal places, $\int_1^3 \dfrac{5}{x}\,dx$ using

(a) integration,
(b) the trapezoidal rule, with (i) 4 intervals, (ii) 8 intervals,
(c) Simpson's rule with (i) 4 intervals, (ii) 8 intervals.
(d) Determine the percentage error in parts (b) and (c) compared with the value obtained in part (a).

(a) $\int_1^3 \dfrac{5}{x}\,dx = 5\,[\ln x]_1^3 = 5\,[\ln 3 - \ln 1] = 5\ln 3 = 5.493$, correct to
3 decimal places.

(b) (i) With 4 intervals, each is of width $\dfrac{3-1}{4} = 0.5$ and ordinates occur at

1.0, 1.5, 2.0, 2.5 and 3.0. Corresponding values of $\dfrac{5}{x}$ are evaluated and shown in the following table.

x	1.0	1.5	2.0	2.5	3.0
$\dfrac{5}{x}$	5.0000	3.3333	2.5000	2.0000	1.6667

From equation (1), using the trapezoidal rule with 4 intervals:

$$\int_1^3 \frac{5}{x}\,dx \approx (0.5)\left[\frac{1}{2}\,(5.0000 + 1.6667) + 3.3333 + 2.5000 + 2.0000\right]$$
$$= 5.583, \text{ correct to 3 decimal places.}$$

(ii) With 8 intervals, each is of width $\dfrac{3-1}{8} = 0.25$ and ordinates occur

at 1.00, 1.25, 1.50, 1.75, ... 3.00

Corresponding values of $\dfrac{5}{x}$ are evaluated and shown in the following table.

x	1.00	1.25	1.50	1.75	2.00	2.25	2.50	2.75	3.00
$\dfrac{5}{x}$	5.0000	4.0000	3.3333	2.8571	2.5000	2.2222	2.0000	1.8182	1.6667

From equation (1), using the trapezoidal rule with 8 intervals:

$$\int_1^3 \frac{5}{x}\,dx \approx (0.25)\left[\frac{1}{2}\,(5.0000 + 1.6667) + 4.0000 + 3.3333 + 2.8571 \right.$$
$$\left. + 2.5000 + 2.2222 + 2.0000 + 1.8182\right]$$

$$= 5.516, \text{ correct to 3 decimal places.}$$

(c) (i) From equation (5), using Simpson's rule with 4 intervals and the table of values in part (b) (i) above:

$$\int_1^3 \frac{5}{x} \, dx \approx \frac{1}{3} \, (0.5) \left[(5.0000 + 1.6667) + 4 \, (3.3333 + 2.0000) \atop + 2 \, (2.5000) \right]$$

= **5.500**, correct to 3 decimal places.

(ii) From equation (5), using Simpson's rule with 8 intervals and the table of values in part (b) (ii) above:

$$\int_1^3 \frac{5}{x} \, dx \approx \frac{1}{3} \, (0.25) \left[(5.0000 + 1.6667) + 4 \, (4.0000 + 2.8571 \atop + 2.2222 + 1.8182) + 2 \, (3.3333 + 2.5000 + 2.0000) \right]$$

$$\approx \frac{1}{3} \, (0.25) \, [6.6667 + 43.5900 + 15.6666]$$

= **5.494**, correct to 3 decimal places.

(d) Percentage error = $\left(\dfrac{\text{Approximate value} - \text{true value}}{\text{true value}} \right)$ x 100%, where

true value = 5.493 from part (a).

With the trapezoidal rule using 4 intervals,

$$\text{percentage error} = \left(\frac{5.583 - 5.493}{5.493} \right) \text{ x } 100\% = \textbf{1.638\%}$$

and using 8 intervals, percentage error = $\left(\dfrac{5.516 - 5.493}{5.493} \right)$ x 100%

= **0.419%**

With Simpson's rule using 4 intervals,

$$\text{percentage error} = \left(\frac{5.500 - 5.493}{5.493} \right) \text{ x } 100\% = \textbf{0.127\%}$$

and using 8 intervals, percentage error = $\left(\dfrac{5.494 - 5.493}{5.493} \right)$ x 100%

= **0.018%**

Thus when evaluating $\displaystyle\int_1^3 \frac{5}{x} \, dx$ the following conclusions may be drawn from above:

(i) the larger the number of intervals chosen the more accurate is the result, and

(ii) Simpson's rule is more accurate than the trapezoidal rule when the same number of intervals are chosen.

Further problems on numerical integration may be found in the following section (5), problems 1 to 28.

5 Further problems

In problems 1 to 5, evaluate the definite integrals using the trapezoidal rule, giving the answers correct to 3 decimal places.

1. $\int_0^2 \frac{1}{1+\theta^2}\, d\theta$ (Use 8 intervals)   [1.106]

2. $\int_1^4 3 \ln 2x\, dx$ (Use 6 intervals)   [13.827]

3. $\int_0^{\frac{\pi}{2}} \frac{1}{1+\sin x}\, dx$ (Use 6 intervals)   [1.006]

4. $\int_0^{\frac{\pi}{2}} \sqrt{(\sin x)}\, dx$ (Use 5 intervals)   [1.162]

5. $\int_0^{\pi} t \sin t\, dt$ (Use 8 intervals)   [3.101]

In problems 6 to 10, evaluate the definite integrals using the mid-ordinate rule, giving the answers correct to 3 decimal places.

6. $\int_1^4 \sqrt{(x^2-1)}\, dx$ (Use 6 intervals)   [6.735]

7. $\int_0^{\frac{\pi}{4}} \sqrt{(\cos^3 \theta)}\, d\theta$ (Use 9 intervals)   [0.674]

8. $\int_0^{1.5} e^{-\frac{1}{3}x^2}\, dx$ (Use 6 intervals)   [1.197]

9. $\int_{0.4}^2 \frac{dx}{1+x^4}$ (Use 8 intervals)   [0.672]

10. $\int_0^{\frac{\pi}{2}} \frac{1}{1+\cos x}\, dx$ (Use 6 intervals)   [0.997]

In problems 11 to 16, evaluate the definite integrals using Simpson's rule, giving the answers correct to 3 decimal places.

11. $\int_{\frac{\pi}{6}}^{\frac{\pi}{3}} \tan \theta \, d\theta$ (Use 6 intervals)   [0.549]

12. $\int_0^2 \frac{1}{1 + x^3} \, dx$ (Use 8 intervals)   [1.090]

13. $\int_0^{\frac{\pi}{3}} \sqrt{(1 - \frac{1}{3} \sin^2 x)} \, dx$ (Use 6 intervals)   [0.994]

14. $\int_1^3 \frac{\ln x}{x} \, dx$ (Use 10 intervals)   [0.603]

15. $\int_0^{0.4} \frac{\sin \theta}{\theta} \, d\theta$ (Use 8 intervals)   [0.380]

16. $\int_0^{\frac{\pi}{4}} \sqrt{(\sec x)} \, dx$ (Use 6 intervals)   [0.831]

In problems 17 and 18 evaluate the definite integrals using (a) integration, (b) the trapezoidal rule, (c) the mid-ordinate rule, and (d) Simpson's rule. In each of the approximate methods give the answers correct to 3 decimal places.

17. $\int_1^3 \frac{9}{x^2} \, dx$ (Use 8 intervals).   [(a) 6 (b) 6.089 (c) 5.956 (d) 6.004]

18. $\int_0^5 \sqrt{(3x + 1)} \, dx$ (Use 10 intervals)   [(a) 14 (b) 13.977 (c) 14.011 (d) 13.998]

In problems 19 to 21, evaluate the definite integrals using (a) the trapezoidal rule, (b) the mid-ordinate rule and (c) Simpson's rule. Use 6 intervals in each case and give answers correct to 3 decimal places.

19. $\int_0^{0.9} \sqrt{(1 - x^2)} \, dx$ [(a) 0.752 (b) 0.758 (c) 0.756]

20. $\int_{0.6}^{2.4} \sqrt{(1 + x^3)} \, dx$ [(a) 4.006 (b) 3.986 (c) 3.992]

21. $\int_0^{\frac{\pi}{2}} \frac{1}{\sqrt{(1 - \frac{1}{2} \sin^2 \theta)}} \, d\theta$ [(a) 1.854 (b) 1.854 (c) 1.854]

22. A curve is given by the following values:

x	0	1.0	2.0	3.0	4.0	5.0	6.0
y	3	6	12	20	30	42	56

The area under the curve between $x = 0$ and $x = 6.0$ is given by $\int_0^{6.0} y \, dx$. Determine the approximate value of this definite integral, correct to 4 significant figures, using Simpson's rule. [138.3]

23. A function of x, $f(x)$, has the following values for corresponding values of x.

x	0	0.1	0.2	0.3	0.4	0.5	0.6
$f(x)$	0	0.0995	0.1960	0.2866	0.3684	0.4388	0.4952

Evaluate $\int_0^{0.6} f(x) \, dx$ using (a) the trapezoidal rule, and (b) Simpson's rule, giving answers correct to 3 decimal places. [(a) 0.164 (b) 0.164]

24. Use Simpson's rule to estimate $\int_1^3 y \, dx$ for the following pairs of (x, y) values.

x	1.00	1.25	1.50	1.75	2.00	2.25	2.50	2.75	3.00
y	0	0.2789	0.6082	0.9793	1.3863	1.8246	2.2907	2.7819	3.2958

[2.944]

25. A vehicle starts from rest and its velocity is measured every second for 6.0 seconds, with values as follows:

time t (s)	0	1.0	2.0	3.0	4.0	5.0	6.0
velocity v (m s^{-1})	0	1.2	2.4	3.7	5.2	6.0	9.2

The distance travelled in 6.0 seconds is given by $\int_0^{6.0} v \, dt$. Estimate this distance using Simpson's rule giving the answer correct to 3 significant figures. [22.7 m]

26. An alternating current i has the following values at equal intervals of 2.0×10^{-3} seconds.

time $\times 10^{-3}$ (s)	0	2.0	4.0	6.0	8.0	10.0	12.0
current i (A)	0	1.7	3.5	5.0	3.7	2.0	0

Charge q, in coulombs, is given by $q = \int_0^{12.0 \times 10^{-3}} i \, dt$. Use Simpson's rule to determine the approximate charge in the 12.0×10^{-3} second period.   [32.8×10^{-3} C]

27. The velocity v of a body moving in a straight line at time t is given in the table below.

t(s)	0	0.5	1.0	1.5	2.0	2.5	3.0	3.5	4.0
v(m s^{-1})	0	0.07	0.13	0.22	0.27	0.32	0.34	0.31	0

The total distance travelled is given by $\int_0^{4.0} v \, dt$. Estimate the total distance travelled in 4.0 s using (a) the trapezoidal rule, and (b) Simpson's rule, giving the answers in centimetres.   [(a) 83 cm (b) 86 cm]

28. Determine the value of $\int_0^2 \dfrac{x}{\sqrt{(2x^2 + 1)}} \, dx$ using integral calculus. Find also the percentage error introduced by estimating the definite integral by (a) the trapezoidal rule, (b) the mid-ordinate rule, and (c) Simpson's rule, using 4 intervals in each case. Give answers correct to 3 decimal places.   [1; (a) −2.073%, (b) 1.063%, (c) 0.213%]

Chapter 17

Differential equations

1 Families of curves

A graph depicting the equations $y = 3x + 1$, $y = 3x + 2$, and $y = 3x - 4$ is shown in Fig. 1, and three parallel straight lines are seen to be the result.

Equations of the form $y = 3x + c$, where c can have any numerical value, will produce an infinite number of parallel straight lines called a **family of curves**.

A few of these can be seen in Fig. 1. Since $y = 3x + c$, $\frac{dy}{dx} = 3$, that is, the slope of every member of the family is 3. When additional information is given, for example, both the **general equation** $y = 3x + c$, and the member of the family passing through the point (2, 2), as shown as P in Fig. 1, then one particular member of the family is identified. The only line meeting both these conditions is the line $y = 3x - 4$. This is established by substituting $x = 2$ and $y = 2$ in the general equation $y = 3x + c$ and determining the value of c. Then, $2 = 3(2) + c$, giving $c = -6 + 2$, i.e. -4. Thus the **particular solution** is $y = 3x - 4$. Similarly, at point Q having coordinates $(-2, -4)$, the particular member of the family meeting both the conditions that it belongs to the family $y = 3x + c$ and that it passes through Q is the line $y = 3x + 2$. The additional information given, to enable a particular member of a family to be selected, is called the **boundary conditions**.

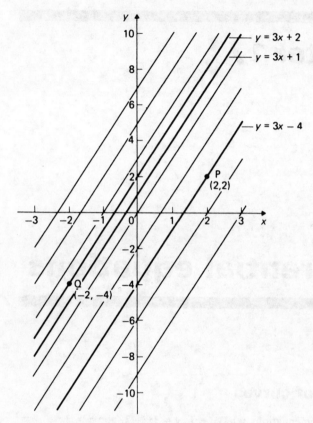

Fig. 1 Some members of the family of curves satisfying the equation $y = 3x + c$

The equation, $\dfrac{\mathrm{d}y}{\mathrm{d}x} = 3$, is called a **differential equation** since it contains a differential coefficient. It is also called a **first-order** differential equation, since it contains the first differential coefficient only, and has no differential coefficients such as $\dfrac{\mathrm{d}^2y}{\mathrm{d}x^2}$ or higher orders.

Another family of an infinite number of curves is produced by drawing a graph depicting the equations $y = 2x^2 + c$. Two of the curves in the family are $y = 2x^2$ (when $c = 0$) and $y = 2x^2 - 12$ (when $c = -12$) and these curves, together with others belonging to the family, are shown in Fig. 2.

The slope at any point of these curves is found by differentiating $y = 2x^2 + c$ and is given by $\dfrac{\mathrm{d}y}{\mathrm{d}x} = 4x$, i.e. the gradient of all of the curves is given by 4 times the value of the abscissa at every point. When boundary con-

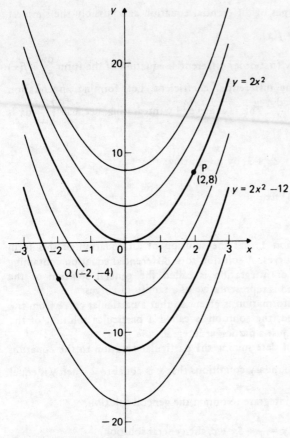

Fig. 2 Some members of the family of curves satisfying the equation $y = 2x^2 + c$

ditions are stated, particular curves can be identified. For example, the curve belonging to the family of curves $y = 2x^2 + c$ and which passes through point P, having coordinates (2, 8), is obtained by substituting $x = 2$ and $y = 8$ in the general equation. This gives $8 = 2(2)^2 + c$, i.e. $c = 0$, and hence the curve is $y = 2x^2$. Similarly, the curve satisfying the general equation and passing through the point Q = (−2, −4) is $y = 2x^2 - 12$.

2 The solution of differential equations of the form $\dfrac{dy}{dx} = f(x)$

Differential equations are used extensively in science and engineering.

There are many types of differential equation and possibly the simplest type is of the form $\frac{dy}{dx} = f(x)$.

The solution of any first-order differential equation of the form $\frac{dy}{dx} = f(x)$ involves eliminating the differential coefficient, i.e., forming an equation which does not contain $\frac{dy}{dx}$. This is achieved by integrating, because $\int \frac{dy}{dx} \, dx$ is equal to y.

For example, when $\frac{dy}{dx} = 2x + 3$, by integrating:

$$\int \frac{dy}{dx} \, dx = \int (2x + 3) \, dx$$

giving $\quad y = x^2 + 3x + c$

It was shown in Section 1 that the solution of an equation of this form produces a family of curves. A solution to a differential equation containing an arbitrary constant of integration is called the **general solution** of the differential equation and is representative of a family of curves.

When additional information is given, so that a particular curve from the family can be identified, the solution is called a **particular solution** of the differential equation or just a **particular integral**.

For example, when determining the particular solution to the equation $\frac{dy}{dx} = x^2 + 5$, given the boundary conditions that x is equal to 2 when y is equal to 5, the first step is to integrate to obtain the general solution.

When $\frac{dy}{dx} = x^2 + 5$, then $y = \frac{x^3}{3} + 5x + c$, the general solution.

Using the information given, i.e. substituting for x and y in the general solution, gives:

$$5 = \frac{(2)^3}{3} + 5(2) + c$$

and so $c = 5 - \frac{8}{3} - 10 = -7\frac{2}{3}$

Hence the particular solution is

$$y = \frac{x^3}{3} + 5x - 7\frac{2}{3}.$$

Worked problems on the solution of differential equations of the form $\frac{dy}{dx} = f(x)$

Problem 1. Find the general solutions to the equations:

(a) $\dfrac{dy}{dx} + \dfrac{5}{x} = 4x$

(b) $x\dfrac{dy}{dx} = 3x^3 - 4x^2 + 5x$

(c) $5\dfrac{dM}{d\theta} = 3e^\theta - 4e^{-\theta}$

(d) $\dfrac{ds}{dt} = u + at$, where u and a are constants

(e) $\dfrac{di}{dt} = \omega I_m \cos \omega t$, where ω and I_m are constants

Each of these equations is of the form $\dfrac{dy}{dx} = f(x)$ and the general solution can be obtained by integration.

(a) $\dfrac{dy}{dx} = 4x - \dfrac{5}{x}$

Integrating: $\displaystyle\int \dfrac{dy}{dx}\, dx = \int \left(4x - \dfrac{5}{x}\right) dx$

$$y = \dfrac{4x^2}{2} - 5 \ln x + c$$

i.e. $\qquad y = 2x^2 - 5 \ln x + c$

(b) $x\dfrac{dy}{dx} = 3x^3 - 4x^2 + 5x$

Dividing throughout by x gives:

$\dfrac{dy}{dx} = 3x^2 - 4x + 5$

Integrating gives: $y = \dfrac{3x^3}{3} - \dfrac{4x^2}{2} + 5x + c$

i.e. $\qquad y = x^3 - 2x^2 + 5x + c$

(c) $5\dfrac{dM}{d\theta} = 3e^\theta - 4e^{-\theta}$

$\dfrac{dM}{d\theta} = \tfrac{1}{5}(3e^\theta - 4e^{-\theta})$

Integrating gives: $M = \tfrac{1}{5}(3e^\theta + 4e^{-\theta}) + c$

(d) $\dfrac{ds}{dt} = u + at$

Integrating gives: $s = ut + \tfrac{1}{2}at^2 + c$

(e) $\dfrac{di}{dt} = \omega I_m \cos \omega t$

Integrating gives: $i = \dfrac{\omega I_m}{\omega} \sin \omega t + c$

i.e. $\qquad i = I_m \sin \omega t + c$

Problem 2. Find the particular solutions of the following equations satisfying the given boundary conditions:

(a) $\dfrac{dy}{dx} + x = 2$ and $y = 3$ when $x = 1$

(b) $x\dfrac{dy}{dx} = 3 - x^3$ and $y = 3\frac{2}{3}$ when $x = 1$

(c) $3\dfrac{dr}{d\theta} + \cos\theta = 0$ and $r = 5$ when $\theta = \dfrac{\pi}{2}$

(d) $\dfrac{dy}{dx} = e^x - 2\sin 2x$ and $y = 2$ when $x = \dfrac{\pi}{4}$

(a) $\dfrac{dy}{dx} = 2 - x$

Integrating gives: $y = 2x - \dfrac{x^2}{2} + c$, the general solution.

Substituting the boundary conditions $y = 3$ and $x = 1$ to evaluate c gives:

$$3 = 2(1) - \dfrac{(1)^2}{2} + c$$

i.e. $c = 1\frac{1}{2}$

Hence the particular solution is $y = 2x - \dfrac{x^2}{2} + 1\frac{1}{2}$

(b) $x\dfrac{dy}{dx} = 3 - x^3$

Dividing throughout by x to express the equation in the form $\dfrac{dy}{dx} = f(x)$ gives:

$$\dfrac{dy}{dx} = \dfrac{3}{x} - x^2$$

Integrating gives: $y = 3\ln x - \dfrac{x^3}{3} + c$, the general solution.

Substituting the boundary conditions gives: $3\frac{2}{3} = 3\ln 1 - \dfrac{(1)^3}{3} + c$

i.e. $\qquad c = 4$

Hence the particular solution is $y = 3\ln x - \dfrac{x^3}{3} + 4$

(c) $3\dfrac{dr}{d\theta} + \cos\theta = 0$

$$\dfrac{dr}{d\theta} = -\tfrac{1}{3}\cos\theta$$

Integrating gives: $r = -\frac{1}{3}\sin\theta + c$, the general solution.

Substituting the boundary conditions gives: $5 = -\frac{1}{3}\sin\frac{\pi}{2} + c$

i.e. $\qquad\qquad\qquad\qquad\qquad\qquad c = 5\frac{1}{3}$

Hence the particular solution is: $r = -\frac{1}{3}\sin\theta + 5\frac{1}{3}$

(d) $\dfrac{dy}{dx} = e^x - 2\sin 2x$

Integrating gives: $y = e^x + \cos 2x + c$, the general solution.

Substituting the boundary conditions gives: $2 = e^{\pi/4} + \cos\frac{\pi}{2} + c$

i.e. $\qquad\qquad\qquad\qquad\qquad\qquad c = 2 - e^{\pi/4}$

Hence the particular solution is $y = e^x + \cos 2x + 2 - e^{\pi/4}$

Expressed in this form, the true value of y is stated. The value of $e^{\pi/4}$ is 2.193 3 correct to 4 decimal places and the result can be expressed as $y = e^x + \cos 2x - 0.193\,3$, correct to 4 decimal places. However, when a result can be accurately expressed in terms of e or π, then it is usually better to leave the result in this form, unless the problem specifies the accuracy required.

Further problems on the solution of differential equations of the form

$\dfrac{dy}{dx} = f(x)$ *may be found in Section 4, Problems 1–30, page 344.*

3 The solution of differential equations of the form $\dfrac{dQ}{dt} = kQ$

The natural laws of growth and decay are of the form $y = Ae^{kx}$, where A and k are constants. For such a law to apply, the rate of change of a variable must be proportional to the variable itself. This can be shown by differentiation. Since

$y = Ae^{kx}$

$\dfrac{dy}{dx} = Ake^{kx}$, i.e. $\dfrac{dy}{dx} = kAe^{kx}$

But Ae^{kx} is equal to y. Hence, $\dfrac{dy}{dx} = ky$

Three of the natural laws are shown below and all such laws can be shown to be of a similar form.

(i) For linear expansion, the amount by which a rod expands when heated depends on the length of the rod, that is, the increase of length with respect to temperature is proportional to the length of the rod. Thus, mathematically:

$$\frac{dl}{d\theta} = kl \text{ and the law is } l = l_0 e^{k\theta}$$

(ii) For Newton's law of cooling, the fall of temperature with respect to time is proportional to the excess of its temperature above that of its surroundings, i.e.

$$\frac{d\theta}{dt} = -k\theta \text{ and the law is } \theta = \theta_0 e^{-kt}$$

(iii) In electrical work, when current decays in a circuit containing resistance and inductance connected in series, the change of current with respect to time is proportional to the current flowing at any instant,

i.e. $\frac{di}{dt} = ki$ and the law is $i = A e^{kt}$ where $k = -\frac{1}{T}$ and t is the time constant of the circuit.

These are just some of many examples of natural or exponential laws. In general, differential equations of the form $\frac{dQ}{dt} = kQ$ depict natural laws and the solutions are always of the form $Q = A e^{kt}$. This can be shown as follows:

Since $\frac{dQ}{dt} = kQ, \frac{dQ}{Q} = k \ dt$

Integrating: $\int \frac{dQ}{Q} = \int k \ dt$

i.e. $\ln Q = kt + c$

By the definition of a logarithm, if $y = e^x$ then $x = \ln y$, i.e. if $\ln y = x$, then $y = e^x$. It follows that when $\ln Q = kt + c$

$$Q = e^{(kt+c)}$$

By the laws of indices, $e^a e^b = e^{(a+b)}$ and applying this principle, gives:

$$Q = e^{kt} e^c$$

But e^c is a constant, say A, thus

$$Q = A e^{kt}$$

Checking by differentiation:

when $Q = A e^{kt}$

$$\frac{dQ}{dt} = kA e^{kt} = kQ$$

Hence $A e^{kt}$ is a solution to the differential equation $\frac{dQ}{dt} = kQ$.

Thus the general solution of any differential equation of the form

$$\frac{dQ}{dt} = kQ \text{ is } Q = Ae^{kt}$$

and when boundary conditions are given, the particular solution can be obtained, as shown in the worked problems following.

Worked problems on the solution of equations of the form $\frac{dQ}{dt} = kQ$

Problem 1. Solve the equation $\frac{dy}{dx} = 6y$ given that $y = 3$ when $x = 0.5$.

Since $\frac{dy}{dx} = 6y$ is of the form $\frac{dQ}{dt} = kQ$, the solution to the general equation will be of the form $Q = Ae^{kt}$, i.e. $y = Ae^{6x}$

Substituting the boundary conditions gives: $3 = Ae^{6(0.5)}$

i.e. $$A = \frac{3}{e^3} = 0.1494$$

Hence the particular solution is $y = \frac{3}{e^3} e^{6x} = 3e^{3(2x-1)}$ or $0.1494e^{6x}$

Problem 2. Determine the particular solutions of the following equations and their given boundary conditions, expressing the values of the constants correct to 4 significant figures:

(a) $\quad \frac{dM}{di} - 4M = 0$ and $M = 5$ when $i = 1$

(b) $\frac{1}{15} \frac{dl}{dm} + \frac{l}{4} = 0$ and $l = 15.41$ when $m = 0.714\ 3$

(a) Rearranging the equation into the form $\frac{dQ}{dt} = kQ$ gives:

$$\frac{dM}{di} = 4M$$

The general solution is of the form $Q = Ae^{kt}$, giving

$$M = Ae^{4i}$$

Substituting the boundary conditions gives: $5 = Ae^{(4)(1)}$

i.e. $$A = \frac{5}{e^4} = 0.091\ 58$$

Hence the particular solution is $M = 0.091\ 58\ e^{4i}$

(b) Writing the equation in the form $\frac{dQ}{dt} = kQ$ gives:

$$\frac{dl}{dm} = -\frac{15}{4} l$$

The general solution is $l = Ae^{-\frac{15}{4}m}$

Substituting the boundary conditions gives: $15.41 = Ae^{\left(-\frac{15}{4}\right)(0.714\ 3)}$

i.e. $A = 224.4$

Hence the particular solution is $l = 224.4\ e^{-3.750m}$

Problem 3. The decay of current in an electrical circuit containing resistance R ohms and inductance L henrys in series is given by $L\dfrac{di}{dt} + Ri = 0$, where i is the current flowing at time t seconds. Determine the general solution of the equation. In such a circuit, R is 5 kΩ, L is 3 henrys and the current falls to 5 A in 0.7 ms. Determine how long it will take for the current to fall to 2 amperes. Express your answer correct to 2 significant figures.

Since $\dfrac{di}{dt} = -\dfrac{R}{L}i$, then the general solution of the equation is
$i = Ae^{-\frac{Rt}{L}}$

By substituting the given values of R, L, i and t, the value of constant A is determined, i.e.

$$5 = Ae^{\left(\frac{-5\times10^3\times0.7\times10^{-3}}{3}\right)}$$

$$= Ae^{-\frac{3.5}{3}}$$

giving $A = 16.056$

To determine the time for i to fall to 2 A, substituting in the general solution for i, A, R and L gives

$$2 = 16.056\ e^{\left(\frac{-5\times10^3\times t}{3}\right)}$$

$$= 16.056\ e^{\left(\frac{-5t}{3}\right)} \text{ when } t \text{ is stated in milliseconds.}$$

Thus, $e^{\left(-\frac{5t}{3}\right)} = \dfrac{2}{16.056} = 0.124\ 56$,

and taking natural logarithms, gives:

$$-\frac{5t}{3}\ln e = \ln 0.124\ 56$$

But $\ln e = 1$, hence $t = -\frac{3}{5}\ln 0.124\ 56 = 1.25$ ms

i.e. **the time for i to fall to 2 A is 1.3 ms**, correct to 2 significant figures.

Problem 4. A copper conductor heats up to 50°C when carrying a current of 200 A. If the temperature coefficient of linear expansion, α_0, for copper is $17 \times 10^{-6}/^\circ$C at 0°C and the equation relating temperature θ with length l is $\dfrac{dl}{d\theta} = \alpha l$, find the increase in length of the conductor at 50°C correct to the nearest centimetre, when l is 1 000 m at 0°C.

Since $\frac{dl}{d\theta} = \alpha l$, then $l = Ae^{\alpha\theta}$, is the general solution.

But l is 1 000 when θ is $0°C$, and substituting these values in the general solution of the equation gives:

$1\,000 = Ae^0$, i.e. $A = 1\,000$

Substituting for A, α and θ in the general equation, gives

$l = 1\,000\,e^{(17\times10^{-6}\times50)} = 1\,000.850\ m$

i.e. **the increase in length of the conductor at $50°C$ is 85 cm**, correct to the nearest centimetre.

Problem 5. The rate of cooling of a body is proportional to the excess of its temperature above that of its surrounding, $\theta°C$.

The equation is: $\frac{d\theta}{dt} = k\theta$, where k is a constant.

A body cools from $90°C$ to $70°C$ in 3.0 minutes at a surrounding temperature of $15°C$. Determine how long it will take for the body to cool to $50°C$.

The general solution of the equation $\frac{d\theta}{dt} = k\theta$ is $\theta = Ae^{kt}$.

Letting the temperature $90°C$ correspond to a time t of zero gives an excess of body temperature above the surroundings of $(90 - 15)$.

Hence, $(90 - 15) = Ae^{(k)(0)}$, i.e. $A = 75$.

3.0 minutes later, the general solution becomes:

$(70 - 15) = 75\,e^{(k)(3)}$

i.e. $e^{3k} = \dfrac{55}{75}$

Taking natural logarithms,

$3k = \ln\dfrac{55}{75}, k = \dfrac{1}{3}\ln\dfrac{55}{75}$

i.e. $k = -0.103\,38$

At $50°C$, $(50 - 15) = 75\,e^{-0.103\,38t}$

$$\frac{35}{75} = e^{-0.103\,38t}$$

Taking natural logarithms gives:

$t = -\dfrac{1}{0.103\,38}\ln\dfrac{35}{75}$

$= 7.37$

That is, **the time for the body to cool to $50°C$ is 7.37 minutes**, or 7 minutes 22 seconds, correct to the nearest second.

Problem 6. The rate of decay of a radioactive material is given by $\frac{dN}{dt} = -\lambda N$ where λ is the decay constant and N the number of radioactive atoms disintegrating per second. Determine the half-life of a zinc isotope, taking the decay constant as 2.22×10^{-4} atoms per second.

The half-life of an element is the time for N to become one-half of its original value. Since $\frac{dN}{dt} = -\lambda N$, then applying the general solution to this equation gives:

$N = Ae^{-\lambda t}$, where the constant A represents the original number of radioactive atoms present since $N = A$ when $t = 0$. For half-life conditions, the ratio $\frac{N}{A}$ is $\frac{1}{2}$, hence

$$\tfrac{1}{2} = e^{-\lambda t} = e^{-2.22 \times 10^{-4} t}$$

Thus, $\ln \tfrac{1}{2} = -2.22 \times 10^{-4} t$

i.e. $t = -\dfrac{1}{2.22 \times 10^{-4}} \ln 0.5$

$= 3\ 122$ seconds or 52 minutes, 2 seconds.

Thus, **the half-life is 52 minutes**, correct to the nearest minute.

Further problems on the solution of equations of the form $\frac{dQ}{dt} = kQ$ may be found in the following section (4), Problems 31—41, page 346.

4   Further problems

Solution of equations of the form $\frac{dy}{dx} = f(x)$

In Problems 1—15, find the general solutions of the equations.

1. $\dfrac{dy}{dx} = 3x - \dfrac{4}{x^2}$ $\left[y = \dfrac{3x^2}{2} + \dfrac{4}{x} + c \right]$

2. $\dfrac{dy}{dx} + 3 = 4x^2$ $\left[y = \dfrac{4x^3}{3} - 3x + c \right]$

3. $3\dfrac{dy}{dx} + \dfrac{2}{\sqrt{x}} = 5\sqrt{x}$ $[y = \tfrac{2}{3}\sqrt{x}(\tfrac{5}{3}x - 2) + c]$

4. $\dfrac{du}{dV} - \dfrac{1}{V} = 4$ $[u = 4V + \ln V + c]$

5. $6 - 5\dfrac{dy}{dx} = \dfrac{1}{x-2}$ $[y = \tfrac{1}{5}(6x - \ln (x - 2)) + c]$

6. $2x^2 - \dfrac{3}{x} + 4\dfrac{dy}{dx} = 0$ $\left[y = \tfrac{1}{4}\left(3 \ln x - 2\dfrac{x^3}{3} \right) + c \right]$

7. $\dfrac{di}{d\theta} = \cos \theta$ $[i = \sin \theta + c]$

8. $6 \dfrac{dV}{dt} = 4 \sin \left(100t + \dfrac{\pi}{6}\right)$ $\left[V = -\dfrac{1}{150} \cos \left(100t + \dfrac{\pi}{6}\right) + c\right]$

9. $\dfrac{di}{dt} - \dfrac{t}{10} + 140 = 0$ $\left[i = \dfrac{t^2}{20} - 140t + c\right]$

10. $3 \dfrac{dv}{dt} + 0.7t^2 - 1.4 = 0$ $[v = \tfrac{1}{3}(4.2t - 0.7t^3) + c]$

11. $\dfrac{dy}{d\theta} = 3e^\theta - \dfrac{4}{e^{2\theta}}$ $\left[y = 3e^\theta + \dfrac{2}{e^{2\theta}} + c\right]$

12. $\dfrac{dV}{dx} = 3x - \dfrac{5}{x} - \sec^2 x$ $\left[V = \dfrac{3x^2}{2} - 5 \ln x - \tan x + c\right]$

13. $\tfrac{1}{2}\dfrac{dy}{dx} + 2x^{\frac{1}{2}} = e^{\frac{x}{2}}$ $\left[y = 4\left(e^{\frac{x}{2}} - \dfrac{2x^{\frac{3}{2}}}{3}\right) + c\right]$

14. $x \dfrac{dy}{dx} = 2 - 3x^2$ $\left[y = 2 \ln x - \dfrac{3x^2}{2} + c\right]$

15. $\dfrac{dM}{d\theta} = \tfrac{1}{2} \sin 3\theta - \tfrac{1}{3} \cos 2\theta$ $[M = -\tfrac{1}{6}(\cos 3\theta + \sin 2\theta) + c]$

In Problems 16–25, determine the particular solutions of the differential equations for the boundary conditions given.

16. $x \dfrac{dy}{dx} - 2 = x^3$ and $y = 1$ when $x = 1$. $\left[y = 2 \ln x + \dfrac{x^3}{3} + \tfrac{2}{3}\right]$

17. $x\left(x - \dfrac{dy}{dx}\right) = 3$ and $y = 2$ when $x = 1$. $\left[y = \dfrac{x^2}{2} - 3 \ln x + 1\tfrac{1}{2}\right]$

18. $\dfrac{ds}{dt} - 4t^2 = 9$ and $s = 27$ when $t = 3$. $\left[s = 9t + \dfrac{4t^3}{3} - 36\right]$

19. $e^{-p} \dfrac{dq}{dp} = 5$ and $q = 2.718$ when $p = 0$. $[q = 5e^p - 2.282]$

20. $3 - \dfrac{dy}{dx} = e^{2x} - 2e^x$ and $y = 7$ when $x = 0$.

$[y = 3x - \tfrac{1}{2}e^{2x} + 2e^x + 5\tfrac{1}{2}]$

21. $\dfrac{dy}{d\theta} - \sin 3\theta = 5$ and $y = \dfrac{5\pi}{6}$ when $\theta = \dfrac{\pi}{6}$. $[y = 5\theta - \tfrac{1}{3} \cos 3\theta]$

22. $3 \sin \left(2\theta - \dfrac{\pi}{3}\right) + 4 \dfrac{dv}{d\theta} = 0$ and $v = 3.7$ when $\theta = \dfrac{2\pi}{3}$.

$\left[v = \tfrac{3}{8}\left(\cos \left(2\theta - \dfrac{\pi}{3}\right)\right) + 4.075\right]$

23. $\tfrac{1}{6}\dfrac{dM}{d\theta} + 1 = \sin \theta$ and $M = 3$ when $\theta = \pi$.

$[M = 3\{(2\pi - 1) - 2 \cos \theta - 2\theta\}]$

24. $\dfrac{2}{(u + 1)^2} = 4 - \dfrac{dz}{du}$ and $z = 14$ when $u = 5$. $\left[z = 4u + \dfrac{2}{u + 1} - 6\tfrac{1}{3}\right]$

25. $\dfrac{1}{2e^x} + 4 = x - 3 \dfrac{dy}{dx}$ and $y = 3$ when $x = 0$.

$\left[y = \tfrac{1}{3}\left\{\dfrac{x^2}{2} + \dfrac{1}{2e^x} - 4x\right\} + 2\tfrac{5}{6}\right]$

26. The bending moment of a beam, M, and shear force F are related by the equation $\dfrac{dM}{dx} = F$, where x is the distance from one end of the beam. Determine M in terms of x when $F = -w(l - x)$ where w and l are constants, and $M = \frac{1}{2}wl^2$ when $x = 0$. $[M = \frac{1}{2}w(l - x)^2]$

27. The angular velocity ω of a flywheel of moment of inertia I is given by $I\dfrac{d\omega}{dt} + N = 0$, where N is a constant. Determine ω in terms of t given that $\omega = \omega_0$ when $t = 0$. $\left[\omega = \omega_0 - \dfrac{Nt}{I} \right]$

28. The gradient of a curve is given by $\dfrac{dy}{dx} = 2x - \dfrac{x^2}{3}$. Determine the equation of the curve if it passes through the point $x = 3$, $y = 4$.

$\left[y = x^2 - \dfrac{x^3}{9} - 2 \right]$

29. The acceleration of a body a is equal to its rate of change of velocity, $\dfrac{dv}{dt}$. Determine an equation for v in terms of t given that the velocity is u when $t = 0$. $[v = u + at]$

30. The velocity of a body v, is equal to its rate of change of distance, $\dfrac{dx}{dt}$. Determine an equation for x in terms of t given $v = u + at$, where u and a are constants and $x = 0$ when $t = 0$. $[x = ut + \frac{1}{2}at^2]$

Solution of equations of the form $\dfrac{dQ}{dt} = kQ$

In Problems 31–33 determine the general solutions to the equations.

31. $\dfrac{dp}{dq} = 9p$ $[p = Ae^{9q}]$

32. $\dfrac{dm}{dn} + 5m = 0$ $[m = Ae^{-5n}]$

33. $\frac{1}{6}\dfrac{dw}{dx} + \frac{3}{5}w = 0$ $[w = Ae^{-\frac{18}{5}x}]$

In Problems 34–36 determine the particular solutions to the equations, expressing the values of the constants correct to 3 significant figures.

34. $\dfrac{dQ}{dt} = 15.0Q$ and $Q = 7.3$ when $t = 0.015$. $[Q = 5.83\,e^{15.0t}]$

35. $\frac{1}{7}\dfrac{dl}{dm} - \frac{1}{3}l = 0$ and $l = 1.7 \times 10^4$ when $m = 3.4 \times 10^{-2}$.

$[l = 1.57 \times 10^4\,e^{2.33m}]$

36. $0.741\dfrac{dy}{dx} + 0.071\,y = 0$ and $y = 73.4$ when $x = 15.7$

$[y = 330\,e^{-0.0958x}]$

37. The difference in tension, T newtons, between two sides of a belt when in contact with a pulley over an angle of θ radians and when it is on the point of slipping, is given by $\frac{dT}{d\theta} = \mu T$, where μ is the coefficient of friction between the material of the belt and that of the pulley at the point of slipping. When $\theta = 0$ radians, the tension is 170 N and the co-efficient of friction as slipping starts is 0.31. Determine the tension at the point of slipping when θ is $\frac{5\pi}{6}$ radians. Also determine the angle of lap in degrees, to give a tension of 340 N just before slipping starts.
   [383 N, 128°]

38. The charge Q coulombs at time t seconds for a capacitor of capacitance C farads when discharging through a resistance of R ohms is given by:
   $$R \frac{dQ}{dt} + \frac{Q}{C} = 0$$
   A circuit contains a resistance of 500 kilohms and a capacitance of 8.7 microfarads, and after 147 milliseconds the charge falls to 7.5 coulombs. Determine the initial charge and the charge after one second, correct to 3 significant figures.   [7.76 C, 6.17 C]

39. The rate of decay of a radioactive substance is given by $\frac{dN}{dt} = -\lambda N$, where λ is the decay constant and N the number of radioactive atoms disintegrating per second. Determine the half-life of radium in years (i.e. the time for N to become one-half of its original value) taking the decay constant for radium as 1.36×10^{-11} atoms per second and assuming a '365-day' year.   [1 616 years]

40. The variation of resistance, R ohms, of a copper conductor with temperature, $\theta°C$, is given by $\frac{dR}{d\theta} = \alpha R$, where α is the temperature coefficient of resistance of copper. Taking α as 39×10^{-4} per °C, determine the resistance of a copper conductor at 30°C, correct to 4 significant figures, when its resistance at 80°C is 57.4 ohms.   [47.23 ohms]

41. The rate of growth of bacteria is directly proportional to the amount of bacteria present. Form a differential equation for the rate of growth when n is the number of bacteria at time t seconds. If the number of bacteria present at $t = 0$ is n_0, solve the equation. When the number of bacteria doubles in one hour, determine by how many times it will have increased in twelve hours.   [$n = n_0 e^{kt}$, 2^{12}]

Appendices

Appendix A   The binomial expansion

The general binomial expansion of $(a + b)^n$, where n is any positive integer, is given by:

$$(a + b)^n = a^n + n\,a^{n-1}\,b + \frac{n\,(n-1)}{(1)\,(2)}\,a^{n-2}\,b^2 + \frac{n\,(n-1)(n-2)}{(1)\,(2)\,(3)}\,a^{n-3}\,b^3 + \ldots,$$

Appendix B   Trigonometrical compound angles

1. Compound angles

Angles such as $(A + B)$ or $(A - B)$ are called **compound angles** since they are the sum or difference of two angles A and B. Each expression of a compound angle has two components. The trigonometrical ratios of compound angles may be expressed in terms of their two component angles. These are often called the **addition and subtraction formulae** and are true for all values of A and B. It may be shown that:

$$\sin\,(A + B) = \sin A \cos B + \cos A \sin B \qquad \ldots (1)$$
$$\sin\,(A - B) = \sin A \cos B - \cos A \sin B \qquad \ldots (2)$$
$$\cos\,(A + B) = \cos A \cos B - \sin A \sin B \qquad \ldots (3)$$
$$\cos\,(A - B) = \cos A \cos B + \sin A \sin B \qquad \ldots (4)$$

2. Changing sums or differences of sines and cosines into products of sines and cosines

From equations (1) and (2) in section 1,

$$\sin\,(A + B) + \sin\,(A - B) = \sin A \cos B + \cos A \sin B + \sin A \cos B - \cos A \sin B$$
$$= 2 \sin A \cos B.$$

In the compound angle formulae let $A + B = x$
and $A - B = y$.

Then $A = \dfrac{x + y}{2}$ and $B = \dfrac{x - y}{2}$.

Then, instead of $\sin (A + B) + \sin (A - B) = 2 \sin A \cos B$ we have

$$\sin x + \sin y = 2 \sin \left(\frac{x + y}{2}\right) \cos \left(\frac{x - y}{2}\right) \qquad \ldots (5)$$

Similarly,

$$\sin x - \sin y = 2 \cos \left(\frac{x + y}{2}\right) \sin \left(\frac{x - y}{2}\right) \qquad \ldots (6)$$

$$\cos x + \cos y = 2 \cos \left(\frac{x + y}{2}\right) \cos \left(\frac{x - y}{2}\right) \qquad \ldots (7)$$

and

$$\cos x - \cos y = -2 \sin \left(\frac{x + y}{2}\right) \sin \left(\frac{x - y}{2}\right) \qquad \ldots (8)$$

3. Double angles

If in equation (1) of section 1, $A = B$ then

$$\sin 2A = 2 \sin A \cos A \qquad \ldots (9)$$

Similarly, if in equation 3, of section 1, $A = B$ then

$$\cos 2A = \cos^2 A - \sin^2 A \qquad \ldots (10)$$

There are two further formulae for $\cos 2A$. Since $\sin^2 A + \cos^2 A = 1$ then $\sin^2 A = 1 - \cos^2 A$. Thus

$$\cos 2A = \cos^2 A - (1 - \cos^2 A) = 2 \cos^2 A - 1 \qquad \ldots (11)$$

Similarly, $\cos 2A = (1 - \sin^2 A) - \sin^2 A = 1 - 2 \sin^2 A \qquad \ldots (12)$

Note that since $\sin 2A = 2 \sin A \cos A$, then $\sin 4A = 2 \sin 2A \cos 2A$
 and since $\cos 2A = 2 \cos^2 A - 1$, then $\cos 6A = 2 \cos^2 3A - 1$,
 and so on.

Appendix C Approximate methods for finding areas of irregular figures

1. Trapezoidal rule

For Fig. 1(a), area of ABCD $= d \left[\left(\frac{y_1 + y_7}{2}\right) + y_2 + y_3 + y_4 + y_5 + y_6 \right]$

i.e. the trapezoidal rule states that the area of an irregular figure is given by:
Area = (width of interval) [$\frac{1}{2}$ (first + last ordinates) + sum of remaining
ordinates]

2. Mid-ordinate rule

For Fig. 1(b), area of PQRS $= d (y_1 + y_2 + y_3 + y_4 + y_5 + y_6)$,
i.e. the mid-ordinate rule states that the area of an irregular figure is given by:
Area = (width of interval) (sum of mid-ordinate)

3. Simpson's rule

To find an area such as ABCD of Fig. 1(a) the base AD **must** be divided into an **even** number of strips of equal width d, thus producing an **odd** number of ordinates, in this case 7.

$$\text{Area of ABCD} = \frac{d}{3} [(y_1 + y_7) + 4 (y_2 + y_4 + y_6) + 2 (y_3 + y_5)]$$

(a)

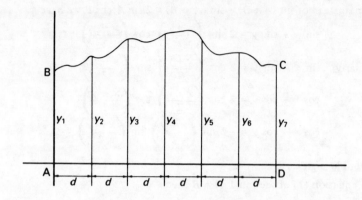

(b)

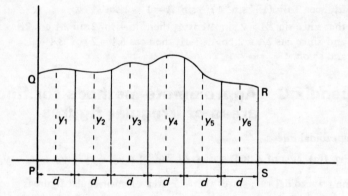

Fig. 1

i.e. Simpson's rule states that the area of an irregular figure is given by:

$$\text{Area} = \tfrac{1}{3}(\text{width of interval}) \left[\begin{pmatrix} \text{first + last} \\ \text{ordinate} \end{pmatrix} + 4 \begin{pmatrix} \text{sum of even} \\ \text{ordinates} \end{pmatrix} + 2 \begin{pmatrix} \text{sum of remaining} \\ \text{odd ordinates} \end{pmatrix} \right]$$

When estimating areas of irregular figures, Simpson's rule is generally regarded as the most accurate of the approximate methods available.

Appendix D   Differential coefficients of common functions by analytical proof

1.   Differential coefficient of ax^n

Let $f(x) = ax^n$
then $f(x + \delta x) = a(x + \delta x)^n$

By definition, $f'(x) = \displaystyle\lim_{\delta x \to 0} \left\{ \dfrac{f(x + \delta x) - f(x)}{\delta x} \right\}$

$\qquad\qquad = \displaystyle\lim_{\delta x \to 0} \left\{ \dfrac{a(x + \delta x)^n - ax^n}{\delta x} \right\}$

$a(x + \delta x)^n$ may be expanded using the binomial expansion (see Appendix A).

$$a(x + \delta x)^n = a\left[x^n + nx^{n-1}\,\delta x + \frac{n(n-1)}{(1)(2)} x^{n-2}\,(\delta x)^2 + \ldots \right]$$

$$= ax^n + an\,x^{n-1}\,\delta x + \frac{a\,n(n-1)}{(1)(2)} x^{n-2}\,(\delta x)^2 + \ldots$$

$$a(x + \delta x)^n - ax^n = an\,x^{n-1}\,\delta x + \frac{a\,n(n-1)}{(1)(2)} x^{n-2}\,(\delta x)^2 + \ldots$$

$$\frac{a(x + \delta x)^n - ax^n}{\delta x} = an\,x^{n-1} + \frac{a\,n(n-1)}{(1)(2)} x^{n-2}\,\delta x + \ldots$$

$$f'(x) = \lim_{\delta x \to 0} \left\{ an\,x^{n-1} + \frac{a\,n(n-1)}{(1)(2)} x^{n-2}\,\delta x + \ldots \right\}$$

i.e. $f'(x) = an\,x^{n-1}$, since all subsequent terms in the bracket will contain δx raised to some power and will become zero when a limiting value is taken. This result is true for all values of n, whether they are positive, negative or fractional.

Hence when $y = f(x) = ax^n$, $f'(x) = an\,x^{n-1}$

2.   Differential coefficient of $\sin x$

Let $f(x) = \sin x$
then $f(x + \delta x) = \sin (x + \delta x)$

By definition, $f'(x) = \displaystyle\lim_{\delta x \to 0} \left\{ \dfrac{f(x + \delta x) - f(x)}{\delta x} \right\}$

$\qquad\qquad = \displaystyle\lim_{\delta x \to 0} \left\{ \dfrac{\sin (x + \delta x) - \sin x}{\delta x} \right\}$

Now $\sin x - \sin y = 2 \cos\left[\dfrac{x + y}{2}\right] \sin\left[\dfrac{x - y}{2}\right]$ (see Appendix B).

Hence $\sin (x + \delta x) - \sin x = 2 \cos\left[\dfrac{(x + \delta x) + x}{2}\right] \sin\left[\dfrac{(x + \delta x) - x}{2}\right]$

$$= 2 \cos \left[x + \frac{\delta x}{2} \right] \sin \left[\frac{\delta x}{2} \right]$$

$$\frac{\sin (x + \delta x) - \sin x}{\delta x} = \frac{2 \cos \left[x + \frac{\delta x}{2} \right] \sin \left[\frac{\delta x}{2} \right]}{\delta x}$$

$$= \cos \left[x + \frac{\delta x}{2} \right] \frac{\sin \left[\frac{\delta x}{2} \right]}{\left[\frac{\delta x}{2} \right]}$$

When δx is small, $\sin \delta x \simeq \delta x$

(For example, if $\delta x = 1°$, $\sin 1° = 0.017\ 5$ and $1°$ in radians $= 0.017\ 5$.)

Thus when δx is small, say, less than $2°$, $\sin \left[\frac{\delta x}{2} \right] = \left[\frac{\delta x}{2} \right]$, correct to 3 significant figures

i.e. $\dfrac{\sin \left[\dfrac{\delta x}{2} \right]}{\left[\dfrac{\delta x}{2} \right]} = 1$

Hence $f'(x) = \displaystyle\lim_{\delta x \to 0} \left\{ \cos \left[x + \frac{\delta x}{2} \right] \frac{\sin \left[\frac{\delta x}{2} \right]}{\left[\frac{\delta x}{2} \right]} \right\}$

i.e. $f'(x) = \cos x$

Hence when $y = f(x) = \sin x$, $f'(x) = \cos x$

3. Differential coefficient of $\cos x$

Let $f(x) = \cos x$

then $f(x + \delta x) = \cos (x + \delta x)$

By definition, $f'(x) = \displaystyle\lim_{\delta x \to 0} \left\{ \frac{f(x + \delta x) - f(x)}{\delta x} \right\}$

$$= \lim_{\delta x \to 0} \left\{ \frac{\cos (x + \delta x) - \cos x}{\delta x} \right\}$$

Now $\cos x - \cos y = -2 \sin \left[\frac{x + y}{2} \right] \sin \left[\frac{x - y}{2} \right]$ (see Appendix B).

Hence $\cos (x + \delta x) - \cos x = -2 \sin \left[\frac{(x + \delta x) + x}{2} \right] \sin \left[\frac{(x + \delta x) - x}{2} \right]$

$$= -2 \sin \left[x + \frac{\delta x}{2} \right] \sin \left[\frac{\delta x}{2} \right]$$

$$\frac{\cos (x + \delta x) - \cos x}{\delta x} = \frac{-2 \sin \left[x + \dfrac{\delta x}{2}\right] \sin \left[\dfrac{\delta x}{2}\right]}{\delta x}$$

$$= - \sin \left[x + \frac{\delta x}{2}\right] \frac{\sin \left[\dfrac{\delta x}{2}\right]}{\left[\dfrac{\delta x}{2}\right]}$$

Hence $f'(x) = \displaystyle\lim_{\delta x \to 0} \left\{ - \sin \left[x + \frac{\delta x}{2}\right] \frac{\sin \left[\dfrac{\delta x}{2}\right]}{\left[\dfrac{\delta x}{2}\right]} \right\}$

$$= - (\sin x), \text{ since in the limit, } \frac{\sin \left[\dfrac{\delta x}{2}\right]}{\left[\dfrac{\delta x}{2}\right]} = 1$$

i.e. $f'(x) = - \sin x$

Hence when $y = f(x) = \cos x$, $f'(x) = \sin x$

4.   Differential coefficient of e^{ax}

Let $f(x) = e^{ax}$

then $f(x + \delta x) = e^{a(x + \delta x)}$

By definition, $f'(x) = \displaystyle\lim_{\delta x \to 0} \left\{ \frac{f(x + \delta x) - f(x)}{\delta x} \right\}$

$$= \lim_{\delta x \to 0} \left\{ \frac{e^{a(x + \delta x)} - e^{ax}}{\delta x} \right\}$$

$$e^{a(x + \delta x)} - e^{ax} = e^{ax} (e^{a\delta x} - 1)$$

Since $e^x = 1 + x + \dfrac{x^2}{2!} + \dfrac{x^3}{3!} + \ldots$

then $e^{a\delta x} = 1 + (a\delta x) + \dfrac{(a\delta x)^2}{2!} + \dfrac{(a\delta x)^3}{3!} + \ldots$

Therefore $e^{ax} (e^{a\delta x} - 1) = e^{ax} \left(1 + a\delta x + \dfrac{(a\delta x)^2}{2!} + \ldots - 1 \right)$

$$= e^{ax} \left(a\delta x + \frac{(a\delta x)^2}{2!} + \ldots \right)$$

$$\frac{e^{a(x + \delta x)} - e^{ax}}{\delta x} = e^{ax} \left(a + \frac{a^2 \delta x}{2!} + \ldots \right)$$

Hence $f'(x) = \displaystyle\lim_{\delta x \to 0} \left\{ e^{ax}\left(a + \dfrac{a^2\delta x}{2!} + \ldots \right) \right\}$

$\qquad = (e^{ax})\,(a)$

i.e. $\qquad f'(x) = ae^{ax}$

Hence when $y = f(x) = e^{ax}$, $f'(x) = ae^{ax}$

5. Differential coefficient of ln ax

Let $f(x) = \ln ax$

then $f(x + \delta x) = \ln a(x + \delta x)$

By definition, $f'(x) = \displaystyle\lim_{\delta x \to 0} \left\{ \dfrac{f(x + \delta x) - f(x)}{\delta x} \right\}$

$\qquad = \displaystyle\lim_{\delta x \to 0} \left\{ \dfrac{\ln a(x + \delta x) - \ln ax}{\delta x} \right\}$

$\ln a(x + \delta x) - \ln ax = \ln ax \left(1 + \dfrac{\delta x}{x} \right) - \ln ax$

$\qquad\qquad = \ln ax + \ln\left(1 + \dfrac{\delta x}{x} \right) - \ln ax$

$\qquad\qquad = \ln\left(1 + \dfrac{\delta x}{x} \right)$

Now $\ln (1 + x) = x - \dfrac{x^2}{2} + \dfrac{x^3}{3} - \ldots$

Therefore $\ln\left(1 + \dfrac{\delta x}{x} \right) = \dfrac{\delta x}{x} - \dfrac{\left(\dfrac{\delta x}{x} \right)^2}{2} + \dfrac{\left(\dfrac{\delta x}{x} \right)^3}{3} - \ldots$

$\dfrac{\ln a(x + \delta x) - \ln ax}{\delta x} = \dfrac{1}{x} - \dfrac{\delta x}{2x^2} + \dfrac{\delta x^2}{3x^3} - \ldots$

Hence $f'(x) = \displaystyle\lim_{\delta x \to 0} \left\{ \dfrac{\ln a(x + \delta x) - \ln ax}{\delta x} \right\}$

$\qquad = \displaystyle\lim_{\delta x \to 0} \left\{ \dfrac{1}{x} - \dfrac{\delta x}{2x^2} + \dfrac{\delta x^2}{3x^3} - \ldots \right\}$

i.e. $\qquad f'(x) = \dfrac{1}{x}$

Hence when $y = f(x) = \ln ax$, $f'(x) = \dfrac{1}{x}$

Index